WASTE NOT

A directory of unwanted domestic and business items collected by UK charities

5TH EDITION

EDITOR
JILL GOLDSWORTHY

© 1997 Charities Aid
Foundation

Published by The Charities
Aid Foundation
Kings Hill
West Malling
Kent ME19 4TA

Telephone
+44 (0)1732 520000

Fax
+44 (0)1732 520001

E-mail address
cafpubs@caf.charitynet.org

Web address
http://www.charitynet.org

Design
Eugenie Dodd Typographics

Typeset by
BPC Whitefriars Ltd

Printed and bound by
Bell & Bain Ltd, Glasgow

A catalogue record for this
book is available from the
British Library

ISBN 1–85934–027–X

Contents

Introduction

Many hundreds of charities have long depended on their charity shops as a valuable source of income obtained simply by collecting and selling on other people's unwanted items. In 1996 a survey of just over 4,500 shops indicated that their combined turnover was approximately £247 million (*NGO Finance*, 1996 Annual Charity Shops Survey), giving true meaning to the maxim that 'one person's rubbish is another's treasure'!

The variety of items that have a worthwhile use to charities is immense. No longer do they collect just Christmas cards, milk bottle tops and second-hand clothes; there is now a lively recycling market for computer hardware and software, musical instruments, Air Miles tokens, telephone cards, etc.

The work of the charity shops is not, however, the whole story; many charities are extremely pleased to accept various items listed in this directory, whether or not they have a retail outlet.

The purpose of this, the 5th edition of *Waste Not*, is to put people who wish to recycle their unwanted items in touch with organisations that can put them to good use. The information contained in this directory has been supplied by the charities themselves. A questionnaire was sent to all the organisations listed, asking them to indicate which items they are willing to receive and whether or not they operate a collection service within their area.

All the organisations which appeared in earlier editions of *Waste Not* were invited to update their details and any organisations which contacted CAF and asked to be included were, naturally, accommodated. In order to extend the scope of the directory, the editorial team also mailed what they judged to be a representative sample of national charities which possess local networks, drawn from right across the range of charitable activities. Inevitably, therefore, which organisations are listed depends partly on a subjective judgement. Organisations which would like to be included in future editions are invited to contact the editorial team at CAF.

With some of the national charities which operate hundreds, or even thousands, of shops it has not been possible to include individual details of all of them. These organisations have indicated to us what items their shops collect and these have been listed against their head office or regional office addresses. If you contact these offices they will be able to guide you towards a local collection point.

About this directory

Structure

The directory is divided into two parts.

Part One begins with a list of all the items that are included in this directory. They have been grouped under general headings: for example, 'Baby equipment' will be found under 'Home and garden', 'Used toner cartridges' under 'Office'. Page numbers by each of these items refer you to the second listing in Part One.

This second listing groups organisations under the items which they will accept and by geographical area. Most of the UK has been divided into counties, for example Kent, Gwynedd and Lothian. London has been divided into postal districts, eg London EC, London SW. Northern Ireland is listed as a complete region.

Part Two provides an alphabetical list of all the organisations included in Part One. This gives full details of the organisations, including address, telephone number and fax number (if supplied), a full list of the items they are interested in and whether or not they operate a collection service.

Example of how to use the directory

You may have a highchair and baby's pram you wish to dispose of. Refer to the opening page of Part One to find out whether these items are listed. Under the general heading of 'Home and garden' you will find a sub-category of 'Baby equipment'. Now turn to the page number indicated and you will find all the organisations that are willing to receive baby equipment listed by geographical area. Look under your local area to find organisations that you could contact.

Now turn to Part Two of the directory, where you will find these organisations listed alphabetically. Here you will find more information on each organisation – address, telephone number, fax number (where provided) and whether or not they operate a collection service, as well as all the other items they collect. You can then choose the charity nearest to you that has a collection service (unless you are able to deliver the item yourself) and contact them to see if they are interested in your items. If there are no organisations in your area, you could look at nearby areas until you find a suitable recipient for your items.

About CAF

CAF, Charities Aid Foundation, is a registered charity with a unique mission – to increase the substance of charity in the UK and overseas. It provides services that are both charitable and financial which help donors make the most of their giving and charities make the most of their resources.

Many of CAF's publications reflect the organisation's purpose: *Dimensions of the Voluntary Sector* offers the definitive financial overview of the sector, while *The Directory of Grant Making Trusts* provides the most comprehensive source of funding information available.

As an integral part of its activities, CAF works to raise standards of management in voluntary organisations. This includes the making of grants by its own Grants Council, sponsorship of the Charity Annual Report and Accounts Awards, seminars, training courses and the Charities Annual Conference, the largest regular gathering of key people from within the voluntary sector. In addition, Charitynet is now established as the leading Internet site on voluntary action.

For decades, CAF has led the way in developing tax-effective services to donors, and these are now used by more than 150,000 individuals and 2,000 of the UK's leading companies. Many are also using CAF's CharityCard, the world's first debit card designed exclusively for charitable giving. CAF's unique range of investment and administration services for charities includes the CafCash High Interest Cheque Account, two common investment funds for longer-term investment and a full appeals and subscription management service.

CAF's activities are not limited to the UK, however. Increasingly, CAF is looking to apply the same principles and develop similar services internationally, in its drive to increase the substance of charity across the world.

CAF
Kings Hill
West Malling
Kent ME19 4TA

Telephone +44(0)1732 520000

Fax +44(0)1732 520001

Web address http://www.charitynet.org

E-mail address cafpubs@caf.charitynet.org

Other publications from CAF

The Directory of Grant Making Trusts 1997–98
15th edition

ISBN 1–85934–025–3
£69.95 (2 volumes)
Published February 1997

Acknowledged as the definitive guide to grant-making trusts in the UK, this directory enables fundraisers to pinpoint those trusts whose funding objectives match their own particular project or area of work.

Split into two volumes for the first time, and containing the details of over 500 additional trusts, the 1997–98 edition has undergone a complete design overhaul in order to make the information it contains even more straightforward and accessible.

The indices which 'lead' the user to the most relevant trusts have also been radically improved and an entirely new classification of types of beneficiary has been adopted. Particularly significantly, the listing of trusts by beneficial area has been reorganised in order to highlight regional funding preferences more clearly.

These improvements will enable fundraisers to obtain an even more detailed understanding of the future funding policies of the trusts listed and thereby to tailor their requests for support more accurately – so reducing the time and money wasted on inappropriate appeals.

Grant-making trusts made grants in excess of £700 million in 1995. The *DGMT* is designed to act as the lifeline between good causes in desperate need of support and this rich vein of funding.

Grantseeker
The interactive CD-ROM for fundraisers

ISBN 1–85934–032–6
£150 + £26.25 VAT
Published April 1997

Drawing on CAF's years of experience as publisher of *The Directory of Grant Making Trusts*, *Grantseeker* is the tailor-made solution to the information needs of trust fundraisers in the electronic age.

Fully interactive, the specially designed search engine will scan the entire *DGMT* database in a matter of seconds on the basis of a user's own selection criteria and generate a ranked 'hit list' of trusts whose funding preferences match their project or cause. Selection criteria particular to the CD include details of grant size and grant type.

Taking full advantage of the 'added value' available via an electronic search tool, *Grantseeker* offers a more sophisticated matching service than can be provided by traditional methods, enabling fundraisers to save weeks of effort and frustration. A simple hypertext link can provide them with the complete *DGMT* entry on a potential funder within moments of loading the CD. The days of ultimate dependence on a paper-based directory are over.

The sample grants data from selected trusts, published separately in the *Grants Index*, appear in the full trust entries featured in *Grantseeker*.

Designed for use by fundraisers with little or no experience of electronic directories, as well as the more technically minded, *Grantseeker* provides step-by-step instructions on every stage of the search process, backed by comprehensive help files. Even the most confirmed Luddite should not be intimidated!

Grantseeker runs under Windows 3.1 or Windows 95.

Focus Series: Children and Youth

ISBN 1–85934–017–2
£19.95
Published July 1996

Environment, Animal Welfare and Heritage

ISBN 1–85934–016–4
£19.95
Published July 1996

Museums, Art Galleries and Performing Arts

ISBN 1–85934–047–4
£19.95
Published March 1997

Designed to make the search for funds easier still, many directories from the Focus Series will collect together, in individual volumes, details of trusts which have expressed an intention to support charitable activity in particular fields.

These directories, the first to appear, focus on trusts supporting causes associated with **Children and Youth**, **Environment, Animal Welfare and Heritage** and **Museums, Art Galleries and Performing Arts** projects. In addition to comprehensive details of the future funding priorities of the trusts listed, information is also provided on recent grants they have made.

Following the design established for the new-look *Directory of Grant Making Trusts*, these three directories will give grant-seekers working in the relevant fields a head-start in identifying sympathetic trusts and presenting well-tailored funding applications.

Applying to a Grant Making Trust

A guide for fundraisers

Anne Villemur
ISBN 1–85934–033–4
£7.95
Published February 1997

Grant-making trusts of all sizes complain that many of the funding applications that they receive fail either to match their stated funding priorities or to provide a coherent explanation of the project or programme for which support is being sought. Consequently, they are not eligible for consideration.

In response to this situation, and drawing on the author's years of experience as editor of *The Directory of Grant Making Trusts*, this book provides step-by-step guidance on drawing up a well-rounded 'case for support' which contains all the information that trustees require when considering an application.

Including practical advice on project costing, selecting appropriate trusts and chasing up applications, *Applying to a Grant Making Trust* is the companion volume to the *DGMT* which users have long been demanding.

Running a Local Fundraising Campaign
A guide for small voluntary organisations

Janet Hilderley

ISBN 1–85934–040–7
£9.95

Published April 1997

For many small charities or regional branches a successful local fundraising campaign can generate lasting results not only in terms of the money raised but also in terms of enhanced public awareness of an organisation's existence and core activities. However, the work involved in planning and running a campaign can be considerable and there are undoubted risks if anything goes wrong.

It was once believed that it was possible to apply the same basic strategy developed for a national campaign to a local situation. Experience has proved that this approach seldom works and that greater account needs to be taken of local circumstances.

This guide provides practical information and advice on the enormous range of activities which can make up a local fundraising campaign and helps readers to assess which options would be most appropriate for their charity.

PART ONE

Organisations by category and geographical area

This section lists the organisations appearing in this book under the items that they are willing to receive and by geographical area. It also includes a list of all the items included in the book grouped under general headings

Clothing, Jewellery, Personal Items

Clothing adults'

Avon

Age Concern (Bedminster)

Age Concern (Bristol)

Age Concern (Clifton)

Age Concern (Knowle)

Age Concern (Weston-super-Mare)

The Home Farm Trust

Service 9 – Bristol's Volunteer Bureau

Bedfordshire

Age Concern (Bedfordshire)

Bedford Refuge (part of Christian Family Care)

Luton Day Centre for the Homeless

Women's Royal Voluntary Service

Berkshire

Age Concern (Reading)

Christian Community Action

Thames Valley Hospice

Buckinghamshire

Age Concern (Milton Keynes)

Age Concern (Bucks)

High Wycombe General Aid Society

Cambridgeshire

Emmaus (Cambridge)

St Theresa's House

SOFA (Peterborough) Limited

Central

Alloa Community Enterprises Limited

Cheshire

Age Concern (Cheshire)

Arthritis Research (Arthritis & Rheumatism Council)

Blacon Project

Sue Ryder Foundation

Cumbria

Age Concern (Carlisle & District)

Age Concern (Northwest Cumbria)

Age Concern (South Lakeland)

Age Concern (Ulverston & District)

Family Advice Centre

Derbyshire

Age Concern (Derbyshire)

Arthritis & Rheumatism Council

Salcare

Treetops Hospice

Devon

Acorn Furniture & Clothing Project

Age Concern (Exeter)

Age Concern (Paignton)

Age Concern (Plymouth)

Age Concern (Torquay)

Arthritis & Rheumatism Council for Research

Exeter CVS Charity Shop

Halcyon Neighbourhood Centre (Furniture & Thrift Store)

League of Friends – Plymouth Psychiatric Service

Seaton & District Hospital League of Friends

Dorset

Age Concern (Blandford Forum)

Age Concern (Boscombe)

Age Concern (Bournemouth)

Age Concern (Poole)

Boscombe Salvation Army Charity Concern

The Friends of Blandford Community Hospital

Gingerbread

Pramacare

Sheltered Work Opportunities Project

East Sussex

Age Concern (Brighton)

Age Concern (East Sussex)

Betts Memorial Heart Foundation

Friends of the Eastbourne Hospitals

The House Project Charity Shop

Hove YMCA

Lewes Volunteer Bureau

Magpie Recycling Co-op Limited

Monday Club

Seaford Volunteers

Sussex Emmaus

Tools For Self Reliance

East Yorkshire

Age Concern (East Riding of Yorkshire)

RSPCA

Essex

Age Concern (Essex)

Barnardos (East Retail Region)

Epping Forest Field Centre

Farleigh (Mid-Essex Hospice)

The Friends of St Francis Hospice (Shops) Ltd

Hamelin Trust

Harlow Council for Voluntary Service

St Helena Hospice

St Luke's Hospice

Scope in Colchester (Castlegate Centre)

Gloucestershire

Full House Furniture and Recycling Service

Grampian

Aberdeen Cyrenians

Aberdeen Women's Aid

Voluntary Service (Aberdeen)

Greater Manchester

Age Concern (Manchester)

Age Concern (Metro Bury)

Age Concern (Metropolitan Rochdale)

Barnardos (North Retail Region)

Manchester & Salford Methodist Mission

The Salvation Army

Wesley Community Project

Gwent

Wastesavers Recycling Association

Gwynedd

Age Concern (Gwynedd a Món)

RSPCA (Meirionnydd Branch)

Hampshire

Rehab – Basingstoke & Alton Cardiac Appeal

Relate (Basingstoke & District)

Wessex Cancer Trust

Women's Aid to Former Yugoslavia

Hereford & Worcester

Arthritis Research Charity Shop

Community Chest

Full House Furniture & Recycling Service

ME Association Hereford & Worcester Group

Hertfordshire

Friends of Danesbury

National Animal Welfare Trust

The Stort Trust

Humberside

Age Concern (Hull)

Kent

Age Concern (Gillingham)

Canterbury Women's Refuge

Cats Protection League (Bexley Branch)

Friends of Animals League

Kent Red Cross Charity Shops

Medway Homes Refuge

RSPCA (Kent Rochester Branch)

St Cecilia's Cheshire Home

St Martin's Emmaus

Seven Springs Boutique

Seven Springs Cheshire Home

Lancashire

Age Concern (Blackburn & District)

Age Concern (Blackpool)

Age Concern (Lytham St Anne's)

Age Concern (Preston & South Ribble)

Emmaus (Greater Manchester)

Homeless in Blackpool

Queens Hall Help Committee

Salvation Army

Save the Children

Leicestershire

Age Concern (Leicester)

British Red Cross

RSPCA (Leicestershire Branch)

Lincolnshire

Care Shop

St Barnabas Hospice Shops

Strut Limited

London E

Crisis

Hackney Pensioners' Association

Immigration Welfare & Legal Advisory Services

Toynbee Hall

Waste Not Recycling

London EC

Help the Aged

Shelter, the National Campaign for Homeless People

London NW

Age Concern (Brent)

Age Concern (Westminster)

Brent Gingerbread

Mind in Camden Charity Shop

Simon Community

London SE

Elimination of Leukaemia Fund

League of Friends of Lewisham Hospital

St Christopher's Hospice

South Norwood Animal Rescue

London SW

Age Concern England

Cardinal Hume Centre for Young Homeless People

Centre '70 Community Shop

Oasis Aids Support Centre

RSPCA (Wimbledon & District)

Trinity Hospice

Wandsworth Housing Support Project

London W

Age Concern (Ealing Borough0

Age Concern (Hammersmith & Fulham)

London WC

The Children's Society

Imperial Cancer Research Fund

Leukaemia Research Fund

Lothian

Age Concern Scotland

Bethany Christian Trust

Cancer Research Campaign Scotland

Royal National Lifeboat Institution

Sue Ryder Foundation

Merseyside

Age Concern (Wirral)

Southport & District Cerebral Palsy Association

Vincent Harkins Day Care Centre

Middlesex

Age Concern (Feltham, Hanworth & Bedfont)

British Red Cross Society

Hillingdon Community Furniture Recycling Project

Norfolk

Centre 81

Dereham Gingerbread Club

Norfolk & Norwich Scope

Norwich Community Workshop

North Yorkshire

Age Concern (Coleraine)

Age Concern (North West Yorkshire)

Age Concern (York)

Emmaus (Scarborough)

Network (Whitby Resource Centre)

St Leonard's Hospice

The Salvation Army

Selby District AVS Charity Shop

Northamptonshire

Daventry Contact

The Salvation Army

Northern Ireland

Age Action Ireland

Arthritis & Rheumatism Council (NI)

Barnardos (Belfast)

Bryson House

Emmaus Liberty Belfast

The Salvation Army Charity Shop

Voluntary Service (Belfast)

War on Want (NI)

Nottinghamshire

Age Concern (Nottinghamshire)

Emmanuel House Day Centre

Family First Limited

The Home Farm Trust

Kirby Volunteer Centre

Nottingham Mencap

RSPCA

Orkney

Age Concern (Orkney)

Oxfordshire

Age Concern (Oxfordshire)

Hearing Dogs for the Deaf

Oxfam

Powys

Replay

Shropshire

Knowle Sports Association

Shropshire & Mid Wales Hospice

Shropshire Children's Scrap Store

Somerset

Age Concern (Clevedon)

Age Concern (Somerset)

British Red Cross Somerset Branch

Imperial Cancer Research Fund

St Margaret's Somerset Hospice

Women's Royal Voluntary Service

South Glamorgan

Age Concern (South Glamorgan)

Track 2000

South Yorkshire

Age Concern (Rotherham)

Arthritis Research

Bentley Association for Supportive Help

League of Friends – Royal Hallamshire Hospital

RSPCA (SYAC)

Salvation Army (Care & Share Shop)

Sheffield Family Services Unit

Staffordshire

Alsager Animals in Need

RSPCA (Burton-on-Trent & District Branch)

Strathclyde

Bethany House

Disability Network

Dundee Voluntary Action

Enable (Scottish Society for the Mentally Handicapped)

The Salvation Army

Suffolk

Age Concern (Suffolk)

Arthritis & Rheumatism Council for Research

Home Farm Trust

St Louis Family Service

Surrey

Age Concern (Sutton Borough (Shop))

British Red Cross

Croydon Voluntary Action

Disability Action Sutton

Hydon Hill Cheshire Home

Mental Aid Projects

Mind in Croydon

Prosa Foundation

Queen Elizabeth's Foundation for Disabled People

St Raphael's Hospice

Surrey Community Recycling and Play Project

Tayside

Brittle Bone Society

Tayside Furniture Project

Tyne & Wear

Age Concern (South Tyneside)

Community Furniture Service

Community Transport

St Oswald's Hospice

South Shields Ladies Lifeboat Comm

Wearside Women in Need

Warwickshire

Emmaus (Coventry & Warwickshire)

Oxfam

RACKS

Rokeby Infant School PTFA

Scope

West Midlands

Age Concern (Solihull)

Barnardos (West Retail Region)

Community Transport

Community Transport – Birmingham Project

Phoenix Sheltered Workshop

Stour Valley Cat Rescue

Walsall Gingerbread Advice Centre

West Sussex

Arthritis & Rheumatism Council for Research

The Missions to Seamen

St Bridget's Cheshire Home

West Yorkshire

Age Concern (Bradford & District)

Age Concern (Calderdale)

Age Concern (Huddersfield & District)

Age Concern (North Kirklees)

Age Concern (Wakefield District)

Batley Family & Community Centre, Community Furniture Service

Bradford Gingerbread Centre

Keighley Council for Voluntary Service

Kirkwood Hospice

RSPCA (Bradford & District Branch)

The Russell Street Project Limited

St George's Crypt

Wiltshire

Age Concern (Thamesdown)

Marie Curie Cancer Care

Prospect Hospice

RSPCA (Marlborough with Andover Branch)

RSPCA (Wiltshire North & Chippenham Branch)

Worcestershire

Malvern Churches Community Network

Clothing children's

Avon

Age Concern (Bedminster)

Age Concern (Bristol)

Age Concern (Clifton)

Age Concern (Knowle)

Age Concern (Weston-super-Mare)

The Home Farm Trust

Service 9 – Bristol's Volunteer Bureau

Bedfordshire

Age Concern (Bedfordshire)

Bedford Refuge (part of Christian Family Care)

Charis Mother & Baby Care (part of Christian Family Care)

Luton Day Centre for the Homeless

Women's Royal Voluntary Service

Berkshire

Age Concern (Reading)

Christian Community Action

Thames Valley Hospice

Buckinghamshire

Age Concern (Milton Keynes)

Age Concern (Bucks)

High Wycombe General Aid Society

Cambridgeshire

Emmaus (Cambridge)

St Theresa's House

SOFA (Peterborough) Limited

Central

Alloa Community Enterprises Limited

Cheshire

Age Concern (Cheshire)

Arthritis Research (Arthritis & Rheumatism Council)

Blacon Project

Sue Ryder Foundation

Cumbria

Age Concern (Carlisle & District)

Age Concern (Northwest Cumbria)

Age Concern (South Lakeland)

Age Concern (Ulverston & District)

Family Advice Centre

Derbyshire

Age Concern (Derbyshire)

Arthritis & Rheumatism Council

Salcare

Treetops Hospice

Devon

Acorn Furniture & Clothing Project

Age Concern (Exeter)

Age Concern (Paignton)

Age Concern (Plymouth)

Age Concern (Torquay)

Arthritis & Rheumatism Council for Research

Exeter CVS Charity Shop

Halcyon Neighbourhood Centre (Furniture & Thrift Store)

League of Friends – Plymouth Psychiatric Service

Seaton & District Hospital League of Friends

Dorset

Age Concern (Blandford Forum)

Age Concern (Boscombe)

Age Concern (Bournemouth)

Age Concern (Poole)

Boscombe Salvation Army Charity Concern

The Friends of Blandford Community Hospital

Gingerbread

Pramacare

East Sussex

Age Concern (Brighton)

Age Concern (East Sussex)

Betts Memorial Heart Foundation

The House Project Charity Shop

Hove YMCA

Lewes Volunteer Bureau

Magpie Recycling Co-op Limited

Sussex Emmaus

East Yorkshire

Age Concern (East Riding of Yorkshire)

RSPCA

Essex

Age Concern (Essex)

Barnardos (East Retail Region)

Epping Forest Field Centre

Farleigh (Mid-Essex Hospice)

The Friends of St Francis Hospice (Shops) Ltd

Hamelin Trust

Harlow Council for Voluntary Service

St Helena Hospice

St Luke's Hospice

Scope in Colchester (Castlegate Centre)

Gloucestershire

Full House Furniture and Recycling Service

Grampian

Aberdeen Women's Aid

Voluntary Service (Aberdeen)

Greater Manchester

Age Concern (Manchester)

Age Concern (Metro Bury)

Age Concern (Metropolitan Rochdale)

Barnardos (North Retail Region)

Manchester & Salford Methodist Mission

Manchester One Parent Family Advice Centre

The Salvation Army

Wesley Community Project

Gwent

Wastesavers Recycling Association

Gwynedd

Age Concern (Gwynedd a Món)

RSPCA (Meirionnydd Branch)

Hampshire

Dorcas Project/Basics Bank

Rehab – Basingstoke & Alton Cardiac Appeal

Wessex Cancer Trust

Women's Aid to Former Yugoslavia

Hereford & Worcester

Arthritis Research Charity Shop

Community Chest

Full House Furniture & Recycling Service

ME Association Hereford & Worcester Group

Hertfordshire

Friends of Danesbury

National Animal Welfare Trust

The Stort Trust

Humberside

Age Concern (Hull)

Kent

Age Concern (Gillingham)

Bexley Downs Syndrome Group

Canterbury Women's Refuge

Cats Protection League (Bexley Branch)

Friends of Animals League

Hope Romania

Kent Red Cross Charity Shops

Medway Homes Refuge

RSPCA (Kent Rochester Branch)

St Cecilia's Cheshire Home

St Martin's Emmaus

Seven Springs Cheshire Home

Lancashire

Age Concern (Blackburn & District)

Age Concern (Blackpool)

Age Concern (Lytham St Anne's)

Age Concern (Preston & South Ribble)

Emmaus (Greater Manchester)

Homeless in Blackpool

Queens Hall Help Committee

Salvation Army

Save the Children

Leicestershire

Age Concern (Leicester)

Baby Gear

British Red Cross

Loughborough Community Care

RSPCA (Leicestershire Branch)

Lincolnshire

Care Shop

St Barnabas Hospice Shops

Strut Limited

London E

Hackney Pensioners' Association

Immigration Welfare & Legal Advisory Services

Toynbee Hall

Waste Not Recycling

London EC

Help the Aged

Shelter, the National Campaign for Homeless People

London NW

Age Concern (Brent)

Age Concern (Westminster)

Brent Gingerbread

Mind in Camden Charity Shop

London SE

Elimination of Leukaemia Fund

League of Friends of Lewisham Hospital

St Christopher's Hospice

Shaftesbury Resources Centre

London SW

Age Concern England

Cardinal Hume Centre for Young Homeless People

Centre '70 Community Shop

Oasis Aids Support Centre

RSPCA (Wimbledon & District)

Trinity Hospice

Wandsworth Housing Support Project

London W

Age Concern (Ealing Borough0

Age Concern (Hammersmith & Fulham)

Catholic Children's Society (Westminster)

London WC

The Children's Society

Imperial Cancer Research Fund

Leukaemia Research Fund

Lothian

Age Concern Scotland

Bethany Christian Trust

Cancer Research Campaign Scotland

Royal National Lifeboat Institution

Sue Ryder Foundation

Merseyside

Age Concern (Wirral)

Southport & District Cerebral Palsy Association

Middlesex

Age Concern (Feltham, Hanworth & Bedfont)

British Red Cross Society

Hillingdon Community Furniture Recycling Project

Norfolk

Centre 81

Dereham Gingerbread Club

Norfolk & Norwich Scope

North Yorkshire

Age Concern (Coleralne)

Age Concern (North West Yorkshire)

Age Concern (York)

Emmaus (Scarborough)

Network (Whitby Resource Centre)

St Leonard's Hospice

The Salvation Army

Selby District AVS Charity Shop

Northampshire

Daventry Contact

The Salvation Army

Northern Ireland

Age Action Ireland

Arthritis & Rheumatism Council (NI)

Barnardos (Belfast)

Bryson House

Emmaus Liberty Belfast

The Salvation Army Charity Shop

Voluntary Service (Belfast)

War on Want (NI)

Nottinghamshire

Age Concern (Nottinghamshire)

Beeston Volunteer Bureau

Emmanuel House Day Centre

Family First Limited

The Home Farm Trust

Kirby Volunteer Centre

Nottingham Mencap

RSPCA

Orkney

Age Concern (Orkney)

Oxfordshire

Age Concern (Oxfordshire)

Hearing Dogs for the Deaf

Oxfam

Powys

Replay

Shropshire

Knowle Sports Association

Shropshire & Mid Wales Hospice

Shropshire Children's Scrap Store

Somerset

Age Concern (Clevedon)

Age Concern (Somerset)

British Red Cross Somerset Branch

Imperial Cancer Research Fund

St Margaret's Somerset Hospice

Women's Royal Voluntary Service

South Glamorgan

Age Concern (South Glamorgan)

Track 2000

South Yorkshire

Age Concern (Rotherham)

Arthritis Research

Bentley Association for Supportive Help

Cot-Age – Child Safety & Nursery Equipment

League of Friends – Royal Hallamshire Hospital

RSPCA (SYAC)

Salvation Army (Care & Share Shop)

Sheffield Family Services Unit

Staffordshire

Alsager Animals in Need

RSPCA (Burton-on-Trent & District Branch)

Strathclyde

Bethany House

Disability Network

Dundee Voluntary Action

Enable (Scottish Society for the Mentally Handicapped)

The Salvation Army

Suffolk

Age Concern (Suffolk)

Arthritis & Rheumatism Council for Research

Home Farm Trust

St Louis Family Service

Surrey

Age Concern (Sutton Borough (Shop))

British Red Cross

Christian Family Concern

Croydon Voluntary Action

Disability Action Sutton

Hydon Hill Cheshire Home

Mental Aid Projects

Mind in Croydon

Prosa Foundation

St Raphael's Hospice

Surrey Community Recycling and Play Project

Tayside

Brittle Bone Society

Tayside Furniture Project

Tyne & Wear

Age Concern (South Tyneside)

Community Transport

St Oswald's Hospice

South Shields Ladies Lifeboat Comm

Wearside Women in Need

Warwickshire

Emmaus (Coventry & Warwickshire)

Oxfam

RACKS

Rokeby Infant School PTFA

Scope

West Midlands

Age Concern (Solihull)

Barnardos (West Retail Region)

Community Transport

Community Transport – Birmingham Project

Phoenix Sheltered Workshop

Stour Valley Cat Rescue

Walsall Gingerbread Advice Centre

West Sussex

Arthritis & Rheumatism Council for Research

St Bridget's Cheshire Home

West Yorkshire

Age Concern (Bradford & District)

Age Concern (Calderdale)

Age Concern (Huddersfield & District)

Age Concern (North Kirklees)

Age Concern (Wakefield District)

Batley Family & Community Centre, Community Furniture Service

Bradford Gingerbread Centre

Keighley Council for Voluntary Service

Kirkwood Hospice

RSPCA (Bradford & District Branch)

The Russell Street Project Limited

St George's Crypt

Wiltshire

Age Concern (Thamesdown)

Marie Curie Cancer Care

Prospect Hospice

RSPCA (Marlborough with Andover Branch)

RSPCA (Wiltshire North & Chippenham Branch)

Worcestershire

Malvern Churches Community Network

Fur coats

Berkshire
Christian Community Action

Thames Valley Hospice

Buckinghamshire
Age Concern (Bucks)

Central
Alloa Community Enterprises Limited

Cheshire
Arthritis Research (Arthritis & Rheumatism Council)

Derbyshire
Salcare

Devon
Acorn Furniture & Clothing Project

Dorset
Boscombe Salvation Army Charity Concern

East Sussex
Sussex Emmaus

Essex
Barnardos (East Retail Region)

Farleigh (Mid-Essex Hospice)

Grampian
Voluntary Service (Aberdeen)

Greater Manchester
Age Concern (Metropolitan Rochdale)

Barnardos (North Retail Region)

Manchester & Salford Methodist Mission

The Salvation Army

Wesley Community Project

Hampshire
Rehab – Basingstoke & Alton Cardiac Appeal

Kent
Age Concern (Gillingham)

Friends of Animals League

Hope Romania

Seven Springs Boutique

Seven Springs Cheshire Home

London E
Hackney Pensioners' Association

Waste Not Recycling

London NW
Age Concern (Brent)

Brent Gingerbread

London SE
Elimination of Leukaemia Fund

London SW
Trinity Hospice

London W
Age Concern (Ealing Borough0

Catholic Children's Society (Westminster)

London WC
Leukaemia Research Fund

Lothian
Age Concern Scotland

Sue Ryder Foundation

Merseyside
Age Concern (Wirral)

Southport & District Cerebral Palsy Association

Middlesex
Hillingdon Community Furniture Recycling Project

Norfolk
Centre 81

North Yorkshire
Age Concern (Coleraine)

Selby District AVS Charity Shop

Northamptonshire
Daventry Contact

Northern Ireland
Age Action Ireland

Barnardos (Belfast)

Voluntary Service (Belfast)

Nottinghamshire
Nottingham Mencap

Shropshire
Knowle Sports Association

South Glamorgan
Track 2000

South Yorkshire
Arthritis Research

Suffolk
St Louis Family Service

Surrey
Hydon Hill Cheshire Home

Prosa Foundation

St Raphael's Hospice

Surrey Community Recycling and Play Project

Tayside
Brittle Bone Society

Tyne & Wear
Age Concern (South Tyneside)

Warwickshire
Rokeby Infant School PTFA

West Midlands
Barnardos (West Retail Region)

West Sussex
Arthritis & Rheumatism Council for Research

Hearing aids

Berkshire

Christian Community Action

Dorset

Boscombe Salvation Army
Charity Concern

East Sussex

Sussex Emmaus

Greater Manchester

The Salvation Army

Wesley Community Project

Hereford & Worcester

Arthritis Research Charity Shop

Kent

Age Concern (Gillingham)

Hope Romania

Middlesex

Hillingdon Community
Furniture Recycling Project

North Yorkshire

Age Concern (North West
Yorkshire)

Northamptonshire

Daventry Contact

Oxfordshire

Age Concern (Oxford)

Strathclyde

Disability Network

Suffolk

Arthritis & Rheumatism Council
for Research

Warwickshire

Emmaus (Coventry &
Warwickshire)

West Sussex

Guild Care

Jewellery

Avon

Age Concern (Bedminster)

Age Concern (Bristol)

Age Concern (Clifton)

Age Concern (Knowle)

Age Concern (Weston-super-
Mare)

The Home Farm Trust

Service 9 – Bristol's Volunteer
Bureau

Bedfordshire

Age Concern (Bedfordshire)

Luton Day Centre for the
Homeless

The Royal Society for the
Protection of Birds

The Salvation Army

Berkshire

Age Concern (Reading)

Christian Community Action

Thames Valley Hospice

Buckinghamshire

Age Concern (Milton Keynes)

Age Concern (Bucks)

High Wycombe General Aid
Society

Cambridgeshire

Cambridge SOFA

Emmaus (Cambridge)

Newark Play Association

SOFA (Peterborough) Limited

Spaywatch

Central

Alloa Community Enterprises
Limited

Cheshire

Age Concern (Cheshire)

Arthritis Research (Arthritis &
Rheumatism Council)

Sue Ryder Foundation

Cumbria

Age Concern (Carlisle & District)

Age Concern (Northwest Cumbria)

Age Concern (South Lakeland)

Age Concern (Ulverston & District)

Derbyshire

Age Concern (Derbyshire)

Arthritis & Rheumatism Council

Salcare

Treetops Hospice

Devon

Age Concern (Exeter)

Age Concern (Paignton)

Age Concern (Plymouth)

Age Concern (Torquay)

Arthritis & Rheumatism Council for Research

Exeter CVS Charity Shop

League of Friends – Plymouth Psychiatric Service

Seaton & District Hospital League of Friends

Dorset

Age Concern (Blandford Forum)

Age Concern (Boscombe)

Age Concern (Bournemouth)

Age Concern (Poole)

Boscombe Salvation Army Charity Concern

Christchurch Hospital League of Friends

The Friends of Blandford Community Hospital

Gingerbread

Pramacare

Sheltered Work Opportunities Project

East Sussex

Age Concern (Brighton)

Age Concern (East Sussex)

Betts Memorial Heart Foundation

Bexhill & District Diabetic Group

Feline Foster

Friends of the Eastbourne Hospitals

The House Project Charity Shop

Hove YMCA

Lewes Volunteer Bureau

Monday Club

Peacehaven & Telscombe Volunteer Bureau

Royal National Lifeboat Institution

Seaford Volunteers

Sussex Emmaus

East Yorkshire

Age Concern (East Riding of Yorkshire)

RSPCA

Essex

Age Concern (Essex)

Barnardos (East Retail Region)

Farleigh (Mid-Essex Hospice)

The Friends of St Francis Hospice (Shops) Ltd

Hamelin Trust

St Helena Hospice

St Luke's Hospice

Scope in Colchester (Castlegate Centre)

Gloucestershire

Full House Furniture and Recycling Service

Grampian

Aberdeen Women's Aid

Voluntary Service (Aberdeen)

Greater Manchester

Age Concern (Manchester)

Age Concern (Metro Bury)

Barnardos (North Retail Region)

Manchester & Salford Methodist Mission

The Salvation Army

Wesley Community Project

Gwynedd

Age Concern (Gwynedd a Món)

RSPCA (Meirionnydd Branch)

RSPCA (West Gwynedd Branch)

Hampshire

National Schizophrenia Fellowship

Rehab – Basingstoke & Alton Cardiac Appeal

Relate (Basingstoke & District)

Wessex Cancer Trust

Hereford & Worcester

Arthritis Research Charity Shop

Community Chest

Full House Furniture & Recycling Service

ME Association Hereford & Worcester Group

Hertfordshire

Dacorum Council for Voluntary Service

Friends of Danesbury

National Animal Welfare Trust

The Stort Trust

Humberside

Age Concern (Hull)

Kent

Age Concern (Gillingham)

Bexley Downs Syndrome Group

British Red Cross Margate Centre

Canterbury Women's Refuge

Cats Protection League (Bexley Branch)

Dartford District Volunteer Bureau

Friends of Animals League

Kent Red Cross Charity Shops

Lord Whisky Sanctuary Fund

RSPCA (Kent Rochester Branch)

St Cecilia's Cheshire Home

St Martin's Emmaus

Seven Springs Boutique

Seven Springs Cheshire Home

Thanet Mind (Mental Health Day Centre)

Lancashire

Age Concern (Blackburn & District)

Age Concern (Blackpool)

Age Concern (Lytham St Anne's)

Age Concern (Preston & South Ribble)

Emmaus (Greater Manchester)

Homeless in Blackpool

Horses & Ponies Protection Association

Queens Hall Help Committee

Salvation Army

Save the Children

Leicestershire

Age Concern (Leicester)

British Red Cross

Cat Action Trust

RSPCA (Leicestershire Branch)

Lincolnshire

Artlandish Limited

Care Shop

Non-Animal Medical Research

St Barnabas Hospice Shops

Strut Limited

London E

Hackney Pensioners' Association

Immigration Welfare & Legal Advisory Services

Toynbee Hall

Walthamstow After School Club

London EC

Help the Aged

Shelter, the National Campaign for Homeless People

London NW

Age Concern (Brent)

Age Concern (Westminster)

Brent Gingerbread

Mind in Camden Charity Shop

London SE

Elimination of Leukaemia Fund

Friends of King's College Hospital

League of Friends of Lewisham Hospital

St Christopher's Hospice

South Norwood Animal Rescue

London SW

Age Concern England

Cardinal Hume Centre for Young Homeless People

Centre '70 Community Shop

Marie Curie Cancer Care

Oasis Aids Support Centre

RSPCA (Richmond, Twickenham & Barnes Branch)

RSPCA (Wimbledon & District)

Trinity Hospice

Wandsworth Housing Support Project

London W

Age Concern (Ealing Borough0

Age Concern (Hammersmith & Fulham)

Catholic Children's Society (Westminster)

Royal National Mission to Deep Sea Fishermen

Scoliosis Association (UK)

London WC

The Children's Society

Imperial Cancer Research Fund

Leukaemia Research Fund

Lothian

Age Concern Scotland

Bethany Christian Trust

Cancer Research Campaign Scotland

The National Bible Society of Scotland

Royal National Lifeboat Institution

Sue Ryder Foundation

Merseyside

Age Concern (Wirral)

Newton Visual Impaired Group

Southport & District Cerebral Palsy Association

Middlesex

Age Concern (Feltham, Hanworth & Bedfont)

British Red Cross Society

Hillingdon Community Furniture Recycling Project

League of Friends of Teddington Memorial Hospital

Norfolk

League of Friends – James Paget Hospital

Norfolk & Norwich Scope

The Norfolk Society

Norwich Community Workshop

North Yorkshire

Age Concern (Coleraine)

Age Concern (North West Yorkshire)

Age Concern (York)

Emmaus (Scarborough)

St Leonard's Hospice

The Salvation Army

Selby District AVS Charity Shop

Northampshire

Caring & Sharing Trust

Daventry Contact

Northern Ireland

Age Action Ireland

Arthritis & Rheumatism Council (NI)

Barnardos (Belfast)

Emmaus Liberty Belfast

The Salvation Army Charity Shop

Voluntary Service (Belfast)

War on Want (NI)

Nottinghamshire

Age Concern (Nottinghamshire)

Beeston Volunteer Bureau

Emmanuel House Day Centre

The Home Farm Trust

Kirby Volunteer Centre

Nottingham Mencap

RSPCA

Orkney

Age Concern (Orkney)

Oxfordshire

Age Concern (Oxford)

Age Concern (Oxfordshire)

The Blue Cross

Hearing Dogs for the Deaf

Katharine House Hospice

Oxfam

The Worldwide Fund for Nature (WWF)

Powys

Replay

Shropshire

Knowle Sports Association

Shropshire & Mid Wales Hospice

Shropshire Children's Scrap Store

Somerset

Age Concern (Clevedon)

Age Concern (Somerset)

British Red Cross Somerset Branch

Imperial Cancer Research Fund

St Margaret's Somerset Hospice

West Somerset Council for Voluntary Service

South Glamorgan

Age Concern (South Glamorgan)

Royal National Lifeboat Institution

Track 2000

South Yorkshire

Age Concern (Rotherham)

Arthritis Research

Bentley Association for Supportive Help

League of Friends – Royal Hallamshire Hospital

RSPCA (SYAC)

Salvation Army (Care & Share Shop)

Sheffield Family Services Unit

Staffordshire

Alsager Animals in Need

RSPCA (Burton-on-Trent & District Branch)

RSPCA (North Staffs Branch)

Strathclyde

Disability Network

Dundee Voluntary Action

Enable (Scottish Society for the Mentally Handicapped)

The Salvation Army

Suffolk

Age Concern (Suffolk)

Arthritis & Rheumatism Council for Research

Home Farm Trust

St Louis Family Service

Surrey

Age Concern (Sutton Borough (Shop))

British Red Cross

Cats in Care

Community Scrap Scheme

Croydon Voluntary Action

Disability Action Sutton

Epsom & Ewell Phab Club

Hydon Hill Cheshire Home

Inner Wheel Club of Ewell

Mental Aid Projects

Mind in Croydon

Queen Elizabeth's Foundation for Disabled People

Royal National Mission To Deep Sea Fishermen

St Raphael's Hospice

Surrey Community Recycling and Play Project

Tayside

Brittle Bone Society

Tyne & Wear

Age Concern (South Tyneside)

St Oswald's Hospice

South Shields Ladies Lifeboat Comm

Warwickshire

Emmaus (Coventry & Warwickshire)

Oxfam

RACKS

Scope

West Midlands

Age Concern (Solihull)

Barnardos (West Retail Region)

Birmingham Play Resource Centre

Phoenix Sheltered Workshop

RSPCA (Birmingham & District Branch)

Stour Valley Cat Rescue

Walsall Gingerbread Advice Centre

West Sussex

Arthritis & Rheumatism Council for Research

St Bridget's Cheshire Home

West Yorkshire

Age Concern (Bradford & District)

Age Concern (Calderdale)

Age Concern (Huddersfield & District)

Age Concern (North Kirklees)

Age Concern (Wakefield District)

Keighley Council for Voluntary Service

Kirkwood Hospice

Pet Animals Welfare Society (PAWS)

RSPCA (Bradford & District Branch)

Wiltshire

Age Concern (Thamesdown)

Marie Curie Cancer Care

Prospect Hospice

RSPCA (Marlborough with Andover Branch)

RSPCA (Wiltshire North & Chippenham Branch)

....

Worcestershire

Malvern Churches Community Network

Spectacles

Bedfordshire

Friends of Biggleswade Hospital

Women's Royal Voluntary Service

....

Berkshire

Christian Community Action

Thames Valley Hospice

....

Cambridgeshire

Emmaus (Cambridge)

....

Cheshire

Sue Ryder Foundation

....

Cumbria

Age Concern (Carlisle & District)

Age Concern (Northwest Cumbria)

Age Concern (Ulverston & District)

....

Derbyshire

Salcare

....

Devon

Arthritis & Rheumatism Council for Research

....

Dorset

Boscombe Salvation Army Charity Concern

....

East Sussex

Lewes Volunteer Bureau

Sussex Emmaus

....

Essex

St Helena Hospice

....

Greater Manchester

The Salvation Army

Wesley Community Project

....

Hereford & Worcester

Arthritis Research Charity Shop

Hertfordshire

The Stort Trust

....

Kent

Bexley Downs Syndrome Group

St Cecilia's Cheshire Home

Seven Springs Cheshire Home

....

Lancashire

Age Concern (Blackpool)

Age Concern (Lytham St Anne's)

Queens Hall Help Committee

....

Lincolnshire

St Barnabas Hospice Shops

....

London E

Hackney Pensioners' Association

....

London EC

Friends of Moorfields Eye Hospital

Shelter, the National Campaign for Homeless People

....

London NW

Brent Gingerbread

Mind in Camden Charity Shop

....

London SE

St Christopher's Hospice

....

London SW

Centre '70 Community Shop

Trinity Hospice

Wandsworth Housing Support Project

....

Lothian

Age Concern Scotland

Sue Ryder Foundation

....

Middlesex

Hillingdon Community Furniture Recycling Project

North Yorkshire

Emmaus (Scarborough)

The Salvation Army

Northamptonshire

Daventry Contact

Northern Ireland

Age Action Ireland

War on Want (NI)

Nottinghamshire

Eastwood Volunteer Bureau

Oxfordshire

Age Concern (Oxford)

Shropshire

Knowle Sports Association

South Glamorgan

Track 2000

Strathclyde

David Livingstone International Disability Network

Suffolk

Arthritis & Rheumatism Council for Research

St Louis Family Service

Surrey

Community Scrap Scheme

Hydon Hill Cheshire Home

Inner Wheel Club of Ewell

SHCVS

Surrey Community Recycling and Play Project

Vision Aid Overseas

Warwickshire

Emmaus (Coventry & Warwickshire)

Scope

West Midlands

Phoenix Sheltered Workshop

West Sussex

British Red Cross

Guild Care

West Yorkshire

Kirkwood Hospice

RSPCA (Bradford & District Branch)

Watches

Avon

Age Concern (Bristol)

Service 9 – Bristol's Volunteer Bureau

Bedfordshire

Age Concern (Bedfordshire)

The Royal Society for the Protection of Birds

Berkshire

Age Concern (Reading)

Christian Community Action

Thames Valley Hospice

Buckinghamshire

Age Concern (Bucks)

High Wycombe General Aid Society

Cambridgeshire

Cambridge SOFA

Central

Alloa Community Enterprises Limited

Cheshire

Age Concern (Cheshire)

Arthritis Research (Arthritis & Rheumatism Council)

Cumbria

Age Concern (Carlisle & District)

Age Concern (Northwest Cumbria)

Age Concern (South Lakeland)

Age Concern (Ulverston & District)

Derbyshire

Age Concern (Derbyshire)

Arthritis & Rheumatism Council

Salcare

Treetops Hospice

Devon

Arthritis & Rheumatism Council for Research

Dorset

Boscombe Salvation Army Charity Concern

Christchurch Hospital League of Friends

The Friends of Blandford Community Hospital

Pramacare

East Sussex

Age Concern (Brighton)

Age Concern (East Sussex)

Betts Memorial Heart Foundation

Bexhill & District Diabetic Group

Feline Foster

Lewes Volunteer Bureau

Royal National Lifeboat Institution

Seaford Volunteers

Sussex Emmaus

East Yorkshire

Age Concern (East Riding of Yorkshire)

RSPCA

Essex

Barnardos (East Retail Region)

Farleigh (Mid-Essex Hospice)

The Friends of St Francis Hospice (Shops) Ltd

Hamelin Trust

St Helena Hospice

St Luke's Hospice

Gloucestershire

Full House Furniture and Recycling Service

Grampian

Aberdeen Women's Aid

Voluntary Service (Aberdeen)

Greater Manchester

Age Concern (Manchester)

Age Concern (Metro Bury)

Barnardos (North Retail Region)

Manchester & Salford Methodist Mission

The Salvation Army

Wesley Community Project

Gwynedd

Age Concern (Gwynedd a Món)

RSPCA (West Gwynedd Branch)

Hampshire

Rehab – Basingstoke & Alton Cardiac Appeal

Relate (Basingstoke & District)

Hereford & Worcester

Arthritis Research Charity Shop

Full House Furniture & Recycling Service

Hertfordshire

Friends of Danesbury

National Animal Welfare Trust

The Stort Trust

Humberside

Age Concern (Hull)

Kent

Age Concern (Gillingham)

Bexley Downs Syndrome Group

British Red Cross Margate Centre

Dartford District Volunteer Bureau

Friends of Animals League

Kent Red Cross Charity Shops

Lord Whisky Sanctuary Fund

RSPCA (Kent Rochester Branch)

St Cecilia's Cheshire Home

St Martin's Emmaus

Seven Springs Cheshire Home

Lancashire

Age Concern (Blackburn & District)

Age Concern (Blackpool)

Age Concern (Lytham St Anne's)

Emmaus (Greater Manchester)

Homeless in Blackpool

Horses & Ponies Protection Association

Queens Hall Help Committee

Save the Children

Leicestershire

Age Concern (Leicester)

British Red Cross

RSPCA (Leicestershire Branch)

Lincolnshire

Care Shop

Non-Animal Medical Research

St Barnabas Hospice Shops

London E

Hackney Pensioners' Association

Immigration Welfare & Legal Advisory Services

Toynbee Hall

Walthamstow After School Club

London EC

Help the Aged

Shelter, the National Campaign for Homeless People

London NW

Age Concern (Brent)

Age Concern (Westminster)

Brent Gingerbread

Mind in Camden Charity Shop

London SE

St Christopher's Hospice

Shaftesbury Resources Centre

South Norwood Animal Rescue

London SW

Age Concern England

Centre '70 Community Shop

The Homeless Furniture Project

Marie Curie Cancer Care

Oasis Aids Support Centre

Trinity Hospice

Wandsworth Housing Support Project

London W

Age Concern (Ealing Borough0

Age Concern (Hammersmith & Fulham)

Royal National Mission to Deep Sea Fishermen

Scoliosis Association (UK)

London WC

The Children's Society

Imperial Cancer Research Fund

Leukaemia Research Fund

Lothian

Age Concern Scotland

Bethany Christian Trust

Cancer Research Campaign Scotland

The National Bible Society of Scotland

Royal National Lifeboat Institution

Sue Ryder Foundation

Merseyside

Age Concern (Wirral)

Newton Visual Impaired Group

Southport & District Cerebral Palsy Association

Vincent Harkins Day Care Centre

Middlesex

Age Concern (Feltham, Hanworth & Bedfont)

British Red Cross Society

Hillingdon Community Furniture Recycling Project

Norfolk

Centre 81

League of Friends – James Paget Hospital

North Yorkshire

Age Concern (North West Yorkshire)

Emmaus (Scarborough)

St Leonard's Hospice

The Salvation Army

Selby District AVS Charity Shop

Northamptonshire

Caring & Sharing Trust

Daventry Contact

Northern Ireland

Age Action Ireland

Barnardos (Belfast)

The Salvation Army Charity Shop

Voluntary Service (Belfast)

War on Want (NI)

Nottinghamshire

Age Concern (Nottinghamshire)

The Home Farm Trust

Kirby Volunteer Centre

RSPCA

Oxfordshire

Age Concern (Oxford)

Age Concern (Oxfordshire)

Katharine House Hospice

Oxfam

The Worldwide Fund for Nature (WWF)

Powys

Replay

Shropshire

Knowle Sports Association

Shropshire & Mid Wales Hospice

Somerset

Age Concern (Somerset)

British Red Cross Somerset Branch

St Margaret's Somerset Hospice

South Glamorgan

Age Concern (South Glamorgan)

Track 2000

South Yorkshire

Age Concern (Rotherham)

Arthritis Research

Bentley Association for Supportive Help

RSPCA (SYAC)

Salvation Army (Care & Share Shop)

Sheffield Family Services Unit

Staffordshire

Alsager Animals in Need

Strathclyde

David Livingstone International Disability Network

Suffolk

Age Concern (Suffolk)

Arthritis & Rheumatism Council for Research

Home Farm Trust

St Louis Family Service

Surrey

Age Concern (Sutton Borough (Shop))

British Red Cross

Community Scrap Scheme

Disability Action Sutton

Hydon Hill Cheshire Home

Mental Aid Projects

Mind in Croydon

St Raphael's Hospice

Surrey Community Recycling and Play Project

Tayside

Brittle Bone Society

Tyne & Wear

Age Concern (South Tyneside)

South Shields Ladies Lifeboat Comm

Warwickshire

Emmaus (Coventry & Warwickshire)

Oxfam

RACKS

Scope

West Midlands

Age Concern (Solihull)

Barnardos (West Retail Region)

Birmingham Play Resource Centre

Phoenix Sheltered Workshop

Stour Valley Cat Rescue

Walsall Gingerbread Advice Centre

West Sussex

Arthritis & Rheumatism Council for Research

St Bridget's Cheshire Home

West Yorkshire

Age Concern (Bradford & District)

Age Concern (Calderdale)

Age Concern (Huddersfield & District)

Cash from Trash in Aid of Charities

Keighley Council for Voluntary Service

Kirkwood Hospice

RSPCA (Bradford & District Branch)

Wiltshire

Age Concern (Thamesdown)

Prospect Hospice

RSPCA (Marlborough with Andover Branch)

Wedding clothes for hire

Avon

Age Concern (Bedminster)

Age Concern (Bristol)

Age Concern (Clifton)

Age Concern (Knowle)

Age Concern (Weston-super-Mare)

Berkshire

Christian Community Action

Central

Alloa Community Enterprises Limited

Cheshire

Arthritis Research (Arthritis & Rheumatism Council)

Sue Ryder Foundation

Derbyshire

Arthritis & Rheumatism Council

Salcare

Devon

Age Concern (Exeter)

Age Concern (Paignton)

Age Concern (Torquay)

Dorset

Age Concern (Blandford Forum)

Age Concern (Boscombe)

Age Concern (Poole)

East Sussex

Age Concern (Brighton)

Essex

Barnardos (East Retail Region)

Farleigh (Mid-Essex Hospice)

The Friends of St Francis Hospice (Shops) Ltd

St Helena Hospice

Greater Manchester

Barnardos (North Retail Region)

Hereford & Worcester

Arthritis Research Charity Shop

Humberside

Age Concern (Hull)

Lancashire

Age Concern (Lytham St Anne's)

Lincolnshire

St Barnabas Hospice Shops

London EC

Help the Aged

London NW

Age Concern (Brent)

Age Concern (Westminster)

Lothian

Sue Ryder Foundation

Middlesex

Hillingdon Community Furniture Recycling Project

Norfolk

Centre 81

Northern Ireland

Arthritis & Rheumatism Council (NI)

Barnardos (Belfast)

The Salvation Army Charity Shop

Nottinghamshire

Age Concern (Nottinghamshire)

Oxfordshire

Age Concern (Oxford)

Oxfam

Shropshire

Knowle Sports Association

Shropshire & Mid Wales Hospice

Somerset

Age Concern (Clevedon)

Imperial Cancer Research Fund

St Margaret's Somerset Hospice

South Glamorgan

Track 2000

South Yorkshire

Arthritis Research

Suffolk

Age Concern (Suffolk)

Home Farm Trust

Warwickshire

Emmaus (Coventry & Warwickshire)

Oxfam

Scope

West Midlands

Age Concern (Solihull)

Barnardos (West Retail Region)

West Sussex

Arthritis & Rheumatism Council for Research

West Yorkshire

Kirkwood Hospice

The Russell Street Project Limited

Home and Garden

Baby equipment

Avon

Age Concern (Bristol)

Bedfordshire

Bedford Refuge (part of Christian Family Care)

Charis Mother & Baby Care (part of Christian Family Care)

Luton Day Centre for the Homeless

Women's Royal Voluntary Service

Berkshire

Age Concern (Reading)

Christian Community Action

Thames Valley Hospice

Buckinghamshire

Age Concern (Milton Keynes)

Age Concern (Bucks)

High Wycombe General Aid Society

Slough Furniture Project

Cambridgeshire

Cambridge SOFA

St Theresa's House

SOFA (Peterborough) Limited

Central

Alloa Community Enterprises Limited

Cheshire

3C Teamwork

Arthritis Research (Arthritis & Rheumatism Council)

Blacon Project

Sue Ryder Foundation

Cumbria

Age Concern (Carlisle & District)

Age Concern (Northwest Cumbria)

Age Concern (South Lakeland)

Age Concern (Ulverston & District)

Family Advice Centre

Derbyshire

Age Concern (Derbyshire)

Arthritis & Rheumatism Council

Derby Furniture Project

Salcare

Treetops Hospice

Devon

Acorn Furniture & Clothing Project

Halcyon Neighbourhood Centre (Furniture & Thrift Store)

Seaton & District Hospital League of Friends

Turntable Furniture Project

Dorset

Boscombe Salvation Army Charity Concern

Gingerbread

Durham

FRADE

East Sussex

Eastbourne Playbus

Hastings Furniture Service

Sussex Emmaus

East Yorkshire

Age Concern (East Riding of Yorkshire)

Hull Resettlement Furniture Service

RSPCA

Essex

Farleigh (Mid-Essex Hospice)

The Friends of St Francis Hospice (Shops) Ltd

Hamelin Trust

Harlow Council for Voluntary Service

St Helena Hospice

St Luke's Hospice

South Essex Community Furniture Service

Gloucestershire

Full House Furniture and Recycling Service

The Furniture Recycling Project

Grampian

Voluntary Service (Aberdeen)

Greater Manchester

Age Concern (Manchester)

Age Concern (Metro Bury)

Bolton Community Transport

Manchester & Salford Methodist Mission

Manchester One Parent Family Advice Centre

The Salvation Army

Wesley Community Project

Gwent

The Community Furniture Project

Gwynedd

RSPCA (Meirionnydd Branch)

Hampshire

Dorcas Project/Basics Bank

Rehab – Basingstoke & Alton Cardiac Appeal

Resettlement Project – South Hants

Hereford & Worcester

Arthritis Research Charity Shop

Community Chest

Full House Furniture & Recycling Service

Furniture Action

Hertfordshire

Base, Dacorum and St Albans Homeless Development Team

Family Support Scheme Stotford & Arlesey (part of Christian Family Care)

Friends of Danesbury

National Animal Welfare Trust

North Herts CVS/Lions Furniture Recycling Scheme

Stevenage Furniture Scheme

Welwyn Hatfield CVS

Humberside

Age Concern (Hull)

Kent

Age Concern (Gillingham)

Bexley Downs Syndrome Group

The Bridge Trust

Canterbury Women's Refuge

Medway Homes Refuge

St Martin's Emmaus

Lancashire

Age Concern (Blackpool)

Age Concern (Lytham St Anne's)

Emmaus (Greater Manchester)

Homeless in Blackpool

Queens Hall Help Committee

Leicester

Leicester Disabled Gardeners Club

Leicestershire Disabled Adventure Club

Leicestershire

Baby Gear

British Red Cross

Loughborough Community Care

Work-Link Project

Lincolnshire

Care Shop

Sleaford & District Furniture Recycling Project

Strut Limited

London E

Immigration Welfare & Legal Advisory Services

Newham Baby Bank

Toynbee Hall

London EC

Shelter, the National Campaign for Homeless People

London NW

Age Concern (Brent)

Age Concern (Westminster)

Brent Gingerbread

London SE

Shaftesbury Resources Centre

London SW

Age Concern England

Cardinal Hume Centre for Young Homeless People

Centre '70 Community Shop

Furniture Aid South Thames

Trinity Hospice

Wandsworth Housing Support Project

London W

Age Concern (Hammersmith & Fulham)

Catholic Children's Society (Westminster)

Lothian

Sue Ryder Foundation

Merseyside

Southport & District Cerebral Palsy Association

Middlesex

Hillingdon Community Furniture

Hillingdon Community Furniture Recycling Project

Hounslow Community Transport Furniture Project

Norfolk

Centre 81

Norfolk & Norwich Scope

North Yorkshire

Craven Voluntary Action

Emmaus (Scarborough)

Network (Whitby Resource Centre)

The Salvation Army

Selby District AVS Charity Shop

Northamptonshire

Daventry Contact

Northern Ireland

Age Action Ireland

Arthritis & Rheumatism Council (NI)

Bryson House

Emmaus Liberty Belfast

The Salvation Army Charity Shop

Voluntary Service (Belfast)

Northumberland

Community Furniture Project

Nottinghamshire

Age Concern (Nottinghamshire)

Beeston Volunteer Bureau

Eastwood Volunteer Bureau

Family First Limited

The Furniture Project

The Home Farm Trust

Kirby Volunteer Centre

Living Room

RSPCA

Oxfordshire

Age Concern (Oxford)

Banbury & District CVS (Furniture Store)

Powys

Replay

Shropshire

Knowle Sports Association

Somerset

British Red Cross Somerset Branch

Furnicare

NCH Action for Children

St Margaret's Somerset Hospice

South Glamorgan

Age Concern (South Glamorgan)

Track 2000

South Yorkshire

Age Concern (Rotherham)

Arthritis Research

Bentley Association for Supportive Help

Cot-Age – Child Safety & Nursery Equipment

Salvation Army (Care & Share Shop)

Sheffield Family Services Unit

Staffordshire

Burton YMCA

RSPCA (North Staffs Branch)

Stafford Furniture Exchange

Strathclyde

Disability Network

Drumchapel Furnishaid Project

Enable (Scottish Society for the Mentally Handicapped)

The Salvation Army

Suffolk

Arthritis & Rheumatism Council for Research

St Louis Family Service

Surrey

Age Concern (Sutton Borough (Shop))

Christian Family Concern

Community Scrap Scheme

Hydon Hill Cheshire Home

Mental Aid Projects

Mind in Croydon

Prosa Foundation

St Raphael's Hospice

Surrey Community Recycling and Play Project

Tayside

Tayside Furniture Project

Tyne & Wear

Age Concern (South Tyneside)

Community Furniture Service

Community Transport

St Oswald's Hospice

Wearside Women in Need

Warwickshire

Emmaus (Coventry & Warwickshire)

West Midlands

Age Concern (Solihull)

Community Transport – Birmingham Project

Phoenix Sheltered Workshop

Walsall Gingerbread Advice Centre

West Sussex

Adur Furniture Network

Arthritis & Rheumatism Council for Research

Bognor Regis and District Council for Voluntary Service

Crawley Furni-Aid

West Yorkshire

Age Concern (Wakefield District)

Batley Family & Community Centre, Community Furniture Service

Bradford Gingerbread Centre

Kirkwood Hospice

RSPCA (Bradford & District Branch)

The Russell Street Project Limited

St George's Crypt

Windhill Community Furniture Store

Wiltshire

Burnbake Trust

RSPCA (Marlborough with Andover Branch)

Worcestershire

Malvern Churches Community Network

Bed linen and mattresses

Avon
Age Concern (Bedminster)

Age Concern (Bristol)

Age Concern (Clifton)

Age Concern (Knowle)

Age Concern (Weston-super-Mare)

The Home Farm Trust

Service 9 – Bristol's Volunteer Bureau

The SOFA Project

Bedfordshire
Bedford Refuge (part of Christian Family Care)

Luton Day Centre for the Homeless

Women's Royal Voluntary Service

Berkshire
Age Concern (Reading)

Christian Community Action

Buckinghamshire
Age Concern (Milton Keynes)

Age Concern (Bucks)

Chiltern Voluntary Services

High Wycombe General Aid Society

Slough Furniture Project

Cambridgeshire
Cambridge SOFA

Emmaus (Cambridge)

St Theresa's House

SOFA (Peterborough) Limited

Central
Alloa Community Enterprises Limited

Cheshire
3C Teamwork

Arthritis Research (Arthritis & Rheumatism Council)

Blacon Project

Cumbria
Age Concern (Carlisle & District)

Age Concern (Northwest Cumbria)

Age Concern (South Lakeland)

Family Advice Centre

Derbyshire
Arthritis & Rheumatism Council

Derby Furniture Project

Salcare

Treetops Hospice

Devon
Acorn Furniture & Clothing Project

Age Concern (Exeter)

Age Concern (Paignton)

Age Concern (Plymouth)

Age Concern (Torquay)

Arthritis & Rheumatism Council for Research

Halcyon Neighbourhood Centre (Furniture & Thrift Store)

League of Friends – Plymouth Psychiatric Service

Seaton & District Hospital League of Friends

Turntable Furniture Project

Dorset
Age Concern (Blandford Forum)

Age Concern (Boscombe)

Age Concern (Poole)

Boscombe Salvation Army Charity Concern

The Friends of Blandford Community Hospital

Gingerbread

Sheltered Work Opportunities Project

Dumfries & Galloway
Dumfries Furniture Project Limited

Durham
FRADE

East Sussex
Hastings Furniture Service

Hove YMCA

Magpie Recycling Co-op Limited

Sussex Emmaus

East Yorkshire
Age Concern (East Riding of Yorkshire)

Hull Resettlement Furniture Service

RSPCA

Essex
Farleigh (Mid-Essex Hospice)

The Friends of St Francis Hospice (Shops) Ltd

Harlow Council for Voluntary Service

St Helena Hospice

St Luke's Hospice

South Essex Community Furniture Service

Gloucestershire
Full House Furniture and Recycling Service

The Furniture Recycling Project

Grampian
Aberdeen Cyrenians

Aberdeen Women's Aid

Voluntary Service (Aberdeen)

Greater Manchester
Age Concern (Manchester)

Age Concern (Metro Bury)

Bolton Community Transport

Manchester & Salford Methodist Mission

The Salvation Army

Wesley Community Project

Gwynedd
RSPCA (Meirionnydd Branch)

Hampshire
Dorcas Project/Basics Bank

Resettlement Project – South Hants

Hereford & Worcester

Arthritis Research Charity Shop

Community Chest

Full House Furniture & Recycling Service

Furniture Action

Hertfordshire

Base, Dacorum and St Albans Homeless Development Team

Friends of Danesbury

National Animal Welfare Trust

North Herts CVS/Lions Furniture Recycling Scheme

Stevenage Furniture Scheme

The Stort Trust

Welwyn Hatfield CVS

Humberside

Age Concern (Hull)

Kent

Age Concern (Gillingham)

The Bridge Trust

Canterbury Women's Refuge

Friends of Animals League

Medway Homes Refuge

St Cecilia's Cheshire Home

St Martin's Emmaus

Seven Springs Cheshire Home

Lancashire

Age Concern (Blackburn & District)

Age Concern (Blackpool)

Age Concern (Lytham St Anne's)

Emmaus (Greater Manchester)

Homeless in Blackpool

Queens Hall Help Committee

Leicester

Leicester Disabled Gardeners Club

Leicestershire Disabled Adventure Club

Leicestershire

Baby Gear

British Red Cross

Loughborough Community Care

Work-Link Project

Lincolnshire

Care Shop

Community Chest Furniture Recycling Project

St Barnabas Hospice Shops

Sleaford & District Furniture Recycling Project

Strut Limited

London E

Crisis

Hackney Pensioners' Association

Toynbee Hall

Waste Not Recycling

London EC

Help the Aged

Shelter, the National Campaign for Homeless People

London NW

Age Concern (Brent)

Age Concern (Westminster)

Brent Gingerbread

Mind in Camden Charity Shop

Simon Community

London SE

League of Friends of Lewisham Hospital

Shaftesbury Resources Centre

London SW

Age Concern England

Furniture Aid South Thames

The Homeless Furniture Project

Oasis Aids Support Centre

RSPCA (Wimbledon & District)

Wandsworth Housing Support Project

London W

Catholic Children's Society (Westminster)

Lothian

Bethany Christian Trust

Cancer Research Campaign Scotland

Edinburgh Furniture Initiative

Sue Ryder Foundation

Merseyside

Age Concern (Wirral)

Southport & District Cerebral Palsy Association

Middlesex

Age Concern (Feltham, Hanworth & Bedfont)

Hillingdon Community Furniture Recycling Project

Hounslow Community Transport Furniture Project

Richmond Fellowship International

Norfolk

Centre 81

Norfolk & Norwich Scope

Norwich Community Workshop

North Yorkshire

Age Concern (Coleraine)

Age Concern (North West Yorkshire)

Craven Voluntary Action

Emmaus (Scarborough)

Network (Whitby Resource Centre)

The Salvation Army

Selby District AVS Charity Shop

Northamptonshire

Daventry Contact

The Salvation Army

Northern Ireland

Age Action Ireland

Arthritis & Rheumatism Council (NI)

Emmaus Liberty Belfast

The Salvation Army Charity Shop

Voluntary Service (Belfast)

War on Want (NI)

Northumberland

Community Furniture Project

Nottinghamshire

Age Concern (Nottinghamshire)

Beeston Volunteer Bureau

Eastwood Volunteer Bureau

Family First Limited

The Furniture Project

Kirby Volunteer Centre

Living Room

Nottingham Mencap

RSPCA

Oxfordshire

Age Concern (Oxford)

Oxfam

Shropshire

Knowle Sports Association

Somerset

Age Concern (Clevedon)

Age Concern (Somerset)

British Red Cross Somerset Branch

Furnicare

St Margaret's Somerset Hospice

Women's Royal Voluntary Service

South Glamorgan

Age Concern (South Glamorgan)

Track 2000

South Yorkshire

Age Concern (Rotherham)

Bentley Association for Supportive Help

RSPCA (SYAC)

Saint Vincent De Paul Furniture Store

Salvation Army (Care & Share Shop)

Sheffield Family Services Unit

Staffordshire

Alsager Animals in Need

Burton YMCA

Stafford Furniture Exchange

Strathclyde

Bethany House

Drumchapel Furnishaid Project

North Ayr Training Group

The Salvation Army

Suffolk

Age Concern (Suffolk)

Arthritis & Rheumatism Council for Research

St Louis Family Service

Surrey

Age Concern (Sutton Borough (Shop))

British Red Cross

Christian Family Concern

Hydestile Wildlife Hospital

Hydon Hill Cheshire Home

Mental Aid Projects

Mind in Croydon

St Raphael's Hospice

Surrey Community Recycling and Play Project

Tayside

Tayside Furniture Project

Tyne & Wear

Age Concern (South Tyneside)

Community Furniture Service

Community Transport

St Oswald's Hospice

Wearside Women in Need

Warwickshire

Emmaus (Coventry & Warwickshire)

Oxfam

RACKS

Scope

West Midlands

Age Concern (Solihull)

Community Transport

Community Transport – Birmingham Project

Community Transport Sandwell

Phoenix Sheltered Workshop

Walsall Gingerbread Advice Centre

West Sussex

Adur Furniture Network

Bognor Regis and District Council for Voluntary Service

Crawley Furni-Aid

Guild Care

West Yorkshire

Age Concern (Bradford & District)

Age Concern (Huddersfield & District)

Age Concern (North Kirklees)

Age Concern (Wakefield District)

Batley Family & Community Centre, Community Furniture Service

Bradford Gingerbread Centre

Keighley Council for Voluntary Service

Kirkwood Hospice

St George's Crypt

Windhill Community Furniture Store

Wiltshire

Burnbake Trust

RSPCA (Marlborough with Andover Branch)

Worcestershire

Malvern Churches Community Network

Bric-a-brac

Avon

Age Concern (Bedminster)

Age Concern (Bristol)

Age Concern (Clifton)

Age Concern (Knowle)

Age Concern (Weston-super-Mare)

The Home Farm Trust

Service 9 – Bristol's Volunteer Bureau

The SOFA Project

Bedfordshire

Age Concern (Bedfordshire)

Friends of Biggleswade Hospital

Luton Day Centre for the Homeless

The Salvation Army

Women's Royal Voluntary Service

Berkshire

Age Concern (Reading)

Christian Community Action

Thames Valley Hospice

Buckinghamshire

Age Concern (Milton Keynes)

Age Concern (Bucks)

High Wycombe General Aid Society

Slough Furniture Project

Cambridgeshire

Cambridge SOFA

Emmaus (Cambridge)

St Theresa's House

SOFA (Peterborough) Limited

Spaywatch

Central

Alloa Community Enterprises Limited

Cheshire

3C Teamwork

Age Concern (Cheshire)

Arthritis Research (Arthritis & Rheumatism Council)

Blacon Project

Raynaud's & Scleroderma Association

Sue Ryder Foundation

Clwyd

Rhyl & District Gingerbread Group

Cumbria

Age Concern (Carlisle & District)

Age Concern (Northwest Cumbria)

Age Concern (South Lakeland)

Age Concern (Ulverston & District)

Family Advice Centre

Derbyshire

Age Concern (Derbyshire)

Arthritis & Rheumatism Council

Derby Furniture Project

Salcare

Treetops Hospice

Devon

Acorn Furniture & Clothing Project

Age Concern (Exeter)

Age Concern (Paignton)

Age Concern (Plymouth)

Age Concern (Torquay)

Arthritis & Rheumatism Council for Research

Exeter CVS Charity Shop

Halcyon Neighbourhood Centre (Furniture & Thrift Store)

League of Friends – Plymouth Psychiatric Service

Seaton & District Hospital League of Friends

Dorset

Age Concern (Blandford Forum)

Age Concern (Boscombe)

Age Concern (Bournemouth)

Age Concern (Poole)

Boscombe Salvation Army Charity Concern

Christchurch Hospital League of Friends

The Friends of Blandford Community Hospital

Gingerbread

Pramacare

Dumfries & Galloway

Dumfries Furniture Project Limited

Durham

FRADE

East Sussex

Age Concern (Brighton)

Betts Memorial Heart Foundation

Bexhill & District Diabetic Group

Feline Foster

Friends of the Eastbourne Hospitals

Hastings Furniture Service

The House Project Charity Shop

Hove YMCA

Lewes Volunteer Bureau

Monday Club

Peacehaven & Telscombe Volunteer Bureau

Seaford Volunteers

Sussex Emmaus

East Yorkshire

Age Concern (East Riding of Yorkshire)

RSPCA

Essex

Age Concern (Essex)

Barnardos (East Retail Region)

Farleigh (Mid-Essex Hospice)

The Friends of St Francis Hospice (Shops) Ltd

Friends of Wallace Kennels

Hamelin Trust

Harlow Council for Voluntary Service

St Helena Hospice

St Luke's Hospice

Scope in Colchester (Castlegate Centre)

South Essex Community Furniture Service

Gloucestershire

Full House Furniture and Recycling Service

The Furniture Recycling Project

Grampian

Aberdeen Women's Aid

Voluntary Service (Aberdeen)

Greater Manchester

Age Concern (Manchester)

Age Concern (Metro Bury)

Barnardos (North Retail Region)

Manchester & Salford Methodist Mission

The Salvation Army

Wesley Community Project

Gwent

The Community Furniture Project

Gwynedd

Age Concern (Gwynedd a Món)

RSPCA (Meirionnydd Branch)

RSPCA (West Gwynedd Branch)

Hampshire

National Schizophrenia Fellowship

Rehab – Basingstoke & Alton Cardiac Appeal

Relate (Basingstoke & District)

Wessex Cancer Trust

Hereford & Worcester

Arthritis Research Charity Shop

Community Chest

Full House Furniture & Recycling Service

ME Association Hereford & Worcester Group

Hertfordshire

Friends of Danesbury

National Animal Welfare Trust

The Stort Trust

Humberside

Age Concern (Hull)

Kent

Age Concern (Gillingham)

Bexley Downs Syndrome Group

British Red Cross Margate Centre

Canterbury Women's Refuge

Cats Protection League (Bexley Branch)

Dartford District Volunteer Bureau

Friends of Animals League

Hope Romania

Kent Red Cross Charity Shops

Lord Whisky Sanctuary Fund

RSPCA (Kent Rochester Branch)

St Cecilia's Cheshire Home

St George's Community Children's Project Limited

St Martin's Emmaus

Seven Springs Cheshire Home

Lancashire

Age Concern (Blackburn & District)

Age Concern (Blackpool)

Age Concern (Lytham St Anne's)

Age Concern (Preston & South Ribble)

Emmaus (Greater Manchester)

Homeless in Blackpool

Horses & Ponies Protection Association

Preston Animal Welfare Society

Queens Hall Help Committee

Salvation Army

Leicester

Leicester Disabled Gardeners Club

Leicestershire Disabled Adventure Club

Leicestershire

Age Concern (Leicester)

British Red Cross

Cat Action Trust

Loughborough Community Care

RSPCA (Leicestershire Branch)

Work-Link Project

Lincolnshire

Care Shop

Strut Limited

London E

Hackney Pensioners' Association

Toynbee Hall

Walthamstow After School Club

London EC

Friends of Moorfields Eye Hospital

Help the Aged

Shelter, the National Campaign for Homeless People

London NW

Age Concern (Brent)

Age Concern (Westminster)

Brent Gingerbread

Mind in Camden Charity Shop

London SE

Friends of King's College Hospital

League of Friends of Lewisham Hospital

St Christopher's Hospice

Shaftesbury Resources Centre

South Norwood Animal Rescue

London SW

Age Concern England

Age Concern (Wandsworth)

Cardinal Hume Centre for Young Homeless People

Centre '70 Community Shop

Oasis Aids Support Centre

RSPCA (Richmond, Twickenham & Barnes Branch)

RSPCA (Wimbledon & District)

Trinity Hospice

Wandsworth Housing Support Project

London W

Age Concern (Hammersmith & Fulham)

Catholic Children's Society (Westminster)

Octavia Hill Housing Trust

Royal National Mission to Deep Sea Fishermen

Scoliosis Association (UK)

London WC

The Children's Society

Imperial Cancer Research Fund

Leukaemia Research Fund

Lothian

Age Concern Scotland

Bethany Christian Trust

Cancer Research Campaign Scotland

Royal National Lifeboat Institution

Sue Ryder Foundation

Merseyside

Age Concern (Wirral)

Newton Visual Impaired Group

South Sefton Helping Hand Service

Southport & District Cerebral Palsy Association

Vincent Harkins Day Care Centre

Middlesex

Age Concern (Feltham, Hanworth & Bedfont)

British Red Cross Society

Enfield Preservation Society

Hillingdon Community Furniture

Hillingdon Community Furniture Recycling Project

Hounslow Community Transport Furniture Project

League of Friends of Teddington Memorial Hospital

Norfolk

Centre 81

League of Friends – James Paget Hospital

Norfolk & Norwich Scope

The Norfolk Society

Royal British Legion

North Yorkshire

Age Concern (Coleraine)

Age Concern (North West Yorkshire)

Age Concern (York)

Emmaus (Scarborough)

Network (Whitby Resource Centre)

St Leonard's Hospice

The Salvation Army

Selby District AVS Charity Shop

Northamptonshire

Daventry Contact

The Salvation Army

Northern Ireland

Age Action Ireland

Arthritis & Rheumatism Council (NI)

Barnardos (Belfast)

Emmaus Liberty Belfast

The Salvation Army Charity Shop

Voluntary Service (Belfast)

War on Want (NI)

Nottinghamshire

Age Concern (Nottinghamshire)

Beeston Volunteer Bureau

Family First Limited

The Furniture Project

The Home Farm Trust

Kirby Volunteer Centre

Living Room

Nottingham Mencap

RSPCA

Orkney

Age Concern (Orkney)

Oxfordshire

Age Concern (Oxford)

Age Concern (Oxfordshire)

The Blue Cross

Hearing Dogs for the Deaf

Nuffield Orthopaedic Centre League of Friends

Oxfam

Powys

Replay

Shropshire

Knowle Sports Association

Shropshire & Mid Wales Hospice

Shropshire Children's Scrap Store

Somerset

1st Taunton (Wilton) Scout Group

Age Concern (Clevedon)

Age Concern (Somerset)

British Red Cross Somerset Branch

Ferne Animal Sanctuary

Furnicare

Imperial Cancer Research Fund

St Margaret's Somerset Hospice

West Somerset Council for Voluntary Service

South Glamorgan

Age Concern (South Glamorgan)

Track 2000

South Yorkshire

Age Concern (Rotherham)

Arthritis Research

Bentley Association for Supportive Help

League of Friends – Royal Hallamshire Hospital

RSPCA (SYAC)

Salvation Army (Care & Share Shop)

Sheffield Family Services Unit

Staffordshire

Alsager Animals in Need

RSPCA (Burton-on-Trent & District Branch)

RSPCA (North Staffs Branch)

Stafford Furniture Exchange

Strathclyde

Bethany House

Disability Network

Drumchapel Furnishaid Project

Dundee Voluntary Action

Enable (Scottish Society for the Mentally Handicapped)

North Ayr Training Group

The Salvation Army

....

Suffolk

Age Concern (Suffolk)

Arthritis & Rheumatism Council for Research

Home Farm Trust

St Louis Family Service

....

Surrey

Age Concern (Sutton Borough (Shop))

British Red Cross

Cats in Care

Community Scrap Scheme

Croydon Voluntary Action

Disability Action Sutton

Epsom & Ewell Phab Club

Hydestile Wildlife Hospital

Hydon Hill Cheshire Home

Mental Aid Projects

Mind in Croydon

St Raphael's Hospice

Surrey Community Recycling and Play Project

....

Tayside

Tayside Furniture Project

....

Tyne & Wear

Age Concern (South Tyneside)

British Lung Foundation (Breathe North)

Community Furniture Service

Community Transport

St Oswald's Hospice

South Shields Ladies Lifeboat Comm

Wearside Women in Need

....

Warwickshire

Emmaus (Coventry & Warwickshire)

Oxfam

RACKS

Scope

....

West Midlands

Age Concern (Solihull)

Barnardos (West Retail Region)

Birmingham Play Resource Centre

Community Transport

Community Transport – Birmingham Project

Community Transport Sandwell

Phoenix Sheltered Workshop

RSPCA (Birmingham & District Branch)

Stour Valley Cat Rescue

Walsall Gingerbread Advice Centre

....

West Sussex

Arthritis & Rheumatism Council for Research

British Red Cross

St Bridget's Cheshire Home

....

West Yorkshire

Age Concern (Bradford & District)

Age Concern (Calderdale)

Age Concern (Huddersfield & District)

Age Concern (North Kirklees)

Age Concern (Wakefield District)

Batley Family & Community Centre, Community Furniture Service

Bradford Gingerbread Centre

Kirkwood Hospice

RSPCA (Bradford & District Branch)

Windhill Community Furniture Store

....

Wiltshire

Age Concern (Thamesdown)

Burnbake Trust

Devres & District PHAB

Marie Curie Cancer Care

Prospect Hospice

RSPCA (Marlborough with Andover Branch)

RSPCA (Swindon Branch)

RSPCA (Wiltshire North & Chippenham Branch)

....

Worcestershire

Malvern Churches Community Network

Clocks

Avon

Age Concern (Bedminster)

Age Concern (Bristol)

Age Concern (Clifton)

Age Concern (Knowle)

Age Concern (Weston-super-Mare)

The SOFA Project

Bedfordshire

Luton Day Centre for the Homeless

Berkshire

Age Concern (Reading)

Christian Community Action

Thames Valley Hospice

Buckinghamshire

Age Concern (Milton Keynes)

Age Concern (Bucks)

High Wycombe General Aid Society

Cambridgeshire

Cambridge SOFA

Emmaus (Cambridge)

SOFA (Peterborough) Limited

Central

Alloa Community Enterprises Limited

Cheshire

3C Teamwork

Age Concern (Cheshire)

Arthritis Research (Arthritis & Rheumatism Council)

Blacon Project

Sue Ryder Foundation

Cumbria

Age Concern (Carlisle & District)

Age Concern (Northwest Cumbria)

Age Concern (South Lakeland)

Age Concern (Ulverston & District)

Family Advice Centre

Derbyshire

Age Concern (Derbyshire)

Derby Furniture Project

Salcare

Treetops Hospice

Devon

Acorn Furniture & Clothing Project

Age Concern (Exeter)

Age Concern (Paignton)

Age Concern (Plymouth)

Age Concern (Torquay)

Arthritis & Rheumatism Council for Research

Dorset

Age Concern (Blandford Forum)

Age Concern (Boscombe)

Age Concern (Poole)

Boscombe Salvation Army Charity Concern

Christchurch Hospital League of Friends

The Friends of Blandford Community Hospital

Gingerbread

Pramacare

Dumfries & Galloway

Dumfries Furniture Project Limited

East Sussex

Betts Memorial Heart Foundation

Bexhill & District Diabetic Group

Feline Foster

Hove YMCA

Lewes Volunteer Bureau

Monday Club

Seaford Volunteers

Sussex Emmaus

East Yorkshire

Age Concern (East Riding of Yorkshire)

RSPCA

Essex

Barnardos (East Retail Region)

Farleigh (Mid-Essex Hospice)

The Friends of St Francis Hospice (Shops) Ltd

Hamelin Trust

St Helena Hospice

St Luke's Hospice

South Essex Community Furniture Service

Gloucestershire

Full House Furniture and Recycling Service

The Furniture Recycling Project

Grampian

Aberdeen Women's Aid

Voluntary Service (Aberdeen)

Greater Manchester

Age Concern (Manchester)

Age Concern (Metro Bury)

Barnardos (North Retail Region)

Manchester & Salford Methodist Mission

The Salvation Army

Wesley Community Project

Gwynedd

Age Concern (Gwynedd a Món)

RSPCA (Meirionnydd Branch)

Hampshire

Rehab – Basingstoke & Alton Cardiac Appeal

Resettlement Project – South Hants

Hereford & Worcester

Arthritis Research Charity Shop

Community Chest

Full House Furniture & Recycling Service

Hertfordshire

Friends of Danesbury

National Animal Welfare Trust

North Herts CVS/Lions Furniture Recycling Scheme

The Stort Trust

Humberside

Age Concern (Hull)

Kent

Age Concern (Gillingham)

Bexley Downs Syndrome Group

The Bridge Trust

British Red Cross Margate Centre

Dartford District Volunteer Bureau

Friends of Animals League

Kent Red Cross Charity Shops

Lord Whisky Sanctuary Fund

RSPCA (Kent Rochester Branch)

St Cecilia's Cheshire Home

St Martin's Emmaus

Seven Springs Cheshire Home

Lancashire

Age Concern (Blackburn & District)

Age Concern (Blackpool)

Age Concern (Lytham St Anne's)

Age Concern (Preston & South Ribble)

Emmaus (Greater Manchester)

Homeless in Blackpool

Horses & Ponies Protection Association

Queens Hall Help Committee

Save the Children

Leicester

Leicester Disabled Gardeners Club

Leicestershire Disabled Adventure Club

Leicestershire

British Red Cross

Cat Action Trust

Loughborough Community Care

RSPCA (Leicestershire Branch)

Lincolnshire

Care Shop

Strut Limited

London E

Hackney Pensioners' Association

Immigration Welfare & Legal Advisory Services

Toynbee Hall

Walthamstow After School Club

London EC

Help the Aged

Shelter, the National Campaign for Homeless People

London NW

Age Concern (Brent)

Age Concern (Westminster)

Brent Gingerbread

Mind in Camden Charity Shop

London SE

St Christopher's Hospice

Shaftesbury Resources Centre

London SW

Age Concern England

Age Concern (Wandsworth)

Cardinal Hume Centre for Young Homeless People

Centre '70 Community Shop

The Homeless Furniture Project

Marie Curie Cancer Care

Oasis Aids Support Centre

Trinity Hospice

Wandsworth Housing Support Project

London W

Age Concern (Hammersmith & Fulham)

Royal National Mission to Deep Sea Fishermen

Scoliosis Association (UK)

London WC

The Children's Society

Imperial Cancer Research Fund

Leukaemia Research Fund

Lothian

Age Concern Scotland

Bethany Christian Trust

Cancer Research Campaign Scotland

The National Bible Society of Scotland

Royal National Lifeboat Institution

Sue Ryder Foundation

Merseyside

Age Concern (Wirral)

Southport & District Cerebral Palsy Association

Vincent Harkins Day Care Centre

Middlesex

Age Concern (Feltham, Hanworth & Bedfont)

British Red Cross Society

Hillingdon Community Furniture Recycling Project

Hounslow Community Transport Furniture Project

Norfolk

Centre 81

League of Friends – James Paget Hospital

Norfolk & Norwich Scope

North Yorkshire

Age Concern (Coleraine)

Age Concern (North West Yorkshire)

Emmaus (Scarborough)

St Leonard's Hospice

The Salvation Army

Selby District AVS Charity Shop

Northampshire

Daventry Contact

Northern Ireland

Age Action Ireland

Arthritis & Rheumatism Council (NI)

Barnardos (Belfast)

Emmaus Liberty Belfast

The Salvation Army Charity Shop

Voluntary Service (Belfast)

War on Want (NI)

Nottinghamshire

Age Concern (Nottinghamshire)

Eastwood Volunteer Bureau

Family First Limited

The Home Farm Trust

Kirby Volunteer Centre

Nottingham Mencap

RSPCA

Oxfordshire

Age Concern (Oxford)

Age Concern (Oxfordshire)

Oxfam

The Worldwide Fund for Nature (WWF)

Powys

Replay

Shropshire

Knowle Sports Association

Shropshire & Mid Wales Hospice

Somerset

Age Concern (Clevedon)

Age Concern (Somerset)

British Red Cross Somerset Branch

Furnicare

Imperial Cancer Research Fund

St Margaret's Somerset Hospice

South Glamorgan

Age Concern (South Glamorgan)

Track 2000

South Yorkshire

Age Concern (Rotherham)

Arthritis Research

Bentley Association for Supportive Help

RSPCA (SYAC)

Salvation Army (Care & Share Shop)

Sheffield Family Services Unit

Staffordshire

Alsager Animals in Need

RSPCA (North Staffs Branch)

Strathclyde

Disability Network

Drumchapel Furnishaid Project

The Salvation Army

Suffolk

Age Concern (Suffolk)

Arthritis & Rheumatism Council for Research

Home Farm Trust

St Louis Family Service

Surrey

Age Concern (Sutton Borough (Shop))

British Red Cross

Community Scrap Scheme

Disability Action Sutton

Hydon Hill Cheshire Home

Mental Aid Projects

Mind in Croydon

St Raphael's Hospice

Surrey Community Recycling and Play Project

Tayside

Tayside Furniture Project

Tyne & Wear

Age Concern (South Tyneside)

Community Furniture Service

St Oswald's Hospice

Warwickshire

Emmaus (Coventry & Warwickshire)

Oxfam

RACKS

Scope

West Midlands

Age Concern (Solihull)

Barnardos (West Retail Region)

Birmingham Play Resource Centre

Community Transport – Birmingham Project

Phoenix Sheltered Workshop

Stour Valley Cat Rescue

Walsall Gingerbread Advice Centre

West Sussex

Arthritis & Rheumatism Council for Research

St Bridget's Cheshire Home

West Yorkshire

Age Concern (Bradford & District)

Age Concern (Calderdale)

Age Concern (Huddersfield & District)

Age Concern (Wakefield District)

Kirkwood Hospice

RSPCA (Bradford & District Branch)

Wiltshire

Prospect Hospice

RSPCA (Marlborough with Andover Branch)

RSPCA (Wiltshire North & Chippenham Branch)

Worcestershire

Malvern Churches Community Network

DIY equipment

Avon
Age Concern (Bristol)

Bedfordshire
Luton Day Centre for the Homeless

Berkshire
Age Concern (Reading)

Christian Community Action

Thames Valley Hospice

Buckinghamshire
Age Concern (Milton Keynes)

Age Concern (Bucks)

Slough Furniture Project

Cambridgeshire
Cambridge SOFA

Emmaus (Cambridge)

The Leonard Cheshire Foundation

Newark Play Association

SOFA (Peterborough) Limited

Spaywatch

Central
Alloa Community Enterprises Limited

Cheshire
3C Teamwork

Age Concern (Cheshire)

Arthritis Research (Arthritis & Rheumatism Council)

Sue Ryder Foundation

Cumbria
Age Concern (Northwest Cumbria)

Age Concern (South Lakeland)

Derbyshire
Salcare

Treetops Hospice

Devon
Acorn Furniture & Clothing Project

Seaton & District Hospital League of Friends

Turntable Furniture Project

Dorset
Boscombe Salvation Army Charity Concern

The Friends of Blandford Community Hospital

Gingerbread

Pramacare

Sheltered Work Opportunities Project

East Sussex
Friends of the Eastbourne Hospitals

Hove YMCA

Lewes Volunteer Bureau

Newhaven Volunteer Bureau

Peacehaven & Telscombe Volunteer Bureau

Seaford Volunteers

Sussex Emmaus

Tools For Self Reliance

East Yorkshire
Age Concern (East Riding of Yorkshire)

Essex
Farleigh (Mid-Essex Hospice)

The Friends of St Francis Hospice (Shops) Ltd

Hamelin Trust

Harlow Council for Voluntary Service

St Helena Hospice

St Luke's Hospice

South Essex Community Furniture Service

Tools Mission Workshop

YMCA Day Camps

Gloucestershire
Full House Furniture and Recycling Service

The Furniture Recycling Project

Grampian
Aberdeen Women's Aid

Voluntary Service (Aberdeen)

Greater Manchester
Age Concern (Manchester)

Age Concern (Metro Bury)

Manchester & Salford Methodist Mission

The Salvation Army

Wesley Community Project

Gwynedd
Age Concern (Gwynedd a Món)

RSPCA (Meirionnydd Branch)

RSPCA (West Gwynedd Branch)

Hampshire
Rehab – Basingstoke & Alton Cardiac Appeal

Wessex Cancer Trust

Hereford & Worcester
Arthritis Research Charity Shop

Full House Furniture & Recycling Service

Hertfordshire
Friends of Danesbury

National Animal Welfare Trust

North Herts CVS/Lions Furniture Recycling Scheme

Stevenage Haven

The Stort Trust

Humberside
Age Concern (Hull)

Kent
Age Concern (Gillingham)

Bexley Downs Syndrome Group

British Red Cross Margate Centre

Friends of Animals League

Lord Whisky Sanctuary Fund

St Martin's Emmaus

Seven Springs Cheshire Home

Lancashire

Age Concern (Blackpool)

Age Concern (Lytham St Anne's)

Age Concern (Preston & South Ribble)

Emmaus (Greater Manchester)

Homeless in Blackpool

Horses & Ponies Protection Association

Queens Hall Help Committee

Save the Children

Leicester

Leicester Disabled Gardeners Club

Leicestershire Disabled Adventure Club

Leicestershire

British Red Cross

Cat Action Trust

Loughborough Community Care

Work-Link Project

Lincolnshire

Artlandish Limited

Care Shop

'Garden Call'

Strut Limited

London E

Crisis

Toynbee Hall

Walthamstow After School Club

London EC

Shelter, the National Campaign for Homeless People

London NW

Age Concern (Brent)

Brent Gingerbread

Inland Waterways Association

Simon Community

London SE

St Christopher's Hospice

Shaftesbury Resources Centre

London SW

Age Concern England

Centre '70 Community Shop

The Homeless Furniture Project

Oasis Aids Support Centre

Trinity Hospice

Wandsworth Housing Support Project

London W

Age Concern (Hammersmith & Fulham)

Furnish

London WC

The Children's Society

Lothian

Sue Ryder Foundation

Merseyside

Age Concern (Wirral)

Southport & District Cerebral Palsy Association

Middlesex

British Red Cross Society

Hillingdon Community Furniture Recycling Project

Richmond Fellowship International

Norfolk

Centre 81

Norwich Community Workshop

North Yorkshire

Emmaus (Scarborough)

St Leonard's Hospice

The Salvation Army

Selby District AVS Charity Shop

Northampshire

Caring & Sharing Trust

Daventry Contact

Northern Ireland

Bryson House

Conservation Volunteers Northern Ireland

Emmaus Liberty Belfast

The Salvation Army Charity Shop

Voluntary Service (Belfast)

Nottinghamshire

Age Concern (Nottinghamshire)

Family First Limited

Kirby Volunteer Centre

RSPCA

Orkney

Age Concern (Orkney)

Oxfordshire

Age Concern (Oxford)

Banbury & District CVS (Furniture Store)

Oxfam

Shropshire

Knowle Sports Association

Shropshire & Mid Wales Hospice

Shropshire Children's Scrap Store

Somerset

British Red Cross Somerset Branch

Imperial Cancer Research Fund

St Margaret's Somerset Hospice

South Glamorgan

Track 2000

South Yorkshire

Arthritis Research

Bentley Association for Supportive Help

Highway Tools & Crafts Centre

RSPCA (SYAC)

Salvation Army (Care & Share Shop)

Sheffield Family Services Unit

Staffordshire

Alsager Animals in Need

RSPCA (North Staffs Branch)

Staffordshire Wildlife Trust

Strathclyde

Disability Network

Drumchapel Furnishaid Project

Suffolk

Arthritis & Rheumatism Council for Research

Tools with a Mission

Surrey

Age Concern (Sutton Borough (Shop))

Community Scrap Scheme

Disability Action Sutton

Epsom & Ewell Phab Club

Hydon Hill Cheshire Home

Mental Aid Projects

Mind in Croydon

St Raphael's Hospice

Surrey Community Recycling and Play Project

Tyne & Wear

Community Furniture Service

Community Transport

St Oswald's Hospice

Warwickshire

Emmaus (Coventry & Warwickshire)

West Midlands

Age Concern (Solihull)

Birmingham Play Resource Centre

Stour Valley Cat Rescue

Walsall Gingerbread Advice Centre

West Yorkshire

Cash from Trash in Aid of Charities

Kirkwood Hospice

RSPCA (Bradford & District Branch)

The Russell Street Project Limited

Wiltshire

Prospect Hospice

RSPCA (Marlborough with Andover Branch)

West Wiltshire Council for Voluntary Service

Worcestershire

Malvern Churches Community Network

Furniture

Avon

The SOFA Project

Bedfordshire

Bedford Refuge (part of Christian Family Care)

Luton Day Centre for the Homeless

Sandy Neighbourhood Centre (part of Christian Family Care)

Berkshire

Age Concern (Reading)

Christian Community Action

Thames Valley Hospice

Buckinghamshire

Age Concern (Milton Keynes)

Age Concern (Bucks)

Chiltern Voluntary Services

High Wycombe General Aid Society

Slough Furniture Project

Cambridgeshire

Cambridge SOFA

Emmaus (Cambridge)

SOFA (Peterborough) Limited

Central

Alloa Community Enterprises Limited

Cheshire

3C Teamwork

Arthritis Research (Arthritis & Rheumatism Council)

Blacon Project

Sue Ryder Foundation

Cumbria

Age Concern (Carlisle & District)

Age Concern (Northwest Cumbria)

Age Concern (South Lakeland)

Age Concern (Ulverston & District)

Family Advice Centre

Derbyshire

Derby Furniture Project

Salcare

Treetops Hospice

Devon

Acorn Furniture & Clothing Project

Age Concern (Plymouth)

Halcyon Neighbourhood Centre (Furniture & Thrift Store)

Seaton & District Hospital League of Friends

Turntable Furniture Project

Dorset

Boscombe Salvation Army Charity Concern

The Friends of Blandford Community Hospital

Gingerbread

Sheltered Work Opportunities Project

Dumfries & Galloway

Dumfries Furniture Project Limited

Durham

FRADE

East Sussex

Hastings Furniture Service

Hove YMCA

Magpie Recycling Co-op Limited

Seaford Volunteers

Sussex Emmaus

East Yorkshire

Hull Resettlement Furniture Service

Essex

Colchester Furniture Project/ Shake

Farleigh (Mid-Essex Hospice)

The Friends of St Francis Hospice (Shops) Ltd

Hamelin Trust

Harlow Council for Voluntary Service

St Helena Hospice

St Luke's Hospice

South Essex Community Furniture Service

Tendring Furniture Scheme

Gloucestershire

Full House Furniture and Recycling Service

The Furniture Recycling Project

Grampian

Aberdeen Women's Aid

Voluntary Service (Aberdeen)

Greater Manchester

Age Concern (Manchester)

Age Concern (Metro Bury)

Bolton Community Transport

The Salvation Army

Wesley Community Project

Gwent

The Community Furniture Project

Gwynedd

Age Concern (Gwynedd a Món)

Hampshire

Dorcas Project/Basics Bank

Portsmouth Community Furniture Recycling

Rehab – Basingstoke & Alton Cardiac Appeal

Resettlement Project – South Hants

Wessex Cancer Trust

Hereford & Worcester

Arthritis Research Charity Shop

Community Chest

Full House Furniture & Recycling Service

Furniture Action

Hertfordshire

Family Support Scheme Stotford & Arlesey (part of Christian Family Care)

Friends of Danesbury

National Animal Welfare Trust

North Herts CVS/Lions Furniture Recycling Scheme

Stevenage Furniture Scheme

Welwyn Hatfield CVS

Humberside

Age Concern (Hull)

Kent

The Bridge Trust

Canterbury Women's Refuge

Council for Voluntary Service

Medway Homes Refuge

St Martin's Emmaus

Seven Springs Cheshire Home

Lancashire

Age Concern (Blackburn & District)

Age Concern (Blackpool)

Age Concern (Lytham St Anne's)

Age Concern (Preston & South Ribble)

Emmaus (Greater Manchester)

Homeless in Blackpool

Queens Hall Help Committee

Leicester

Leicester Disabled Gardeners Club

Leicestershire Disabled Adventure Club

Leicestershire

Loughborough Community Care

Work-Link Project

Lincolnshire

Artlandish Limited

Care Shop

Community Chest Furniture Recycling Project

St Barnabas Hospice Shops

Sleaford & District Furniture Recycling Project

Strut Limited

London E

Immigration Welfare & Legal Advisory Services

Toynbee Hall

London NW

Age Concern (Brent)

Brent Gingerbread

London SE

Shaftesbury Resources Centre

London SW

Age Concern England

Cardinal Hume Centre for Young Homeless People

Centre '70 Community Shop

Furniture Aid South Thames

The Homeless Furniture Project

Oasis Aids Support Centre

Trinity Hospice

Wandsworth Housing Support Project

London W

Age Concern (Ealing Borough0

Catholic Children's Society (Westminster)

Furnish

Lothian

Bethany Christian Trust

Edinburgh Furniture Initiative

Royal National Lifeboat Institution

Sue Ryder Foundation

Merseyside

Age Concern (Wirral)

Merseyside Council for Voluntary Service

South Sefton Helping Hand Service

Middlesex

Hillingdon Community Furniture

Hillingdon Community Furniture Recycling Project

Hounslow Community Transport Furniture Project

North Yorkshire

Craven Voluntary Action

Emmaus (Scarborough)

Network (Whitby Resource Centre)

Selby District AVS Charity Shop

Northamptonshire

Daventry Contact

Northern Ireland

Age Action Ireland

Arthritis & Rheumatism Council (NI)

Bryson House

Conservation Volunteers Northern Ireland

Emmaus Liberty Belfast

The Salvation Army Charity Shop

Voluntary Service (Belfast)

War on Want (NI)

Northumberland

Community Furniture Project

Nottinghamshire

Age Concern (Nottinghamshire)

Eastwood Volunteer Bureau

Family First Limited

The Furniture Project

Kirby Volunteer Centre

Living Room

RSPCA

Orkney

Age Concern (Orkney)

Oxfordshire

Age Concern (Oxford)

Banbury & District CVS (Furniture Store)

Oxfam

Shropshire

Knowle Sports Association

Somerset

British Red Cross Somerset Branch

Furnicare

St Margaret's Somerset Hospice

West Somerset Council for Voluntary Service

South Glamorgan

Track 2000

South Yorkshire

Age Concern (Rotherham)

Arthritis Research

Bentley Association for Supportive Help

Highway Tools & Crafts Centre

RSPCA (SYAC)

Saint Vincent De Paul Furniture Store

Salvation Army (Care & Share Shop)

Sheffield Family Services Unit

Staffordshire

Burton YMCA

RSPCA (North Staffs Branch)

Stafford Furniture Exchange

Strathclyde

Bethany House

Drumchapel Furnishaid Project

Enable (Scottish Society for the Mentally Handicapped)

North Ayr Training Group

The Salvation Army

Suffolk

St Louis Family Service

Surrey

Age Concern (Sutton Borough (Shop))

Christian Family Concern

Disability Action Sutton

Hydon Hill Cheshire Home

Mental Aid Projects

Merton Furniture Project

Mind in Croydon

Prosa Foundation

St Raphael's Hospice

Surrey Community Recycling and Play Project

....

Tayside

Tayside Furniture Project

....

Tyne & Wear

Age Concern (South Tyneside)

Community Furniture Service

Community Transport

St Oswald's Hospice

Wearside Women in Need

....

Warwickshire

Emmaus (Coventry & Warwickshire)

....

West Midlands

Birmingham Play Resource Centre

Community Transport

Community Transport – Birmingham Project

Community Transport Sandwell

Stour Valley Cat Rescue

Walsall Gingerbread Advice Centre

....

West Sussex

Adur Furniture Network

Arthritis & Rheumatism Council for Research

Bognor Regis and District Council for Voluntary Service

Crawley Furni-Aid

Guild Care

....

West Yorkshire

Batley Family & Community Centre, Community Furniture Service

Keighley Council for Voluntary Service

Kirkwood Hospice

RSPCA (Bradford & District Branch)

The Russell Street Project Limited

Windhill Community Furniture Store

....

Wiltshire

Burnbake Trust

Prospect Hospice

RSPCA (Marlborough with Andover Branch)

Swindon Gingerbread

....

Worcestershire

Malvern Churches Community Network

Gardening equipment

Avon

Age Concern (Bristol)

....

Bedfordshire

Bedford Refuge (part of Christian Family Care)

Luton Day Centre for the Homeless

Sandy Neighbourhood Centre (part of Christian Family Care)

....

Berkshire

Age Concern (Reading)

Christian Community Action

Thames Valley Hospice

....

Buckinghamshire

Age Concern (Milton Keynes)

Age Concern (Bucks)

Chiltern Voluntary Services

High Wycombe General Aid Society

....

Cambridgeshire

Cambridge SOFA

Emmaus (Cambridge)

Newark Play Association

SOFA (Peterborough) Limited

Spaywatch

....

Central

Alloa Community Enterprises Limited

....

Cheshire

3C Teamwork

Age Concern (Cheshire)

Arthritis Research (Arthritis & Rheumatism Council)

Blacon Project

Sue Ryder Foundation

....

Cumbria

Age Concern (Carlisle & District)

Age Concern (Northwest Cumbria)

Age Concern (South Lakeland)

Age Concern (Ulverston & District)

....

Derbyshire

Derby Furniture Project

Salcare

Treetops Hospice

....

Devon

Acorn Furniture & Clothing Project

Halcyon Neighbourhood Centre (Furniture & Thrift Store)

League of Friends – Plymouth Psychiatric Service

Seaton & District Hospital League of Friends

Turntable Furniture Project

....

Dorset

Boscombe Salvation Army Charity Concern

Gingerbread

Sheltered Work Opportunities Project

....

East Sussex

Hove YMCA

Lewes Volunteer Bureau

Newhaven Volunteer Bureau

Peacehaven & Telscombe Volunteer Bureau

Seaford Volunteers

Sussex Emmaus

Tools For Self Reliance

....

East Yorkshire

Age Concern (East Riding of Yorkshire)

....

Essex

Barnardos (East Retail Region)

Farleigh (Mid-Essex Hospice)

The Friends of St Francis Hospice (Shops) Ltd

Hamelin Trust

Harlow Council for Voluntary Service

St Helena Hospice

St Luke's Hospice

South Essex Community Furniture Service

....

Gloucestershire

Full House Furniture and Recycling Service

The Furniture Recycling Project

....

Grampian

Aberdeen Women's Aid

Voluntary Service (Aberdeen)

....

Greater Manchester

Age Concern (Manchester)

Age Concern (Metro Bury)

Barnardos (North Retail Region)

Manchester & Salford Methodist Mission

The Salvation Army

Wesley Community Project

....

Gwynedd

Age Concern (Gwynedd a Món)

RSPCA (Meirionnydd Branch)

RSPCA (West Gwynedd Branch)

....

Hampshire

Dorcas Project/Basics Bank

National Schizophrenia Fellowship

Rehab – Basingstoke & Alton Cardiac Appeal

Resettlement Project – South Hants

Wessex Cancer Trust

....

Hereford & Worcester

Arthritis Research Charity Shop

Full House Furniture & Recycling Service

....

Hertfordshire

Family Support Scheme Stotford & Arlesey (part of Christian Family Care)

Friends of Danesbury

National Animal Welfare Trust

North Herts CVS/Lions Furniture Recycling Scheme

Stevenage Haven

The Stort Trust

Welwyn Hatfield CVS

....

Humberside

Age Concern (Hull)

....

Kent

Age Concern (Gillingham)

Bexley Downs Syndrome Group

The Bridge Trust

British Red Cross Margate Centre

Canterbury Women's Refuge

Friends of Animals League

Lord Whisky Sanctuary Fund

Medway Homes Refuge

St Martin's Emmaus

Seven Springs Cheshire Home

Thanet Mind (Mental Health Day Centre)

....

Lancashire

Age Concern (Blackburn & District)

Age Concern (Blackpool)

Age Concern (Lytham St Anne's)

Age Concern (Preston & South Ribble)

Emmaus (Greater Manchester)

Homeless in Blackpool

Queens Hall Help Committee

....

Leicester

Leicester Disabled Gardeners Club

Leicestershire Disabled Adventure Club

....

Leicestershire

British Red Cross

Cat Action Trust

Loughborough Community Care

Work-Link Project

Lincolnshire

Care Shop

'Garden Call'

St Barnabas Hospice Shops

Strut Limited

London E

Toynbee Hall

Walthamstow After School Club

London EC

Shelter, the National Campaign for Homeless People

London NW

Age Concern (Brent)

Brent Gingerbread

Inland Waterways Association

Simon Community

London SE

League of Friends of Lewisham Hospital

Shaftesbury Resources Centre

London SW

Age Concern England

The Homeless Furniture Project

Oasis Aids Support Centre

Trinity Hospice

London W

Age Concern (Hammersmith & Fulham)

Lothian

Bethany Christian Trust

Sue Ryder Foundation

Merseyside

Age Concern (Wirral)

Merseyside Council for Voluntary Service

Southport & District Cerebral Palsy Association

Middlesex

Age Concern (Feltham, Hanworth & Bedfont)

British Red Cross Society

Hillingdon Community Furniture Recycling Project

Richmond Fellowship International

Norfolk

Norfolk & Norwich Scope

North Yorkshire

Craven Voluntary Action

Emmaus (Scarborough)

Network (Whitby Resource Centre)

Selby District AVS Charity Shop

Northampshire

Caring & Sharing Trust

Daventry Contact

Northern Ireland

Barnardos (Belfast)

Bryson House

Conservation Volunteers Northern Ireland

Emmaus Liberty Belfast

The Salvation Army Charity Shop

Voluntary Service (Belfast)

War on Want (NI)

Nottinghamshire

Age Concern (Nottinghamshire)

Eastwood Volunteer Bureau

Emmanuel House Day Centre

Kirby Volunteer Centre

RSPCA

Orkney

Age Concern (Orkney)

Oxfordshire

Age Concern (Oxford)

Banbury & District CVS (Furniture Store)

The Blue Cross

Oxfam

Shropshire

Knowle Sports Association

Somerset

Furnicare

Imperial Cancer Research Fund

NCH Action for Children

St Margaret's Somerset Hospice

Wellington Basins Project

South Glamorgan

Age Concern (South Glamorgan)

Track 2000

South Yorkshire

Arthritis Research

Bentley Association for Supportive Help

RSPCA (SYAC)

Salvation Army (Care & Share Shop)

Sheffield Family Services Unit

Staffordshire

RSPCA (North Staffs Branch)

Staffordshire Wildlife Trust

Strathclyde

David Livingstone International

Drumchapel Furnishaid Project

Suffolk

Arthritis & Rheumatism Council for Research

St Louis Family Service

Surrey

Age Concern (Sutton Borough (Shop))

Disability Action Sutton

Hydon Hill Cheshire Home

Mental Aid Projects

Mind in Croydon

St Raphael's Hospice

Tyne & Wear

Community Furniture Service

Community Transport

St Oswald's Hospice

Warwickshire

Emmaus (Coventry & Warwickshire)

West Midlands

Barnardos (West Retail Region)

Birmingham Play Resource Centre

Community Transport – Birmingham Project

Phoenix Sheltered Workshop

RSPCA (Birmingham & District Branch)

Walsall Gingerbread Advice Centre

West Sussex

Arthritis & Rheumatism Council for Research

Guild Care

West Yorkshire

Keighley Council for Voluntary Service

Kirkwood Hospice

The Russell Street Project Limited

Wiltshire

Burnbake Trust

Prospect Hospice

RSPCA (Marlborough with Andover Branch)

Swindon Gingerbread

West Wiltshire Council for Voluntary Service

Worcestershire

Malvern Churches Community Network

Household items (ironing boards etc)

Avon

Age Concern (Bedminster)

Age Concern (Bristol)

Age Concern (Clifton)

Age Concern (Knowle)

Age Concern (Weston-super-Mare)

Service 9 – Bristol's Volunteer Bureau

The SOFA Project

Bedfordshire

Bedford Refuge (part of Christian Family Care)

Luton Day Centre for the Homeless

Berkshire

Age Concern (Reading)

Christian Community Action

Thames Valley Hospice

Buckinghamshire

Age Concern (Milton Keynes)

Age Concern (Bucks)

Chiltern Voluntary Services

High Wycombe General Aid Society

Slough Furniture Project

Cambridgeshire

Cambridge SOFA

Emmaus (Cambridge)

SOFA (Peterborough) Limited

Central

Alloa Community Enterprises Limited

Cheshire

3C Teamwork

Age Concern (Cheshire)

Arthritis Research (Arthritis & Rheumatism Council)

Blacon Project

Sue Ryder Foundation

Cumbria

Age Concern (Carlisle & District)

Age Concern (Northwest Cumbria)

Age Concern (South Lakeland)

Age Concern (Ulverston & District)

Family Advice Centre

Derbyshire

Age Concern (Derbyshire)

Derby Furniture Project

Salcare

Treetops Hospice

Devon

Acorn Furniture & Clothing Project

Age Concern (Exeter)

Age Concern (Paignton)

Age Concern (Torquay)

Halcyon Neighbourhood Centre (Furniture & Thrift Store)

League of Friends – Plymouth Psychiatric Service

Seaton & District Hospital League of Friends

Turntable Furniture Project

Dorset

Age Concern (Blandford Forum)

Age Concern (Boscombe)

Age Concern (Poole)

Boscombe Salvation Army Charity Concern

The Friends of Blandford Community Hospital

Gingerbread

Dumfries & Galloway

Dumfries Furniture Project Limited

Durham

FRADE

East Sussex

Friends of the Eastbourne Hospitals

Hastings Furniture Service

Hove YMCA

Household items

Monday Club

Peacehaven & Telscombe Volunteer Bureau

Sussex Emmaus

....

East Yorkshire

Age Concern (East Riding of Yorkshire)

Hull Resettlement Furniture Service

RSPCA

....

Essex

Barnardos (East Retail Region)

Farleigh (Mid-Essex Hospice)

The Friends of St Francis Hospice (Shops) Ltd

Hamelin Trust

Harlow Council for Voluntary Service

St Helena Hospice

St Luke's Hospice

Scope in Colchester (Castlegate Centre)

South Essex Community Furniture Service

....

Gloucestershire

Full House Furniture and Recycling Service

The Furniture Recycling Project

....

Grampian

Aberdeen Cyrenians

Aberdeen Women's Aid

Voluntary Service (Aberdeen)

....

Greater Manchester

Age Concern (Manchester)

Age Concern (Metro Bury)

Barnardos (North Retail Region)

Bolton Community Transport

Manchester & Salford Methodist Mission

The Salvation Army

Wesley Community Project

....

Gwent

The Community Furniture Project

Gwynedd

Age Concern (Gwynedd a Món)

RSPCA (Meirionnydd Branch)

RSPCA (West Gwynedd Branch)

....

Hampshire

Dorcas Project/Basics Bank

Rehab – Basingstoke & Alton Cardiac Appeal

Resettlement Project – South Hants

Wessex Cancer Trust

....

Hereford & Worcester

Arthritis Research Charity Shop

Community Chest

Full House Furniture & Recycling Service

Furniture Action

....

Hertfordshire

Base, Dacorum and St Albans Homeless Development Team

Friends of Danesbury

National Animal Welfare Trust

North Herts CVS/Lions Furniture Recycling Scheme

Stevenage Furniture Scheme

Stevenage Haven

The Stort Trust

Welwyn Hatfield CVS

....

Humberside

Age Concern (Hull)

....

Kent

Age Concern (Gillingham)

Bexley Downs Syndrome Group

The Bridge Trust

Canterbury Women's Refuge

Friends of Animals League

Lord Whisky Sanctuary Fund

Medway Homes Refuge

St Cecilia's Cheshire Home

St Martin's Emmaus

Seven Springs Cheshire Home

Lancashire

Age Concern (Blackburn & District)

Age Concern (Blackpool)

Age Concern (Lytham St Anne's)

Age Concern (Preston & South Ribble)

Emmaus (Greater Manchester)

Homeless in Blackpool

Queens Hall Help Committee

Salvation Army

....

Leicester

Leicester Disabled Gardeners Club

Leicestershire Disabled Adventure Club

....

Leicestershire

British Red Cross

Loughborough Community Care

Work-Link Project

....

Lincolnshire

Care Shop

Community Chest Furniture Recycling Project

St Barnabas Hospice Shops

Sleaford & District Furniture Recycling Project

Strut Limited

....

London E

Toynbee Hall

....

London EC

Shelter, the National Campaign for Homeless People

....

London NW

Age Concern (Brent)

Age Concern (Westminster)

Brent Gingerbread

Mind in Camden Charity Shop

Simon Community

London SE

League of Friends of Lewisham Hospital

St Christopher's Hospice

Shaftesbury Resources Centre

London SW

Age Concern England

Cardinal Hume Centre for Young Homeless People

Centre '70 Community Shop

Furniture Aid South Thames

The Homeless Furniture Project

Oasis Aids Support Centre

Trinity Hospice

Wandsworth Housing Support Project

London W

Catholic Children's Society (Westminster)

Furnish

Octavia Hill Housing Trust

London WC

The Children's Society

Lothian

Bethany Christian Trust

Cancer Research Campaign Scotland

Edinburgh Furniture Initiative

Royal National Lifeboat Institution

Sue Ryder Foundation

Merseyside

Age Concern (Wirral)

Merseyside Council for Voluntary Service

Southport & District Cerebral Palsy Association

Middlesex

Hillingdon Community Furniture

Hillingdon Community Furniture Recycling Project

Hounslow Community Transport Furniture Project

Norfolk

Centre 81

CSV Vocal Project

Norfolk & Norwich Scope

North Yorkshire

Age Concern (Coleraine)

Age Concern (North West Yorkshire)

Craven Voluntary Action

Emmaus (Scarborough)

Network (Whitby Resource Centre)

St Leonard's Hospice

The Salvation Army

Selby District AVS Charity Shop

Northampton

Daventry Contact

Northern Ireland

Age Action Ireland

Arthritis & Rheumatism Council (NI)

Barnardos (Belfast)

Bryson House

Emmaus Liberty Belfast

The Salvation Army Charity Shop

Voluntary Service (Belfast)

War on Want (NI)

Northumberland

Community Furniture Project

Nottinghamshire

Age Concern (Nottinghamshire)

Beeston Volunteer Bureau

Eastwood Volunteer Bureau

Emmanuel House Day Centre

Family First Limited

The Furniture Project

The Home Farm Trust

Kirby Volunteer Centre

Living Room

RSPCA

Orkney

Age Concern (Orkney)

Oxfordshire

Age Concern (Oxford)

Age Concern (Oxfordshire)

Banbury & District CVS (Furniture Store)

Oxfam

Powys

Replay

Shropshire

Knowle Sports Association

Shropshire & Mid Wales Hospice

Somerset

Age Concern (Clevedon)

British Red Cross Somerset Branch

Furnicare

St Margaret's Somerset Hospice

South Glamorgan

Age Concern (South Glamorgan)

Track 2000

South Yorkshire

Age Concern (Rotherham)

Arthritis Research

Bentley Association for Supportive Help

Highway Tools & Crafts Centre

RSPCA (SYAC)

Saint Vincent De Paul Furniture Store

Salvation Army (Care & Share Shop)

Sheffield Family Services Unit

Staffordshire

Burton YMCA

RSPCA (North Staffs Branch)

Stafford Furniture Exchange

Strathclyde

Bethany House

Drumchapel Furnishaid Project

Enable (Scottish Society for the Mentally Handicapped)

North Ayr Training Group

The Salvation Army

Suffolk

Arthritis & Rheumatism Council for Research

Home Farm Trust

St Louis Family Service

Surrey

Age Concern (Sutton Borough (Shop))

Christian Family Concern

Croydon Voluntary Action

Disability Action Sutton

Hydon Hill Cheshire Home

Mental Aid Projects

Mind in Croydon

Prosa Foundation

St Raphael's Hospice

Surrey Community Recycling and Play Project

Tayside

Tayside Furniture Project

Tyne & Wear

Age Concern (South Tyneside)

Community Furniture Service

Community Transport

St Oswald's Hospice

Warwickshire

Emmaus (Coventry & Warwickshire)

RACKS

Scope

West Midlands

Barnardos (West Retail Region)

Community Transport

Community Transport – Birmingham Project

Community Transport Sandwell

Phoenix Sheltered Workshop

Stour Valley Cat Rescue

Walsall Gingerbread Advice Centre

West Sussex

Adur Furniture Network

Bognor Regis and District Council for Voluntary Service

Crawley Furni-Aid

West Yorkshire

Age Concern (Bradford & District)

Age Concern (Wakefield District)

Batley Family & Community Centre, Community Furniture Service

Bradford Gingerbread Centre

Keighley Council for Voluntary Service

Kirkwood Hospice

RSPCA (Bradford & District Branch)

The Russell Street Project Limited

Windhill Community Furniture Store

Wiltshire

Burnbake Trust

Prospect Hospice

RSPCA (Marlborough with Andover Branch)

RSPCA (Wiltshire North & Chippenham Branch)

Swindon Gingerbread

Worcestershire

Malvern Churches Community Network

Motorbike engines, car engines, spare parts

Dorset

Boscombe Salvation Army Charity Concern

Gingerbread

East Sussex

Sussex Emmaus

Kent

St Martin's Emmaus

Leicester

Leicester Disabled Gardeners Club

Leicestershire Disabled Adventure Club

Shropshire

Knowle Sports Association

South Glamorgan

Track 2000

Warwickshire

Emmaus (Coventry & Warwickshire)

Non perishable foods

Bedfordshire

Bedford Refuge (part of Christian Family Care)

Luton Day Centre for the Homeless

Sandy Neighbourhood Centre (part of Christian Family Care)

Berkshire

Age Concern (Reading)

Christian Community Action

Buckinghamshire

High Wycombe General Aid Society

Cambridgeshire

Spaywatch

Cheshire

Arthritis Research (Arthritis & Rheumatism Council)

Cumbria

Age Concern (Carlisle & District)

Age Concern (Northwest Cumbria)

Derbyshire

Salcare

Dorset

Boscombe Salvation Army Charity Concern

Gingerbread

Sheltered Work Opportunities Project

East Sussex

Seaford Volunteers

Sussex Emmaus

Grampian

Aberdeen Cyrenians

Aberdeen Women's Aid

Greater Manchester

Manchester & Salford Methodist Mission

The Salvation Army

Wesley Community Project

Gwynedd

RSPCA (Meirionnydd Branch)

Hampshire

Dorcas Project/Basics Bank

National Schizophrenia Fellowship

Women's Aid to Former Yugoslavia

Hertfordshire

Base, Dacorum and St Albans Homeless Development Team

Family Support Scheme Stotford & Arlesey (part of Christian Family Care)

National Animal Welfare Trust

Stevenage Haven

Humberside

Age Concern (Hull)

Kent

5th Dartford Scout Group

Bexley Downs Syndrome Group

British Red Cross Margate Centre

Canterbury Women's Refuge

Hope Romania

Medway Homes Refuge

St Martin's Emmaus

Lancashire

Age Concern (Blackburn & District)

Age Concern (Lytham St Anne's)

Emmaus (Greater Manchester)

Homeless in Blackpool

Queens Hall Help Committee

Save the Children

Leicester

Leicester Disabled Gardeners Club

Leicestershire Disabled Adventure Club

Leicestershire

British Red Cross

London E

Crisis

Hackney Pensioners' Association

Immigration Welfare & Legal Advisory Services

Toynbee Hall

Walthamstow After School Club

London NW

Brent Gingerbread

London SE

Shaftesbury Resources Centre

London SW

Cardinal Hume Centre for Young Homeless People

Oasis Aids Support Centre

London W

Catholic Children's Society (Westminster)

Lothian

Bethany Christian Trust

Merseyside

Merseyside Council for Voluntary Service

Newton Visual Impaired Group

Southport & District Cerebral Palsy Association

Vincent Harkins Day Care Centre

Middlesex

Age Concern (Feltham, Hanworth & Bedfont)

Richmond Fellowship International

Norfolk

Norfolk & Norwich Scope

Norwich Community Workshop

North Yorkshire

Selby District AVS Charity Shop

Northamptonshire

Daventry Contact

Northern Ireland

Emmaus Liberty Belfast

Voluntary Service (Belfast)

Nottinghamshire

Emmanuel House Day Centre

RSPCA

Somerset

NCH Action for Children

South Yorkshire

Age Concern (Rotherham)

The M25 Group

RSPCA (SYAC)

Salvation Army (Care & Share Shop)

Sheffield Family Services Unit

Staffordshire

RSPCA (North Staffs Branch)

Strathclyde

Bethany House

David Livingstone International

Suffolk

St Louis Family Service

Surrey

Hydestile Wildlife Hospital

Mind in Croydon

Prosa Foundation

SHCVS

Tyne & Wear

South Shields Ladies Lifeboat Comm

Wearside Women in Need

Warwickshire

Emmaus (Coventry & Warwickshire)

West Midlands

Walsall Gingerbread Advice Centre

West Yorkshire

Age Concern (Huddersfield & District)

Bradford Gingerbread Centre

Kirkwood Hospice

RSPCA (Bradford & District Branch)

The Russell Street Project Limited

St George's Crypt

Wiltshire

RSPCA (Marlborough with Andover Branch)

Swindon Gingerbread

Worcestershire

Malvern Churches Community Network

Pets' equipment

Berkshire

Age Concern (Reading)

Christian Community Action

Thames Valley Hospice

Cambridgeshire

Cambridge SOFA

Central

Alloa Community Enterprises Limited

Cheshire

3C Teamwork

Age Concern (Cheshire)

Arthritis Research (Arthritis & Rheumatism Council)

East Sussex

Feline Foster

Seaford Volunteers

Sussex Emmaus

East Yorkshire

RSPCA

Essex

Friends of Wallace Kennels

St Helena Hospice

St Luke's Hospice

Greater Manchester

Age Concern (Manchester)

Gwynedd

RSPCA (Meirionnydd Branch)

RSPCA (West Gwynedd Branch)

Hereford & Worcester

Community Chest

Hertfordshire

National Animal Welfare Trust

Kent

Age Concern (Gillingham)

Friends of Animals League

Lord Whisky Sanctuary Fund

Lancashire

Emmaus (Greater Manchester)

Homeless in Blackpool

Horses & Ponies Protection Association

Leicester

Leicester Disabled Gardeners Club

Leicestershire Disabled Adventure Club

Leicestershire

Cat Action Trust

RSPCA (Leicestershire Branch)

London E

Crisis

Hackney Pensioners' Association

London NW

Age Concern (Brent)

RSPCA (Mayhew Animal Home)

London SE

South Norwood Animal Rescue

London SW

Age Concern England

Centre '70 Community Shop

Oasis Aids Support Centre

London WC

The Children's Society

Lothian

Sue Ryder Foundation

North Yorkshire

Emmaus (Scarborough)

Selby District AVS Charity Shop

Northern Ireland

The Salvation Army Charity Shop

Voluntary Service (Belfast)

Nottinghamshire

RSPCA

Oxfordshire

The Blue Cross

Shropshire

Knowle Sports Association

South Yorkshire

RSPCA (SYAC)

Staffordshire

Alsager Animals in Need

RSPCA (North Staffs Branch)

Suffolk

Arthritis & Rheumatism Council for Research

Surrey

Hydestile Wildlife Hospital

Warwickshire

Emmaus (Coventry & Warwickshire)

RACKS

West Midlands

Age Concern (Solihull)

Phoenix Sheltered Workshop

Stour Valley Cat Rescue

Walsall Gingerbread Advice Centre

West Yorkshire

Pet Animals Welfare Society (PAWS)

RSPCA (Bradford & District Branch)

Wiltshire

RSPCA (Marlborough with Andover Branch)

RSPCA (Swindon Branch)

RSPCA (Wiltshire North & Chippenham Branch)

Toiletries

Avon

Age Concern (Bedminster)

Age Concern (Bristol)

Age Concern (Clifton)

Age Concern (Knowle)

Age Concern (Weston-super-Mare)

The Home Farm Trust

Service 9 – Bristol's Volunteer Bureau

Bedfordshire

Bedford Refuge (part of Christian Family Care)

Charis Mother & Baby Care (part of Christian Family Care)

Luton Day Centre for the Homeless

Berkshire

Age Concern (Reading)

Christian Community Action

Thames Valley Hospice

Buckinghamshire

Age Concern (Bucks)

High Wycombe General Aid Society

Cambridgeshire

Newark Play Association

St Theresa's House

Central

Alloa Community Enterprises Limited

Cheshire

Age Concern (Cheshire)

Arthritis Research (Arthritis & Rheumatism Council)

Sue Ryder Foundation

Cumbria

Age Concern (Carlisle & District)

Age Concern (Northwest Cumbria)

Age Concern (South Lakeland)

Age Concern (Ulverston & District)

Derbyshire

Age Concern (Derbyshire)

Arthritis & Rheumatism Council

Salcare

Devon

Age Concern (Exeter)

Age Concern (Paignton)

Age Concern (Torquay)

Arthritis & Rheumatism Council for Research

League of Friends – Plymouth Psychiatric Service

Seaton & District Hospital League of Friends

Dorset

Age Concern (Blandford Forum)

Age Concern (Boscombe)

Age Concern (Poole)

Boscombe Salvation Army Charity Concern

Christchurch Hospital League of Friends

The Friends of Blandford Community Hospital

Gingerbread

Pramacare

Sheltered Work Opportunities Project

East Sussex

Betts Memorial Heart Foundation

Feline Foster

Friends of the Eastbourne Hospitals

Hove YMCA

Sussex Emmaus

East Yorkshire

Age Concern (East Riding of Yorkshire)

RSPCA

Essex

Barnardos (East Retail Region)

The Friends of St Francis Hospice (Shops) Ltd

Friends of Wallace Kennels

Hamelin Trust

St Helena Hospice

St Luke's Hospice

Scope in Colchester (Castlegate Centre)

Gloucestershire

Full House Furniture and Recycling Service

Grampian

Aberdeen Cyrenians

Aberdeen Women's Aid

Voluntary Service (Aberdeen)

Greater Manchester

Age Concern (Manchester)

Barnardos (North Retail Region)

Manchester & Salford Methodist Mission

The Salvation Army

Gwynedd

RSPCA (Meirionnydd Branch)

RSPCA (West Gwynedd Branch)

Hampshire

National Schizophrenia Fellowship

Relate (Basingstoke & District)

Wessex Cancer Trust

Women's Aid to Former Yugoslavia

Hereford & Worcester

ME Association Hereford & Worcester Group

Hertfordshire

Base, Dacorum and St Albans Homeless Development Team

Friends of Danesbury

National Animal Welfare Trust

Stevenage Haven

The Stort Trust

Humberside

Age Concern (Hull)

Kent

5th Dartford Scout Group

Age Concern (Gillingham)

Bexley Downs Syndrome Group

The Bridge Trust

British Red Cross Margate Centre

Canterbury Women's Refuge

Cats Protection League (Bexley Branch)

Dartford District Volunteer Bureau

Friends of Animals League

Hope Romania

Kent Red Cross Charity Shops

Lord Whisky Sanctuary Fund

Medway Homes Refuge

RSPCA (Kent Rochester Branch)

St Cecilia's Cheshire Home

St Martin's Emmaus

Seven Springs Cheshire Home

Lancashire

Age Concern (Blackburn & District)

Age Concern (Blackpool)

Age Concern (Lytham St Anne's)

Age Concern (Preston & South Ribble)

Emmaus (Greater Manchester)

Homeless in Blackpool

Queens Hall Help Committee

Save the Children

Leicester

Leicester Disabled Gardeners Club

Leicestershire Disabled Adventure Club

Leicestershire

Age Concern (Leicester)

Baby Gear

British Red Cross

Cat Action Trust

Loughborough Community Care

RSPCA (Leicestershire Branch)

Work-Link Project

Lincolnshire

Bransby Home of Rest for Horses

Strut Limited

London E

Crisis

Hackney Pensioners' Association

Immigration Welfare & Legal Advisory Services

Walthamstow After School Club

London EC

Friends of Moorfields Eye Hospital

London NW

Age Concern (Brent)

Age Concern (Westminster)

Brent Gingerbread

London SE

Friends of King's College Hospital

League of Friends of Lewisham Hospital

South Norwood Animal Rescue

London SW

Age Concern (Wandsworth)

Oasis Aids Support Centre

RSPCA (Richmond, Twickenham & Barnes Branch)

RSPCA (Wimbledon & District)

London W

Age Concern (Hammersmith & Fulham)

Catholic Children's Society (Westminster)

London WC

Imperial Cancer Research Fund

Leukaemia Research Fund

Lothian

Bethany Christian Trust

Sue Ryder Foundation

Merseyside

Merseyside Council for Voluntary Service

Newton Visual Impaired Group

Southport & District Cerebral Palsy Association

Vincent Harkins Day Care Centre

Middlesex

Age Concern (Feltham, Hanworth & Bedfont)

British Red Cross Society

Richmond Fellowship International

Norfolk

Norfolk & Norwich Scope

North Yorkshire

Age Concern (Coleraine)

Emmaus (Scarborough)

St Leonard's Hospice

The Salvation Army

Selby District AVS Charity Shop

Northern Ireland

Age Action Ireland

Arthritis & Rheumatism Council (NI)

Barnardos (Belfast)

Emmaus Liberty Belfast

Voluntary Service (Belfast)

War on Want (NI)

Nottinghamshire

Age Concern (Nottinghamshire)

Beeston Volunteer Bureau

Emmanuel House Day Centre

The Home Farm Trust

Kirby Volunteer Centre

RSPCA

Oxfordshire

Age Concern (Oxford)

Age Concern (Oxfordshire)

The Blue Cross

Katharine House Hospice

Oxfam

Shropshire

Knowle Sports Association

Shropshire & Mid Wales Hospice

Shropshire Children's Scrap Store

Somerset

Age Concern (Clevedon)

Imperial Cancer Research Fund

South Glamorgan

Age Concern (South Glamorgan)

South Yorkshire

Arthritis Research

Bentley Association for Supportive Help

League of Friends – Royal Hallamshire Hospital

The M25 Group

RSPCA (SYAC)

Salvation Army (Care & Share Shop)

Sheffield Family Services Unit

Staffordshire

Alsager Animals in Need

RSPCA (Burton-on-Trent & District Branch)

RSPCA (North Staffs Branch)

Strathclyde

Bethany House

Enable (Scottish Society for the Mentally Handicapped)

The Salvation Army

Suffolk

Age Concern (Suffolk)

Arthritis & Rheumatism Council for Research

Home Farm Trust

St Louis Family Service

Surrey

Age Concern (Sutton Borough (Shop))

British Red Cross

Cats in Care

Christian Family Concern

Disability Action Sutton

Epsom & Ewell Phab Club

Inner Wheel Club of Ewell

Mental Aid Projects

Mind in Croydon

Prosa Foundation

St Raphael's Hospice

SHCVS

Tyne & Wear

British Lung Foundation (Breathe North)

St Oswald's Hospice

South Shields Ladies Lifeboat Comm

Warwickshire

Emmaus (Coventry & Warwickshire)

RACKS

Scope

West Midlands

Age Concern (Solihull)

Barnardos (West Retail Region)

Phoenix Sheltered Workshop

Stour Valley Cat Rescue

Walsall Gingerbread Advice Centre

West Sussex

Arthritis & Rheumatism Council for Research

West Yorkshire

Age Concern (Bradford & District)

Age Concern (Huddersfield & District)

Age Concern (North Kirklees)

Bradford Gingerbread Centre

Kirkwood Hospice

Pet Animals Welfare Society (PAWS)

RSPCA (Bradford & District Branch)

The Russell Street Project Limited

Wiltshire

Devres & District PHAB

RSPCA (Marlborough with Andover Branch)

RSPCA (Swindon Branch)

RSPCA (Wiltshire North & Chippenham Branch)

Worcestershire

Malvern Churches Community Network

Office

Computer hardware and software

Avon
Age Concern (Bristol)

Bedfordshire
The Bedfordshire Region of the National Deaf Children's Society

Hospital Radio Bedford

Luton Day Centre for the Homeless

Berkshire
Christian Community Action

Buckinghamshire
Milton Keynes Council of Voluntary Organisations

Cambridgeshire
Cambridge SOFA

Emmaus (Cambridge)

The Leonard Cheshire Foundation

Central
Alloa Community Enterprises Limited

Cheshire
3C Teamwork

Raynaud's & Scleroderma Association

Sue Ryder Foundation

Cumbria
Age Concern (Northwest Cumbria)

Jennifer Trust for SMA

Derbyshire
Salcare

Dorset
Pramacare

Sheltered Work Opportunities Project

East Sussex
Lewes Volunteer Bureau

Magpie Recycling Co-op Limited

Newhaven Volunteer Bureau

Sussex Emmaus

Essex
Farleigh (Mid-Essex Hospice)

Hamelin Trust

Harlow Council for Voluntary Service

St Luke's Hospice

YMCA Day Camps

Gloucestershire
Full House Furniture and Recycling Service

The Furniture Recycling Project

Grampian
Aberdeen Cyrenians

Aberdeen Women's Aid

Voluntary Service (Aberdeen)

Greater Manchester
Age Concern (Manchester)

Bolton Community Transport

Manchester & Salford Methodist Mission

The Salvation Army

Wesley Community Project

Hampshire
National Schizophrenia Fellowship

Portsmouth Community Furniture Recycling

Rehab – Basingstoke & Alton Cardiac Appeal

Women's Aid to Former Yugoslavia

Hereford & Worcester
Full House Furniture & Recycling Service

Hertfordshire

Base, Dacorum and St Albans Homeless Development Team

National Animal Welfare Trust

The Stort Trust

Humberside

Age Concern (Hull)

Isle of Wight

IW RCC (Wight Play Project)

Kent

British Red Cross Margate Centre

Council for Voluntary Service

Friends of Animals League

Kent Information Federation

Kent Red Cross Charity Shops

Medway Homes Refuge

St Martin's Emmaus

Seven Springs Cheshire Home

Lancashire

Age Concern (Lytham St Anne's)

Age Concern (Preston & South Ribble)

Burnley Community Business & Resource Centre

Chorley & South Ribble Crossroads Care Scheme

Emmaus (Greater Manchester)

Lancaster District CVS

Queens Hall Help Committee

Save the Children

Leicester

Leicester Disabled Gardeners Club

Leicestershire Disabled Adventure Club

Leicestershire

The Gideons International

RSPCA (Leicestershire Branch)

London

Comic Relief

London E

Immigration Welfare & Legal Advisory Services

Toynbee Hall

Walthamstow After School Club

London EC

Shelter, the National Campaign for Homeless People

London N

Voluntary Action (Haringey)

London NW

Brent Gingerbread

Simon Community

London SE

African Foundation for Development (Afford)

Outset

London SW

Age Concern England

Cancer Prevention Research Trust

Cardinal Hume Centre for Young Homeless People

Centre '70 Community Shop

The Homeless Furniture Project

Oasis Aids Support Centre

Trinity Hospice

Wandsworth Housing Support Project

London W

Age Concern (Hammersmith & Fulham)

London WC

Leukaemia Research Fund

Lothian

Bethany Christian Trust

The National Bible Society of Scotland

Sue Ryder Foundation

Merseyside

Age Concern (Wirral)

Merseyside Council for Voluntary Service

Middlesex

British Red Cross Society

Hounslow Community Transport Furniture Project

Richmond Fellowship International

Norfolk

Centre 81

Norfolk & Norwich Scope

Northampshire

Caring & Sharing Trust

Northern Ireland

Age Action Ireland

Conservation Volunteers Northern Ireland

Emmaus Liberty Belfast

Nottinghamshire

Emmanuel House Day Centre

Family First Limited

Kirby Volunteer Centre

Nottingham Mencap

Oxfordshire

Age Concern (Oxford)

Oxfam

Shropshire

Knowle Sports Association

Somerset

St Margaret's Somerset Hospice

South Glamorgan

Track 2000

South Yorkshire

Bentley Association for Supportive Help

RSPCA (SYAC)

Salvation Army (Care & Share Shop)

Sheffield Family Services Unit

....

Staffordshire

RSPCA (North Staffs Branch)

Stafford Furniture Exchange

Staffordshire Wildlife Trust

....

Strathclyde

David Livingstone International

....

Surrey

British Red Cross

Community Scrap Scheme

Disability Action Sutton

Disabled Photographers' Society

Epsom & Ewell Phab Club

Feed the Minds

Hydestile Wildlife Hospital

Mental Aid Projects

Merton Voluntary Service Council

Mind in Croydon

Prosa Foundation

Queen Elizabeth's Foundation for Disabled People

St Raphael's Hospice

SHCVS

Surrey Community Recycling and Play Project

....

Tayside

Tayside Furniture Project

....

Tyne & Wear

Community Furniture Service

Community Transport

....

Warwickshire

Emmaus (Coventry & Warwickshire)

Scope

....

West Midlands

Birmingham Play Resource Centre

Community Transport

Walsall Gingerbread Advice Centre

....

West Sussex

Bognor Regis and District Council for Voluntary Service

Guild Care

West Sussex Dyslexia Association

....

West Yorkshire

Bradford Gingerbread Centre

The Russell Street Project Limited

....

Wiltshire

Prospect Hospice

RSPCA (Marlborough with Andover Branch)

....

Worcestershire

Malvern Churches Community Network

Office equipment and stationery

Avon

Age Concern (Bristol)

Service 9 – Bristol's Volunteer Bureau

....

Bedfordshire

Luton Day Centre for the Homeless

....

Berkshire

Age Concern (Reading)

Christian Community Action

....

Buckinghamshire

Age Concern (Bucks)

Chiltern Voluntary Services

Milton Keynes Council of Voluntary Organisations

....

Cambridgeshire

Cambridge SOFA

Emmaus (Cambridge)

Newark Play Association

Spaywatch

....

Central

Alloa Community Enterprises Limited

....

Cheshire

3C Teamwork

Arthritis Research (Arthritis & Rheumatism Council)

Raynaud's & Scleroderma Association

Sue Ryder Foundation

....

Cumbria

Age Concern (Northwest Cumbria)

Age Concern (South Lakeland)

Jennifer Trust for SMA

....

Derbyshire

Derby Furniture Project

Salcare

Devon

Acorn Furniture & Clothing Project

Turntable Furniture Project

Dorset

Pramacare

Sheltered Work Opportunities Project

Dumfries & Galloway

Dumfries Furniture Project Limited

Durham

FRADE

East Sussex

Bexhill & District Diabetic Group

Eastbourne Playbus

Hove YMCA

Lewes Volunteer Bureau

Magpie Recycling Co-op Limited

Newhaven Volunteer Bureau

Sussex Emmaus

Essex

Epping Forest Field Centre

Hamelin Trust

Harlow Council for Voluntary Service

St Helena Hospice

St Luke's Hospice

YMCA Day Camps

Gloucestershire

Full House Furniture and Recycling Service

The Furniture Recycling Project

Grampian

Aberdeen Cyrenians

Aberdeen Women's Aid

Voluntary Service (Aberdeen)

Greater Manchester

Age Concern (Manchester)

Bolton Community Transport

Manchester & Salford Methodist Mission

The Salvation Army

Wesley Community Project

Gwent

The Community Furniture Project

Gwynedd

Age Concern (Gwynedd a Món)

RSPCA (Meirionnydd Branch)

Hampshire

National Schizophrenia Fellowship

Portsmouth Community Furniture Recycling

Rehab – Basingstoke & Alton Cardiac Appeal

Women's Aid to Former Yugoslavia

Hereford & Worcester

Arthritis Research Charity Shop

Full House Furniture & Recycling Service

Hertfordshire

Base, Dacorum and St Albans Homeless Development Team

Dacorum Council for Voluntary Service

National Animal Welfare Trust

Stevenage Haven

The Stort Trust

Humberside

Age Concern (Hull)

Kent

Age Concern (Gillingham)

Bexley Downs Syndrome Group

British Red Cross Margate Centre

Canterbury Women's Refuge

Council for Voluntary Service

Epilepsy Network Gravesend

Friends of Animals League

Kent Information Federation

Kent Red Cross Charity Shops

Lord Whisky Sanctuary Fund

Medway Homes Refuge

St Cecilia's Cheshire Home

St George's Community Children's Project Limited

St Martin's Emmaus

Seven Springs Cheshire Home

Thanet Phobic Group

Lancashire

Age Concern (Blackpool)

Age Concern (Lytham St Anne's)

Age Concern (Preston & South Ribble)

Burnley Community Business & Resource Centre

Chorley & South Ribble Crossroads Care Scheme

Emmaus (Greater Manchester)

Homeless in Blackpool

Lancaster District CVS

Queens Hall Help Committee

Save the Children

Leicester

Leicester Disabled Gardeners Club

Leicestershire Disabled Adventure Club

Leicestershire

British Red Cross

Cat Action Trust

The Gideons International

RSPCA (Leicestershire Branch)

Work-Link Project

London E

Immigration Welfare & Legal Advisory Services

Toynbee Hall

Walthamstow After School Club

London N

Voluntary Action (Haringey)

London NW

Age Concern (Brent)

Brent Gingerbread

Simon Community

London SE

African Foundation for Development (Afford)

London SW

Cancer Prevention Research Trust

Cardinal Hume Centre for Young Homeless People

Centre '70 Community Shop

The Homeless Furniture Project

Oasis Aids Support Centre

Wandsworth Housing Support Project

London W

Age Concern (Hammersmith & Fulham)

Catholic Children's Society (Westminster)

London WC

Leukaemia Research Fund

Lothian

Bethany Christian Trust

Sue Ryder Foundation

Merseyside

Age Concern (Wirral)

Merseyside Council for Voluntary Service

Southport & District Cerebral Palsy Association

Middlesex

Age Concern (Feltham, Hanworth & Bedfont)

British Red Cross Society

Enfield Preservation Society

Hounslow Community Transport Furniture Project

Richmond Fellowship International

Norfolk

Centre 81

Dereham Gingerbread Club

Mini-Scrapbox

Norfolk & Norwich Scope

Norwich Community Workshop

North Yorkshire

Craven Voluntary Action

Network (Whitby Resource Centre)

Selby District AVS Charity Shop

Northamptonshire

Caring & Sharing Trust

Northern Ireland

Age Action Ireland

Conservation Volunteers Northern Ireland

Emmaus Liberty Belfast

Nottinghamshire

Age Concern (Nottinghamshire)

Beeston Volunteer Bureau

Emmanuel House Day Centre

Family First Limited

Kirby Volunteer Centre

Living Room

Nottingham Mencap

RSPCA

Oxfordshire

Age Concern (Oxford)

Banbury & District CVS (Furniture Store)

Oxfam

Powys

Replay

Shropshire

Knowle Sports Association

Shropshire & Mid Wales Hospice

Shropshire Children's Scrap Store

Somerset

British Red Cross Somerset Branch

Ferne Animal Sanctuary

Imperial Cancer Research Fund

St Margaret's Somerset Hospice

South Glamorgan

Track 2000

South Yorkshire

Age Concern (Rotherham)

Bentley Association for Supportive Help

Highway Tools & Crafts Centre

RSPCA (SYAC)

Salvation Army (Care & Share Shop)

Sheffield Family Services Unit

Staffordshire

Burton YMCA

Directorate of Health Promotion

RSPCA (North Staffs Branch)

Stafford Furniture Exchange

Staffordshire Wildlife Trust

Strathclyde

David Livingstone International

Suffolk

Arthritis & Rheumatism Council for Research

Surrey

British Red Cross

Disability Action Sutton

Epsom & Ewell Phab Club

Feed the Minds

Hydestile Wildlife Hospital

Hydon Hill Cheshire Home

Inner Wheel Club of Ewell

Mental Aid Projects

Merton Voluntary Service Council

Mind in Croydon

Prosa Foundation

Queen Elizabeth's Foundation for Disabled People

St Raphael's Hospice

SHCVS

Surrey Community Recycling and Play Project

Tayside

Tayside Furniture Project

Tyne & Wear

British Lung Foundation
(Breathe North)

Community Furniture Service

Community Transport

Wearside Women in Need

Warwickshire

Emmaus (Coventry &
Warwickshire)

Scope

West Midlands

Birmingham Play Resource
Centre

Community Transport

Community Transport –
Birmingham Project

Walsall Gingerbread Advice
Centre

West Sussex

Arthritis & Rheumatism Council
for Research

Bognor Regis and District
Council for Voluntary Service

Guild Care

West Yorkshire

Cash from Trash in Aid of
Charities

Keighley Council for Voluntary
Service

The Russell Street Project
Limited

Wiltshire

Prospect Hospice

RSPCA (Marlborough with
Andover Branch)

RSPCA (Swindon Branch)

Swindon Children's Scrapstore

Worcestershire

Malvern Churches Community
Network

Used toner cartridges

Avon

Actionaid National Recycling
Unit

Bedfordshire

Friends of Biggleswade Hospital

Berkshire

The Guide Dogs for the Blind
Association

Central

Alloa Community Enterprises
Limited

Cheshire

Raynaud's & Scleroderma
Association

Dorset

Pramacare

East Sussex

Friends of the Eastbourne
Hospitals

Magpie Recycling Co-op Limited

Sussex Emmaus

Essex

St Luke's Hospice

Gloucestershire

Gloucestershire Resource Centre

Greater Manchester

Age Concern (Manchester)

Royal National Lifeboat
Institution

Wesley Community Project

Gwent

Wastesavers Recycling
Association

Hampshire

Wessex Cancer Trust

Lancashire

Emmaus (Greater Manchester)

Leicester

Leicester Disabled Gardeners
Club

Leicestershire Disabled
Adventure Club

Leicestershire

RSPCA (Leicestershire Branch)

London WC

The Children's Society

Leukaemia Research Fund

Lothian

Cancer Research Campaign
Scotland

Royal National Lifeboat
Institution

Sue Ryder Foundation

Northern Ireland

Age Action Ireland

Nottinghamshire

Age Concern (Nottinghamshire)

Oxfordshire

Age Concern (Oxford)

Imperial Cancer Research Fund

Oxfam

Shropshire

Knowle Sports Association

Shropshire & Mid Wales Hospice

Shropshire Children's Scrap
Store

Somerset

1st Taunton (Wilton) Scout
Group

Imperial Cancer Research Fund

South Glamorgan

Royal National Lifeboat
Institution

Staffordshire

Directorate of Health
Promotion

Surrey

Inner Wheel Club of Ewell

Queen Elizabeth's Foundation
for Disabled People

St Raphael's Hospice

Tyne & Wear

British Lung Foundation
(Breathe North)

West Midlands

Birmingham Play Resource
Centre

West Yorkshire

Cash from Trash in Aid of
Charities

Imperial Cancer Research Fund

Leisure

Arts & crafts equipment

Avon

Age Concern (Bedminster)

Age Concern (Bristol)

Age Concern (Clifton)

Age Concern (Knowle)

Age Concern (Weston-super-Mare)

Service 9 – Bristol's Volunteer Bureau

Bedfordshire

Bedford Refuge (part of Christian Family Care)

Luton Day Centre for the Homeless

Sandy Neighbourhood Centre (part of Christian Family Care)

Berkshire

Age Concern (Reading)

Christian Community Action

Thames Valley Hospice

Buckinghamshire

Age Concern (Bucks)

The National Society for Epilepsy

Cambridgeshire

Cambridge SOFA

Emmaus (Cambridge)

The Leonard Cheshire Foundation

Newark Play Association

SOFA (Peterborough) Limited

Spaywatch

Central

Alloa Community Enterprises Limited

Cheshire

3C Teamwork

Age Concern (Cheshire)

Arthritis Research (Arthritis & Rheumatism Council)

PSS – Toy Library & Resource Centre

Cumbria

Age Concern (Carlisle & District)

Age Concern (Northwest Cumbria)

Age Concern (South Lakeland)

Family Advice Centre

Derbyshire

Arthritis & Rheumatism Council

Salcare

Treetops Hospice

Devon

Age Concern (Exeter)

Age Concern (Paignton)

Age Concern (Plymouth)

Age Concern (Torquay)

Halcyon Neighbourhood Centre (Furniture & Thrift Store)

League of Friends – Plymouth Psychiatric Service

Seaton & District Hospital League of Friends

Dorset

Age Concern (Blandford Forum)

Age Concern (Boscombe)

Age Concern (Poole)

Boscombe Salvation Army Charity Concern

Gingerbread

Pramacare

East Sussex

Age Concern (Brighton)

Eastbourne Playbus

Lewes Volunteer Bureau

Newhaven Volunteer Bureau

Seaford Volunteers

Sussex Emmaus

East Yorkshire

Age Concern (East Riding of Yorkshire)

RSPCA

Essex

Barnardos (East Retail Region)

Farleigh (Mid-Essex Hospice)

The Friends of St Francis Hospice (Shops) Ltd

Hamelin Trust

St Helena Hospice

St Luke's Hospice

Scope in Colchester (Castlegate Centre)

YMCA Day Camps

Gloucestershire

Full House Furniture and Recycling Service

Gloucestershire Resource Centre

Grampian

Aberdeen Cyrenians

Voluntary Service (Aberdeen)

Greater Manchester

Age Concern (Manchester)

Age Concern (Metro Bury)

Barnardos (North Retail Region)

Manchester & Salford Methodist Mission

Manchester One Parent Family Advice Centre

The Salvation Army

Wesley Community Project

Gwynedd

RSPCA (Meirionnydd Branch)

RSPCA (West Gwynedd Branch)

Hampshire

National Schizophrenia Fellowship

Rehab – Basingstoke & Alton Cardiac Appeal

Totton & Eling Community Association

Wessex Cancer Trust

Hereford & Worcester

Arthritis Research Charity Shop

Full House Furniture & Recycling Service

Hertfordshire

Base, Dacorum and St Albans Homeless Development Team

Family Support Scheme Stotford & Arlesey (part of Christian Family Care)

Friends of Danesbury

National Animal Welfare Trust

The Stort Trust

Humberside

Age Concern (Hull)

Isle of Wight

IW RCC (Wight Play Project)

Kent

5th Dartford Scout Group

Age Concern (Gillingham)

Bexley Downs Syndrome Group

British Red Cross Margate Centre

Canterbury Women's Refuge

Friends of Animals League

Kent Red Cross Charity Shops

Lord Whisky Sanctuary Fund

RSPCA (Kent Rochester Branch)

St George's Community Children's Project Limited

St Martin's Emmaus

Seven Springs Cheshire Home

Thanet Mind (Mental Health Day Centre)

Lancashire

Age Concern (Blackburn & District)

Age Concern (Blackpool)

Age Concern (Lytham St Anne's)

Burnley Community Business & Resource Centre

Emmaus (Greater Manchester)

Homeless in Blackpool

Queens Hall Help Committee

Salvation Army

Save the Children

Leicester

Leicester Disabled Gardeners Club

Leicestershire Disabled Adventure Club

Leicestershire

Blaby & Whetstone Boys Club

British Red Cross

Cat Action Trust

Loughborough Community Care

Work-Link Project

Lincolnshire

Artlandish Limited

Care Shop

London E

Crisis

Walthamstow After School Club

London EC

Help the Aged

Shelter, the National Campaign for Homeless People

London NW

Age Concern (Brent)

Age Concern (Westminster)

Brent Gingerbread

Mind in Camden Charity Shop

London SE

League of Friends of Lewisham Hospital

London SW

Age Concern England

Cardinal Hume Centre for Young Homeless People

The Homeless Furniture Project

Oasis Aids Support Centre

London W

Age Concern (Hammersmith & Fulham)

Catholic Children's Society (Westminster)

London WC

The Children's Society

Imperial Cancer Research Fund

Lothian

Bethany Christian Trust

Cancer Research Campaign Scotland

Sue Ryder Foundation

Merseyside

Age Concern (Wirral)

Southport & District Cerebral Palsy Association

Middlesex

Age Concern (Feltham, Hanworth & Bedfont)

British Red Cross Society

Richmond Fellowship International

Norfolk

Centre 81

CSV Vocal Project

Dereham Gingerbread Club

Norfolk & Norwich Scope

Norwich Community Workshop

North Yorkshire

Age Concern (Coleraine)

Age Concern (North West Yorkshire)

Emmaus (Scarborough)

St Leonard's Hospice

Selby District AVS Charity Shop

Northamptonshire

Caring & Sharing Trust

Northern Ireland

Barnardos (Belfast)

Emmaus Liberty Belfast

The Salvation Army Charity Shop

Voluntary Service (Belfast)

Nottinghamshire

Age Concern (Nottinghamshire)

Croctal (Crochet & Other Handcrafts)

Emmanuel House Day Centre

Kirby Volunteer Centre

Nottingham Mencap

RSPCA

Oxfordshire

Age Concern (Oxford)

Age Concern (Oxfordshire)

Powys

Replay

Shropshire

Knowle Sports Association

Shropshire & Mid Wales Hospice

Shropshire Children's Scrap Store

Somerset

Age Concern (Clevedon)

British Red Cross Somerset Branch

Imperial Cancer Research Fund

NCH Action for Children

St Margaret's Somerset Hospice

Wellington Basins Project

South Glamorgan

Age Concern (South Glamorgan)

Track 2000

South Yorkshire

Age Concern (Rotherham)

Bentley Association for Supportive Help

Highway Tools & Crafts Centre

Salvation Army (Care & Share Shop)

Staffordshire

Alsager Animals in Need

Newcastle Play Council

Strathclyde

Bethany House

Enable (Scottish Society for the Mentally Handicapped)

Suffolk

Age Concern (Suffolk)

Arthritis & Rheumatism Council for Research

Home Farm Trust

Surrey

Age Concern (Sutton Borough (Shop))

Christian Family Concern

Epsom & Ewell Phab Club

Hydestile Wildlife Hospital

Hydon Hill Cheshire Home

Inner Wheel Club of Ewell

Mental Aid Projects

Mind in Croydon

Queen Elizabeth's Foundation for Disabled People

St Raphael's Hospice

Surrey Community Recycling and Play Project

Tayside

Montrose Scrapstore

Tyne & Wear

St Oswald's Hospice

Warwickshire

Emmaus (Coventry & Warwickshire)

Oxfam

Scope

West Midlands

Age Concern (Solihull)

Barnardos (West Retail Region)

Birmingham Play Resource Centre

Stour Valley Cat Rescue

Walsall Gingerbread Advice Centre

West Sussex

Guild Care

Wallis Centre

West Yorkshire

Age Concern (Bradford & District)

Age Concern (Calderdale)

Age Concern (Wakefield District)

Keighley Council for Voluntary Service

Kirkwood Hospice

The Russell Street Project Limited

Wiltshire

RSPCA (Marlborough with Andover Branch)

Swindon Children's Scrapstore

Worcestershire

Malvern Churches Community Network

Bicycles

Avon

The SOFA Project

Bedfordshire

Bedford Refuge (part of Christian Family Care)

Luton Day Centre for the Homeless

Berkshire

Christian Community Action

Thames Valley Hospice

Buckinghamshire

Age Concern (Milton Keynes)

Cambridgeshire

Cambridge SOFA

Emmaus (Cambridge)

SOFA (Peterborough) Limited

Central

Alloa Community Enterprises Limited

Cheshire

3C Teamwork

Sue Ryder Foundation

Cumbria

Age Concern (Northwest Cumbria)

Age Concern (South Lakeland)

Derbyshire

Derby Furniture Project

Salcare

Devon

Acorn Furniture & Clothing Project

Dorset

Boscombe Salvation Army Charity Concern

Gingerbread

East Sussex

Hove YMCA

Sussex Emmaus

Essex

Barnardos (East Retail Region)

Farleigh (Mid-Essex Hospice)

The Friends of St Francis Hospice (Shops) Ltd

Hamelin Trust

Harlow Council for Voluntary Service

St Helena Hospice

St Luke's Hospice

Gloucestershire

Full House Furniture and Recycling Service

The Furniture Recycling Project

Grampian

Aberdeen Cyrenians

Aberdeen Women's Aid

Voluntary Service (Aberdeen)

Greater Manchester

Age Concern (Manchester)

Age Concern (Metro Bury)

Barnardos (North Retail Region)

The Salvation Army

Wesley Community Project

Hampshire

Dorcas Project/Basics Bank

Rehab – Basingstoke & Alton Cardiac Appeal

Hereford & Worcester

Arthritis Research Charity Shop

Full House Furniture & Recycling Service

Hertfordshire

Friends of Danesbury

National Animal Welfare Trust

The Stort Trust

Humberside

Age Concern (Hull)

Kent

Bexley Downs Syndrome Group

British Red Cross Margate Centre

Canterbury Women's Refuge

Friends of Animals League

Hope Romania

Lord Whisky Sanctuary Fund

St George's Community Children's Project Limited

St Martin's Emmaus

Lancashire

Age Concern (Lytham St Anne's)

Emmaus (Greater Manchester)

Homeless in Blackpool

Queens Hall Help Committee

Leicester

Leicester Disabled Gardeners Club

Leicestershire Disabled Adventure Club

Leicestershire

RSPCA (Leicestershire Branch)

Work-Link Project

Lincolnshire

Care Shop

Strut Limited

London E

Toynbee Hall

Walthamstow After School Club

London EC

Shelter, the National Campaign for Homeless People

London NW

Age Concern (Brent)

Age Concern (Westminster)

Brent Gingerbread

Simon Community

London SE

Shaftesbury Resources Centre

London SW

Age Concern England

Centre '70 Community Shop

The Homeless Furniture Project

Oasis Aids Support Centre

Trinity Hospice

Wandsworth Housing Support Project

London W

Age Concern (Hammersmith & Fulham)

Catholic Children's Society (Westminster)

London WC

Leukaemia Research Fund

Lothian

Age Concern Scotland

Bethany Christian Trust

Sue Ryder Foundation

Merseyside

Age Concern (Wirral)

Southport & District Cerebral Palsy Association

Middlesex

Richmond Fellowship International

Norfolk

Norfolk & Norwich Scope

North Yorkshire

Emmaus (Scarborough)

Network (Whitby Resource Centre)

St Leonard's Hospice

The Salvation Army

Selby District AVS Charity Shop

Northamptonshire

Daventry Contact

Northern Ireland

Age Action Ireland

Barnardos (Belfast)

Conservation Volunteers Northern Ireland

Emmaus Liberty Belfast

The Salvation Army Charity Shop

Nottinghamshire

Age Concern (Nottinghamshire)

Family First Limited

The Furniture Project

Kirby Volunteer Centre

RSPCA

Oxfordshire

Age Concern (Oxford)

Oxfam

Shropshire

Knowle Sports Association

Shropshire & Mid Wales Hospice

Somerset

British Red Cross Somerset Branch

Imperial Cancer Research Fund

St Margaret's Somerset Hospice

South Glamorgan

Age Concern (South Glamorgan)

Track 2000

South Yorkshire

Arthritis Research

Bentley Association for Supportive Help

RSPCA (SYAC)

Salvation Army (Care & Share Shop)

Sheffield Family Services Unit

Staffordshire

RSPCA (North Staffs Branch)

Strathclyde

The Salvation Army

Suffolk

Arthritis & Rheumatism Council for Research

St Louis Family Service

Surrey

Disability Action Sutton

Mental Aid Projects

Mind in Croydon

Prosa Foundation

St Raphael's Hospice

Surrey Community Recycling and Play Project

Tayside

Tayside Furniture Project

Tyne & Wear

Age Concern (South Tyneside)

Community Furniture Service

Community Transport

St Oswald's Hospice

Warwickshire

Emmaus (Coventry & Warwickshire)

RACKS

West Midlands

Age Concern (Solihull)

Barnardos (West Retail Region)

Birmingham Play Resource Centre

Community Transport

Phoenix Sheltered Workshop

RSPCA (Birmingham & District Branch)

Walsall Gingerbread Advice Centre

Wiltshire

RSPCA (Marlborough with Andover Branch)

Worcestershire

Malvern Churches Community Network

Books hardback

Avon

Age Concern (Bedminster)

Age Concern (Bristol)

Age Concern (Clifton)

Age Concern (Knowle)

Age Concern (Weston-super-Mare)

Service 9 – Bristol's Volunteer Bureau

The SOFA Project

Bedfordshire

Age Concern (Bedfordshire)

Friends of Biggleswade Hospital

Luton Day Centre for the Homeless

Berkshire

Age Concern (Reading)

Christian Community Action

Thames Valley Hospice

Berwickshire

Royal National Mission to Deep Sea Fishermen

Buckinghamshire

Age Concern (Milton Keynes)

Age Concern (Bucks)

Cambridgeshire

Cambridge SOFA

Emmaus (Cambridge)

The Leonard Cheshire Foundation

SOFA (Peterborough) Limited

SOS Children's Villages UK

Spaywatch

Central

Alloa Community Enterprises Limited

Cheshire

3C Teamwork

Age Concern (Cheshire)

Arthritis Research (Arthritis & Rheumatism Council)

Raynaud's & Scleroderma Association

Sue Ryder Foundation

Cumbria

Age Concern (Carlisle & District)

Age Concern (Northwest Cumbria)

Age Concern (South Lakeland)

Age Concern (Ulverston & District)

Family Advice Centre

Derbyshire

Age Concern (Derbyshire)

Arthritis & Rheumatism Council

Derby Furniture Project

Salcare

Treetops Hospice

Devon

Acorn Furniture & Clothing Project

Age Concern (Exeter)

Age Concern (Paignton)

Age Concern (Plymouth)

Age Concern (Torquay)

Arthritis & Rheumatism Council for Research

Exeter CVS Charity Shop

League of Friends – Plymouth Psychiatric Service

Seaton & District Hospital League of Friends

Dorset

Age Concern (Blandford Forum)

Age Concern (Boscombe)

Age Concern (Bournemouth)

Age Concern (Poole)

Boscombe Salvation Army Charity Concern

The Friends of Blandford Community Hospital

Pramacare

Sheltered Work Opportunities Project

East Sussex

Age Concern (Brighton)

Betts Memorial Heart Foundation

Friends of the Eastbourne Hospitals

Hove YMCA

Lewes Volunteer Bureau

Monday Club

Newhaven Volunteer Bureau

Sussex Emmaus

Tools For Self Reliance

East Yorkshire

Age Concern (East Riding of Yorkshire)

RSPCA

Essex

Barnardos (East Retail Region)

Farleigh (Mid-Essex Hospice)

Hamelin Trust

St Helena Hospice

St Luke's Hospice

Gloucestershire

Full House Furniture and Recycling Service

The Furniture Recycling Project

Grampian

Aberdeen Cyrenians

Aberdeen Women's Aid

Voluntary Service (Aberdeen)

Greater Manchester

Age Concern (Manchester)

Age Concern (Metro Bury)

Age Concern (Metropolitan Rochdale)

Barnardos (North Retail Region)

Bolton Community Transport

Manchester & Salford Methodist Mission

The Salvation Army

Wesley Community Project

Gwynedd

Age Concern (Gwynedd a Món)

RSPCA (Meirionnydd Branch)

RSPCA (West Gwynedd Branch)

Hampshire

Rehab – Basingstoke & Alton Cardiac Appeal

Relate (Basingstoke & District)

Wessex Cancer Trust

Hereford & Worcester

Arthritis Research Charity Shop

Community Chest

Full House Furniture & Recycling Service

ME Association Hereford & Worcester Group

Hertfordshire

Friends of Danesbury

National Animal Welfare Trust

The Stort Trust

Humberside

Age Concern (Hull)

Kent

Bexley Downs Syndrome Group

British Red Cross Margate Centre

Canterbury Women's Refuge

Cats Protection League (Bexley Branch)

Friends of Animals League

Hope Romania

Kent Red Cross Charity Shops

Lord Whisky Sanctuary Fund

RSPCA (Kent Rochester Branch)

St Cecilia's Cheshire Home

St Martin's Emmaus

Seven Springs Cheshire Home

Thanet Mind (Mental Health Day Centre)

Lancashire

Age Concern (Blackburn & District)

Age Concern (Blackpool)

Age Concern (Lytham St Anne's)

Age Concern (Preston & South Ribble)

Emmaus (Greater Manchester)

Homeless in Blackpool

Preston Animal Welfare Society

Queens Hall Help Committee

Salvation Army

Leicester

Leicester Disabled Gardeners Club

Leicestershire Disabled Adventure Club

Leicestershire

Age Concern (Leicester)

British Red Cross

Cat Action Trust

Loughborough Community Care

RSPCA (Leicestershire Branch)

Work-Link Project

Lincolnshire

Artlandish Limited

Bransby Home of Rest for Horses

Care Shop

St Barnabas Hospice Shops

Strut Limited

London E

Crisis

Hackney Pensioners' Association

Immigration Welfare & Legal Advisory Services

Toynbee Hall

Walthamstow After School Club

London EC

Friends of Moorfields Eye Hospital

Help the Aged

Shelter, the National Campaign for Homeless People

London NW

Age Concern (Brent)

Age Concern (Westminster)

Brent Gingerbread

Inland Waterways Association

Mind in Camden Charity Shop

London SE

Book Aid

Book Aid International

Elimination of Leukaemia Fund

Friends of King's College Hospital

St Christopher's Hospice

London SW

Age Concern England

Age Concern (Wandsworth)

Centre '70 Community Shop

The Homeless Furniture Project

Oasis Aids Support Centre

RSPCA (Wimbledon & District)

Trinity Hospice

Wandsworth Housing Support Project

London W

Age Concern (Ealing Borough0

Age Concern (Hammersmith & Fulham)

London WC

The Children's Society

Imperial Cancer Research Fund

Leukaemia Research Fund

Lothian

Age Concern Scotland

Bethany Christian Trust

Cancer Research Campaign Scotland

Royal National Lifeboat Institution

Sue Ryder Foundation

Merseyside

Age Concern (Wirral)

Southport & District Cerebral Palsy Association

Vincent Harkins Day Care Centre

Wirral Rehab T/AS Speaks Volumes

Middlesex

Age Concern (Feltham, Hanworth & Bedfont)

British Red Cross Society

Hillingdon Community Furniture

Hillingdon Community Furniture Recycling Project

Hounslow Community Transport Furniture Project

Richmond Fellowship International

Norfolk

Centre 81

Dereham Gingerbread Club

League of Friends – James Paget Hospital

Norfolk & Norwich Muscular Dystrophy Group

Norfolk & Norwich Scope

The Norfolk Society

Norwich Community Workshop

North Yorkshire

Age Concern (Coleraine)

Age Concern (North West Yorkshire)

Age Concern (York)

Emmaus (Scarborough)

Network (Whitby Resource Centre)

St Leonard's Hospice

The Salvation Army

Selby District AVS Charity Shop

Northampshire

Daventry Contact

The Salvation Army

Northern Ireland

Age Action Ireland

Arthritis & Rheumatism Council (NI)

Barnardos (Belfast)

Conservation Volunteers Northern Ireland

Emmaus Liberty Belfast

The Salvation Army Charity Shop

Voluntary Service (Belfast)

War on Want (NI)

Nottinghamshire

Age Concern (Nottinghamshire)

Beeston Volunteer Bureau

Croctal (Crochet & Other Handcrafts)

Emmanuel House Day Centre

Family First Limited

The Home Farm Trust

Kirby Volunteer Centre

Nottingham Mencap

Oxfordshire

Age Concern (Oxford)

Age Concern (Oxfordshire)

The Blue Cross

Nuffield Orthopaedic Centre League of Friends

Oxfam

Powys

Replay

Shropshire

Knowle Sports Association

Shropshire & Mid Wales Hospice

Somerset

Age Concern (Clevedon)

Age Concern (Somerset)

British Red Cross Somerset Branch

Imperial Cancer Research Fund

NCH Action for Children

St Margaret's Somerset Hospice

Wellington Basins Project

West Somerset Council for Voluntary Service

South Glamorgan

Age Concern (South Glamorgan)

Track 2000

South Yorkshire

Age Concern (Rotherham)

Arthritis Research

RSPCA (SYAC)

Salvation Army (Care & Share Shop)

Sheffield Family Services Unit

Staffordshire

Alsager Animals in Need

Burton YMCA

Newcastle Play Council

RSPCA (Burton-on-Trent & District Branch)

RSPCA (North Staffs Branch)

Staffordshire Wildlife Trust

Strathclyde

Dundee Voluntary Action

Enable (Scottish Society for the Mentally Handicapped)

Suffolk

Age Concern (Suffolk)

Arthritis & Rheumatism Council for Research

Home Farm Trust

St Louis Family Service

Surrey

Age Concern (Sutton Borough (Shop))

British Red Cross

Croydon Voluntary Action

Disability Action Sutton

Feed the Minds

Hydestile Wildlife Hospital

Hydon Hill Cheshire Home

Inner Wheel Club of Ewell

Mental Aid Projects

Mind in Croydon

Prosa Foundation

St Raphael's Hospice

Tayside

Brittle Bone Society

Montrose Scrapstore

Tyne & Wear

Age Concern (South Tyneside)

Community Furniture Service

Community Transport

South Shields Ladies Lifeboat Comm

Warwickshire

Emmaus (Coventry & Warwickshire)

Oxfam

RACKS

Scope

West Midlands

Age Concern (Solihull)

Barnardos (West Retail Region)

Birmingham Play Resource Centre

Community Transport – Birmingham Project

Phoenix Sheltered Workshop

Stour Valley Cat Rescue

Walsall Gingerbread Advice Centre

West Sussex

Arthritis & Rheumatism Council for Research

Guild Care

West Yorkshire

Age Concern (Bradford & District)

Age Concern (Huddersfield & District)

Age Concern (North Kirklees)

Age Concern (Wakefield District)

Keighley Council for Voluntary Service

Kirkwood Hospice

Pet Animals Welfare Society (PAWS)

RSPCA (Bradford & District Branch)

Wiltshire

Burnbake Trust

RSPCA (Marlborough with Andover Branch)

RSPCA (Wiltshire North & Chippenham Branch)

Worcestershire

Malvern Churches Community Network

Books paperback

Avon

Age Concern (Bedminster)

Age Concern (Bristol)

Age Concern (Clifton)

Age Concern (Knowle)

Age Concern (Weston-super-Mare)

The Home Farm Trust

Service 9 – Bristol's Volunteer Bureau

The SOFA Project

Bedfordshire

Age Concern (Bedfordshire)

Friends of Biggleswade Hospital

Luton Day Centre for the Homeless

Berkshire

Age Concern (Reading)

Christian Community Action

Thames Valley Hospice

Berwickshire

Royal National Mission to Deep Sea Fishermen

Buckinghamshire

Age Concern (Milton Keynes)

Age Concern (Bucks)

Cambridgeshire

Cambridge SOFA

Emmaus (Cambridge)

SOFA (Peterborough) Limited

SOS Children's Villages UK

Spaywatch

Central

Alloa Community Enterprises Limited

Cheshire

3C Teamwork

Age Concern (Cheshire)

Arthritis Research (Arthritis & Rheumatism Council)

Raynaud's & Scleroderma Association

Sue Ryder Foundation

Cumbria

Age Concern (Carlisle & District)

Age Concern (Northwest Cumbria)

Age Concern (South Lakeland)

Age Concern (Ulverston & District)

Family Advice Centre

Derbyshire

Age Concern (Derbyshire)

Arthritis & Rheumatism Council

Derby Furniture Project

Salcare

Treetops Hospice

Devon

Acorn Furniture & Clothing Project

Age Concern (Exeter)

Age Concern (Paignton)

Age Concern (Plymouth)

Age Concern (Torquay)

Arthritis & Rheumatism Council for Research

Exeter CVS Charity Shop

League of Friends – Plymouth Psychiatric Service

Seaton & District Hospital League of Friends

Dorset

Age Concern (Blandford Forum)

Age Concern (Boscombe)

Age Concern (Bournemouth)

Age Concern (Poole)

Boscombe Salvation Army Charity Concern

Christchurch Hospital League of Friends

The Friends of Blandford Community Hospital

Pramacare

Sheltered Work Opportunities Project

East Sussex

Age Concern (Brighton)

Betts Memorial Heart Foundation

Friends of the Eastbourne Hospitals

Hove YMCA

Lewes Volunteer Bureau

Monday Club

Newhaven Volunteer Bureau

Sussex Emmaus

Tools For Self Reliance

East Yorkshire

Age Concern (East Riding of Yorkshire)

RSPCA

Essex

Barnardos (East Retail Region)

Farleigh (Mid-Essex Hospice)

Friends of Wallace Kennels

Hamelin Trust

St Helena Hospice

St Luke's Hospice

Scope in Colchester (Castlegate Centre)

Gloucestershire

Full House Furniture and Recycling Service

The Furniture Recycling Project

Grampian

Aberdeen Cyrenians

Aberdeen Women's Aid

Voluntary Service (Aberdeen)

Greater Manchester

Age Concern (Metro Bury)

Age Concern (Metropolitan Rochdale)

Barnardos (North Retail Region)

Bolton Community Transport

Manchester & Salford Methodist Mission

The Salvation Army

Wesley Community Project

Gwynedd

Age Concern (Gwynedd a Món)

RSPCA (Meirionnydd Branch)

RSPCA (West Gwynedd Branch)

Hampshire

Rehab – Basingstoke & Alton Cardiac Appeal

Relate (Basingstoke & District)

Wessex Cancer Trust

Hereford & Worcester

Arthritis Research Charity Shop

Community Chest

Full House Furniture & Recycling Service

ME Association Hereford & Worcester Group

Hertfordshire

Friends of Danesbury

National Animal Welfare Trust

The Stort Trust

Humberside

Age Concern (Hull)

Kent

5th Dartford Scout Group

Age Concern (Gillingham)

Bexley Downs Syndrome Group

British Red Cross Margate Centre

Canterbury Women's Refuge

Cats Protection League (Bexley Branch)

Dartford District Volunteer Bureau

Friends of Animals League

Hope Romania

Kent Red Cross Charity Shops

Lord Whisky Sanctuary Fund

RSPCA (Kent Rochester Branch)

St Cecilia's Cheshire Home

St George's Community Children's Project Limited

St Martin's Emmaus

Seven Springs Cheshire Home

Thanet Mind (Mental Health Day Centre)

Lancashire

Age Concern (Blackburn & District)

Age Concern (Blackpool)

Age Concern (Lytham St Anne's)

Age Concern (Preston & South Ribble)

Emmaus (Greater Manchester)

Homeless in Blackpool

Preston Animal Welfare Society

Queens Hall Help Committee

Salvation Army

Leicester

Leicester Disabled Gardeners Club

Leicestershire Disabled Adventure Club

Leicestershire

Age Concern (Leicester)

British Red Cross

Cat Action Trust

Loughborough Community Care

RSPCA (Leicestershire Branch)

Work-Link Project

Lincolnshire

Bransby Home of Rest for Horses

Care Shop

St Barnabas Hospice Shops

Strut Limited

London E

Crisis

Hackney Pensioners' Association

Immigration Welfare & Legal Advisory Services

Toynbee Hall

Walthamstow After School Club

London EC

Friends of Moorfields Eye Hospital

Help the Aged

Shelter, the National Campaign for Homeless People

London NW

Age Concern (Brent)

Age Concern (Westminster)

Brent Gingerbread

Mind in Camden Charity Shop

London SE

Book Aid

Book Aid International

Elimination of Leukaemia Fund

Friends of King's College Hospital

League of Friends of Lewisham Hospital

St Christopher's Hospice

South Norwood Animal Rescue

London SW

Age Concern England

Age Concern (Wandsworth)

Centre '70 Community Shop

The Homeless Furniture Project

Oasis Aids Support Centre

RSPCA (Wimbledon & District)

Trinity Hospice

Wandsworth Housing Support Project

London W

Age Concern (Ealing Borough0

Age Concern (Hammersmith & Fulham)

London WC

The Children's Society

Imperial Cancer Research Fund

Leukaemia Research Fund

Lothian

Age Concern Scotland

Bethany Christian Trust

Cancer Research Campaign Scotland

Sue Ryder Foundation

Merseyside

Age Concern (Wirral)

Southport & District Cerebral Palsy Association

Vincent Harkins Day Care Centre

Wirral Rehab T/AS Speaks Volumes

Middlesex

Age Concern (Feltham, Hanworth & Bedfont)

British Red Cross Society

Hillingdon Community Furniture

Hillingdon Community Furniture Recycling Project

Hounslow Community Transport Furniture Project

Norfolk

Centre 81

Dereham Gingerbread Club

League of Friends – James Paget Hospital

Norfolk & Norwich Muscular Dystrophy Group

Norfolk & Norwich Scope

The Norfolk Society

Norwich Community Workshop

Royal British Legion

North Yorkshire

Age Concern (Coleraine)

Age Concern (North West Yorkshire)

Age Concern (York)

Emmaus (Scarborough)

Network (Whitby Resource Centre)

St Leonard's Hospice

The Salvation Army

Selby District AVS Charity Shop

Northamptonshire

Daventry Contact

The Salvation Army

Northern Ireland

Age Action Ireland

Arthritis & Rheumatism Council (NI)

Barnardos (Belfast)

Conservation Volunteers Northern Ireland

Emmaus Liberty Belfast

The Salvation Army Charity Shop

Voluntary Service (Belfast)

War on Want (NI)

Nottinghamshire

Beeston Volunteer Bureau

Croctal (Crochet & Other Handcrafts)

Emmanuel House Day Centre

Family First Limited

The Home Farm Trust

Kirby Volunteer Centre

Nottingham Mencap

RSPCA

Oxfordshire

Age Concern (Oxford)

Age Concern (Oxfordshire)

The Blue Cross

Nuffield Orthopaedic Centre League of Friends

Oxfam

Powys

Replay

Shropshire

Knowle Sports Association

Shropshire & Mid Wales Hospice

Somerset

Age Concern (Clevedon)

Age Concern (Somerset)

British Red Cross Somerset Branch

Imperial Cancer Research Fund

St Margaret's Somerset Hospice

West Somerset Council for Voluntary Service

South Glamorgan

Age Concern (South Glamorgan)

Track 2000

South Yorkshire

Age Concern (Rotherham)

Arthritis Research

League of Friends – Royal Hallamshire Hospital

RSPCA (SYAC)

Salvation Army (Care & Share Shop)

Staffordshire

Alsager Animals in Need

Burton YMCA

Newcastle Play Council

RSPCA (Burton-on-Trent & District Branch)

RSPCA (North Staffs Branch)

Staffordshire Wildlife Trust

Strathclyde

Dundee Voluntary Action

Enable (Scottish Society for the Mentally Handicapped)

The Salvation Army

Suffolk

Age Concern (Suffolk)

Arthritis & Rheumatism Council for Research

Home Farm Trust

St Louis Family Service

Surrey

Age Concern (Sutton Borough (Shop))

British Red Cross

Croydon Voluntary Action

Disability Action Sutton

Epsom & Ewell Phab Club

Feed the Minds

Hydestile Wildlife Hospital

Hydon Hill Cheshire Home

Inner Wheel Club of Ewell

Mental Aid Projects

Mind in Croydon

Prosa Foundation

Royal National Mission To Deep Sea Fishermen

St Raphael's Hospice

Tayside

Brittle Bone Society

Montrose Scrapstore

Tyne & Wear

Age Concern (South Tyneside)

Community Furniture Service

Community Transport

St Oswald's Hospice

South Shields Ladies Lifeboat Comm

Warwickshire

Emmaus (Coventry & Warwickshire)

Oxfam

RACKS

Scope

West Midlands

Age Concern (Solihull)

Barnardos (West Retail Region)

Birmingham Play Resource Centre

Community Transport – Birmingham Project

Phoenix Sheltered Workshop

Stour Valley Cat Rescue

Walsall Gingerbread Advice Centre

West Sussex

Arthritis & Rheumatism Council for Research

British Red Cross

Guild Care

The Missions to Seamen

West Yorkshire

Age Concern (Bradford & District)

Age Concern (Calderdale)

Age Concern (Huddersfield & District)

Age Concern (North Kirklees)

Age Concern (Wakefield District)

Keighley Council for Voluntary Service

Kirkwood Hospice

Pet Animals Welfare Society (PAWS)

RSPCA (Bradford & District Branch)

Wiltshire

Burnbake Trust

Marie Curie Cancer Care

RSPCA (Marlborough with Andover Branch)

Worcestershire

Malvern Churches Community Network

Fabric remnants

Avon

Age Concern (Bedminster)

Age Concern (Bristol)

Age Concern (Clifton)

Age Concern (Knowle)

Age Concern (Weston-super-Mare)

Service 9 – Bristol's Volunteer Bureau

Bedfordshire

Luton Day Centre for the Homeless

Berkshire

Age Concern (Reading)

Christian Community Action

Thames Valley Hospice

Buckinghamshire

The National Society for Epilepsy

Cambridgeshire

Emmaus (Cambridge)

Newark Play Association

SOFA (Peterborough) Limited

Spaywatch

Central

Alloa Community Enterprises Limited

Cheshire

Age Concern (Cheshire)

Arthritis Research (Arthritis & Rheumatism Council)

PSS – Toy Library & Resource Centre

Raynaud's & Scleroderma Association

Sue Ryder Foundation

Cumbria

Age Concern (Carlisle & District)

Age Concern (Northwest Cumbria)

Age Concern (South Lakeland)

Derbyshire

Age Concern (Derbyshire)

Salcare

Treetops Hospice

Devon

Acorn Furniture & Clothing Project

Age Concern (Exeter)

Age Concern (Paignton)

Age Concern (Plymouth)

Age Concern (Torquay)

Halcyon Neighbourhood Centre (Furniture & Thrift Store)

League of Friends – Plymouth Psychiatric Service

Seaton & District Hospital League of Friends

South Devon Play and Resource Centre Scrapstore (SPARC)

Dorset

Age Concern (Blandford Forum)

Age Concern (Boscombe)

Age Concern (Bournemouth)

Age Concern (Poole)

Boscombe Salvation Army Charity Concern

The Friends of Blandford Community Hospital

Gingerbread

Pramacare

East Sussex

Betts Memorial Heart Foundation

Eastbourne Playbus

Friends of the Eastbourne Hospitals

Hove YMCA

Lewes Volunteer Bureau

Sussex Emmaus

East Yorkshire

Age Concern (East Riding of Yorkshire)

Hull Resettlement Furniture Service

Essex

Barnardos (East Retail Region)

Farleigh (Mid-Essex Hospice)

St Helena Hospice

St Luke's Hospice

Scope in Colchester (Castlegate Centre)

Tools Mission Workshop

Gloucestershire

Full House Furniture and Recycling Service

Gloucestershire Resource Centre

Grampian

Voluntary Service (Aberdeen)

Greater Manchester

Age Concern (Manchester)

Barnardos (North Retail Region)

Manchester & Salford Methodist Mission

The Salvation Army

Gwent

Wastesavers Recycling Association

Gwynedd

RSPCA (Meirionnydd Branch)

Hampshire

National Schizophrenia Fellowship

Rehab – Basingstoke & Alton Cardiac Appeal

Southampton Scrap Store

Wessex Cancer Trust

Women's Aid to Former Yugoslavia

Hereford & Worcester

Arthritis Research Charity Shop

Community Chest

Hertfordshire

Friends of Danesbury

National Animal Welfare Trust

Humberside

Age Concern (Hull)

Isle of Wight

IW RCC (Wight Play Project)

Kent

5th Dartford Scout Group

Age Concern (Gillingham)

British Red Cross Margate Centre

Dover District Volunteer Bureau

Kent Red Cross Charity Shops

Lord Whisky Sanctuary Fund

St Cecilla's Cheshire Home

St George's Community Children's Project Limited

St Martin's Emmaus

Seven Springs Cheshire Home

Thanet Mind (Mental Health Day Centre)

Lancashire

Age Concern (Blackburn & District)

Age Concern (Blackpool)

Age Concern (Lytham St Anne's)

Age Concern (Preston & South Ribble)

Burnley Community Business & Resource Centre

Emmaus (Greater Manchester)

Homeless in Blackpool

Queens Hall Help Committee

Save the Children

Leicester

Leicester Disabled Gardeners Club

Leicestershire Disabled Adventure Club

Leicestershire

Baby Gear

British Red Cross

Loughborough Community Care

Work-Link Project

Lincolnshire

Non-Animal Medical Research

St Barnabas Hospice Shops

Strut Limited

London E

Crisis

Hackney Pensioners' Association

Toynbee Hall

Walthamstow After School Club

Waste Not Recycling

London EC

Help the Aged

Shelter, the National Campaign for Homeless People

London NW

Age Concern (Brent)

Age Concern (Westminster)

Mind in Camden Charity Shop

London SE

League of Friends of Lewisham Hospital

St Christopher's Hospice

London SW

The Homeless Furniture Project

Trinity Hospice

London W

Age Concern (Hammersmith & Fulham)

Octavia Hill Housing Trust

London WC

The Children's Society

Lothian

Bethany Christian Trust

Cancer Research Campaign Scotland

Sue Ryder Foundation

Merseyside

St Helen's Opportunity for Play

Southport & District Cerebral Palsy Association

Middlesex

Age Concern (Feltham, Hanworth & Bedfont)

British Red Cross Society

Richmond Fellowship International

Norfolk

CSV Vocal Project

Norfolk & Norwich Scope

Norwich Community Workshop

North Yorkshire

Age Concern (Coleraine)

Emmaus (Scarborough)

Network (Whitby Resource Centre)

St Leonard's Hospice

The Salvation Army

Selby District AVS Charity Shop

Northamphire

Daventry Contact

The Salvation Army

Northern Ireland

Age Action Ireland

Arthritis & Rheumatism Council (NI)

Barnardos (Belfast)

The Salvation Army Charity Shop

Voluntary Service (Belfast)

War on Want (NI)

Nottinghamshire

Age Concern (Nottinghamshire)

Beeston Volunteer Bureau

Family First Limited

The Home Farm Trust

Kirby Volunteer Centre

Newark & Sherwood Play Support Group

Orkney

Age Concern (Orkney)

Powys

Replay

Shropshire

Knowle Sports Association

Shropshire & Mid Wales Hospice

Shropshire Children's Scrap Store

Somerset

Age Concern (Clevedon)

Age Concern (Somerset)

British Red Cross Somerset Branch

Imperial Cancer Research Fund

St Margaret's Somerset Hospice

South Glamorgan

Track 2000

South Yorkshire

Arthritis Research

Highway Tools & Crafts Centre

Staffordshire

Newcastle Play Council

RSPCA (North Staffs Branch)

Strathclyde

Enable (Scottish Society for the Mentally Handicapped)

Suffolk

Age Concern (Suffolk)

Arthritis & Rheumatism Council for Research

Home Farm Trust

St Louis Family Service

Tools with a Mission

Surrey

Age Concern (Sutton Borough (Shop))

Community Scrap Scheme

Disability Action Sutton

Epsom & Ewell Phab Club

Hydestile Wildlife Hospital

Hydon Hill Cheshire Home

Inner Wheel Club of Ewell

Mental Aid Projects

Mind in Croydon

Queen Elizabeth's Foundation for Disabled People

St Raphael's Hospice

Surrey Community Recycling and Play Project

Tayside

Montrose Scrapstore

Tayside Furniture Project

Tyne & Wear

Community Furniture Service

Community Transport

St Oswald's Hospice

Warwickshire

Emmaus (Coventry & Warwickshire)

Oxfam

RACKS

Rokeby Infant School PTFA

Scope

West Midlands

Barnardos (West Retail Region)

Birmingham Play Resource Centre

Community Transport – Birmingham Project

Phoenix Sheltered Workshop

Stour Valley Cat Rescue

Walsall Gingerbread Advice Centre

West Sussex

Wallis Centre

West Yorkshire

Age Concern (Bradford & District)

Age Concern (Calderdale)

Age Concern (Huddersfield & District)

Age Concern (Wakefield District)

Keighley Council for Voluntary Service

Kirkwood Hospice

RSPCA (Bradford & District Branch)

The Russell Street Project Limited

Wiltshire

RSPCA (Marlborough with Andover Branch)

RSPCA (Wiltshire North & Chippenham Branch)

Swindon Children's Scrapstore

Worcestershire

Malvern Churches Community Network

Knitting, crochet and sewing equipment

Avon

Age Concern (Bedminster)

Age Concern (Bristol)

Age Concern (Clifton)

Age Concern (Knowle)

Age Concern (Weston-super-Mare)

Service 9 – Bristol's Volunteer Bureau

Bedfordshire

Luton Day Centre for the Homeless

Berkshire

Age Concern (Reading)

Christian Community Action

Thames Valley Hospice

Buckinghamshire

Age Concern (Milton Keynes)

Age Concern (Bucks)

The National Society for Epilepsy

Cambridgeshire

Cambridge SOFA

Emmaus (Cambridge)

Newark Play Association

Spaywatch

Central

Alloa Community Enterprises Limited

Cheshire

3C Teamwork

Age Concern (Cheshire)

Arthritis Research (Arthritis & Rheumatism Council)

PSS – Toy Library & Resource Centre

Sue Ryder Foundation

Cumbria

Age Concern (Carlisle & District)

Age Concern (Northwest Cumbria)

Age Concern (South Lakeland)

Derbyshire

Age Concern (Derbyshire)

Arthritis & Rheumatism Council

Salcare

Treetops Hospice

Devon

Acorn Furniture & Clothing Project

Age Concern (Exeter)

Age Concern (Paignton)

Age Concern (Plymouth)

Age Concern (Torquay)

Halcyon Neighbourhood Centre (Furniture & Thrift Store)

League of Friends – Plymouth Psychiatric Service

Seaton & District Hospital League of Friends

Dorset

Age Concern (Blandford Forum)

Age Concern (Boscombe)

Age Concern (Bournemouth)

Age Concern (Poole)

Christchurch Hospital League of Friends

The Friends of Blandford Community Hospital

Gingerbread

Pramacare

East Sussex

Betts Memorial Heart Foundation

Hove YMCA

Lewes Volunteer Bureau

Sussex Emmaus

East Yorkshire

Age Concern (East Riding of Yorkshire)

Hull Resettlement Furniture Service

Essex

Barnardos (East Retail Region)

Farleigh (Mid-Essex Hospice)

The Friends of St Francis Hospice (Shops) Ltd

Hamelin Trust

St Helena Hospice

St Luke's Hospice

Scope in Colchester (Castlegate Centre)

Tools Mission Workshop

Gloucestershire

Full House Furniture and Recycling Service

Grampian

Aberdeen Women's Aid

Voluntary Service (Aberdeen)

Greater Manchester

Age Concern (Manchester)

Age Concern (Metro Bury)

Barnardos (North Retail Region)

Manchester & Salford Methodist Mission

The Salvation Army

Wesley Community Project

Gwynedd

RSPCA (Meirionnydd Branch)

RSPCA (West Gwynedd Branch)

Hampshire

National Schizophrenia Fellowship

Rehab – Basingstoke & Alton Cardiac Appeal

Totton & Eling Community Association

Women's Aid to Former Yugoslavia

Hereford & Worcester

Arthritis Research Charity Shop

Community Chest

Full House Furniture & Recycling Service

Hertfordshire

National Animal Welfare Trust

The Stort Trust

Humberside

Age Concern (Hull)

Isle of Wight

IW RCC (Wight Play Project)

Kent

Age Concern (Gillingham)

Bexley Downs Syndrome Group

British Red Cross Margate Centre

Cats Protection League (Bexley Branch)

Kent Red Cross Charity Shops

Lord Whisky Sanctuary Fund

St Cecilia's Cheshire Home

St Martin's Emmaus

Seven Springs Cheshire Home

Thanet Mind (Mental Health Day Centre)

Lancashire

Age Concern (Blackburn & District)

Age Concern (Blackpool)

Age Concern (Lytham St Anne's)

Age Concern (Preston & South Ribble)

Emmaus (Greater Manchester)

Homeless in Blackpool

Queens Hall Help Committee

Save the Children

Leicester

Leicester Disabled Gardeners Club

Leicestershire Disabled Adventure Club

Leicestershire

British Red Cross

Cat Action Trust

Loughborough Community Care

RSPCA (Leicestershire Branch)

Work-Link Project

Lincolnshire

Non-Animal Medical Research

St Barnabas Hospice Shops

Strut Limited

London E

Crisis

Hackney Pensioners' Association

Toynbee Hall

Walthamstow After School Club

London EC

Help the Aged

Shelter, the National Campaign for Homeless People

London NW

Age Concern (Brent)

Age Concern (Westminster)

London SE

Friends of King's College Hospital

League of Friends of Lewisham Hospital

St Christopher's Hospice

London SW

Age Concern England

Trinity Hospice

London W

Age Concern (Hammersmith & Fulham)

Octavia Hill Housing Trust

London WC

The Children's Society

Imperial Cancer Research Fund

Lothian

Bethany Christian Trust

Cancer Research Campaign Scotland

Sue Ryder Foundation

Merseyside

Newton Visual Impaired Group

Southport & District Cerebral Palsy Association

Middlesex

Age Concern (Feltham, Hanworth & Bedfont)

British Red Cross Society

Hillingdon Community Furniture Recycling Project

Richmond Fellowship International

Norfolk

Centre 81

CSV Vocal Project

Norfolk & Norwich Scope

Norwich Community Workshop

North Yorkshire

Age Concern (Coleraine)

Emmaus (Scarborough)

Network (Whitby Resource Centre)

St Leonard's Hospice

The Salvation Army

Selby District AVS Charity Shop

Northampshire

Daventry Contact

Northern Ireland

Age Action Ireland

Arthritis & Rheumatism Council (NI)

Barnardos (Belfast)

Emmaus Liberty Belfast

The Salvation Army Charity Shop

Voluntary Service (Belfast)

Nottinghamshire

Age Concern (Nottinghamshire)

Croctal (Crochet & Other Handcrafts)

The Home Farm Trust

Kirby Volunteer Centre

Oxfordshire

Age Concern (Oxford)

Age Concern (Oxfordshire)

Nuffield Orthopaedic Centre League of Friends

Oxfam

Powys

Replay

Shropshire

Knowle Sports Association

Shropshire & Mid Wales Hospice

Shropshire Children's Scrap Store

Somerset

Age Concern (Clevedon)

Age Concern (Somerset)

British Red Cross Somerset Branch

Imperial Cancer Research Fund

St Margaret's Somerset Hospice

South Glamorgan

Age Concern (South Glamorgan)

Track 2000

South Yorkshire

Arthritis Research

Bentley Association for Supportive Help

RSPCA (SYAC)

Salvation Army (Care & Share Shop)

Staffordshire

Alsager Animals in Need

RSPCA (North Staffs Branch)

Strathclyde

Enable (Scottish Society for the Mentally Handicapped)

Suffolk

Age Concern (Suffolk)

Arthritis & Rheumatism Council for Research

Home Farm Trust

St Louis Family Service

Tools with a Mission

Surrey

Age Concern (Sutton Borough (Shop))

Community Scrap Scheme

Disability Action Sutton

Epsom & Ewell Phab Club

Hydon Hill Cheshire Home

Inner Wheel Club of Ewell

Mental Aid Projects

Mind in Croydon

Prosa Foundation

Queen Elizabeth's Foundation for Disabled People

St Raphael's Hospice

Surrey Community Recycling and Play Project

Tayside

Montrose Scrapstore

Tyne & Wear

Community Furniture Service

St Oswald's Hospice

South Shields Ladies Lifeboat Comm

Warwickshire

Emmaus (Coventry & Warwickshire)

RACKS

Scope

West Midlands

Age Concern (Solihull)

Barnardos (West Retail Region)

Birmingham Play Resource Centre

Phoenix Sheltered Workshop

Stour Valley Cat Rescue

Walsall Gingerbread Advice Centre

West Sussex

Arthritis & Rheumatism Council for Research

Guild Care

West Yorkshire

Age Concern (Bradford & District)

Age Concern (Calderdale)

Age Concern (Huddersfield & District)

Age Concern (Wakefield District)

Keighley Council for Voluntary Service

Kirkwood Hospice

RSPCA (Bradford & District Branch)

The Russell Street Project Limited

Wiltshire

RSPCA (Marlborough with Andover Branch)

RSPCA (Wiltshire North & Chippenham Branch)

Swindon Children's Scrapstore

Worcestershire

Malvern Churches Community Network

Knitting wool

Avon

Age Concern (Bedminster)

Age Concern (Bristol)

Age Concern (Clifton)

Age Concern (Knowle)

Age Concern (Weston-super-Mare)

Service 9 – Bristol's Volunteer Bureau

Bedfordshire

Friends of Biggleswade Hospital

Luton Day Centre for the Homeless

Women's Royal Voluntary Service

Berkshire

Age Concern (Reading)

Christian Community Action

Thames Valley Hospice

Buckinghamshire

Age Concern (Milton Keynes)

Age Concern (Bucks)

High Wycombe General Aid Society

The National Society for Epilepsy

Cambridgeshire

Cambridge SOFA

Newark Play Association

Spaywatch

Central

Alloa Community Enterprises Limited

Cheshire

3C Teamwork

Age Concern (Cheshire)

Arthritis Research (Arthritis & Rheumatism Council)

PSS – Toy Library & Resource Centre

Sue Ryder Foundation

Cumbria

Age Concern (Carlisle & District)

Age Concern (Northwest Cumbria)

Age Concern (South Lakeland)

Age Concern (Ulverston & District)

Derbyshire

Age Concern (Derbyshire)

Arthritis & Rheumatism Council

Salcare

Treetops Hospice

Devon

Acorn Furniture & Clothing Project

Age Concern (Exeter)

Age Concern (Paignton)

Age Concern (Plymouth)

Age Concern (Torquay)

Arthritis & Rheumatism Council for Research

Halcyon Neighbourhood Centre (Furniture & Thrift Store)

League of Friends – Plymouth Psychiatric Service

Seaton & District Hospital League of Friends

South Devon Play and Resource Centre Scrapstore (SPARC)

Dorset

Age Concern (Blandford Forum)

Age Concern (Boscombe)

Age Concern (Bournemouth)

Age Concern (Poole)

Boscombe Salvation Army Charity Concern

Christchurch Hospital League of Friends

The Friends of Blandford Community Hospital

Gingerbread

Pramacare

Rowan Cottage

East Sussex

Age Concern (Brighton)

Betts Memorial Heart Foundation

Friends of the Eastbourne
Hospitals

Hove YMCA

Lewes Volunteer Bureau

Sussex Emmaus

East Yorkshire

Age Concern (East Riding of
Yorkshire)

RSPCA

Essex

Barnardos (East Retail Region)

Farleigh (Mid-Essex Hospice)

The Friends of St Francis
Hospice (Shops) Ltd

St Helena Hospice

St Luke's Hospice

Scope in Colchester (Castlegate
Centre)

Tools Mission Workshop

Gloucestershire

Full House Furniture and
Recycling Service

Grampian

Aberdeen Women's Aid

Voluntary Service (Aberdeen)

Greater Manchester

Age Concern (Metropolitan
Rochdale)

Barnardos (North Retail Region)

The Salvation Army

Wesley Community Project

Gwynedd

RSPCA (Meirionnydd Branch)

RSPCA (West Gwynedd Branch)

Hampshire

National Schizophrenia
Fellowship

Rehab – Basingstoke & Alton
Cardiac Appeal

Southampton Scrap Store

Totton & Eling Community
Association

Women's Aid to Former
Yugoslavia

Hereford & Worcester

Arthritis Research Charity Shop

Community Chest

Hertfordshire

Friends of Danesbury

National Animal Welfare Trust

The Stort Trust

Humberside

Age Concern (Hull)

Isle of Wight

IW RCC (Wight Play Project)

Kent

5th Dartford Scout Group

Age Concern (Gillingham)

British Red Cross Margate
Centre

Cats Protection League (Bexley
Branch)

Dover District Volunteer Bureau

Friends of Animals League

Kent Red Cross Charity Shops

Lord Whisky Sanctuary Fund

St Cecilia's Cheshire Home

St George's Community
Children's Project Limited

St Martin's Emmaus

Seven Springs Cheshire Home

Thanet Mind (Mental Health
Day Centre)

Lancashire

Age Concern (Blackburn &
District)

Age Concern (Blackpool)

Age Concern (Lytham St Anne's)

Age Concern (Preston & South
Ribble)

Emmaus (Greater Manchester)

Homeless in Blackpool

Queens Hall Help Committee

Save the Children

Leicester

Leicester Disabled Gardeners
Club

Leicestershire Disabled
Adventure Club

Leicestershire

Age Concern (Leicester)

Baby Gear

British Red Cross

Loughborough Community
Care

RSPCA (Leicestershire Branch)

Work-Link Project

Lincolnshire

Artlandish Limited

St Barnabas Hospice Shops

Strut Limited

London E

Crisis

Hackney Pensioners' Association

Toynbee Hall

Walthamstow After School Club

London EC

Help the Aged

Shelter, the National Campaign
for Homeless People

London NW

Age Concern (Brent)

Age Concern (Westminster)

Mind in Camden Charity Shop

London SE

Friends of King's College
Hospital

League of Friends of Lewisham
Hospital

St Christopher's Hospice

South Norwood Animal Rescue

London SW

Age Concern England

Centre '70 Community Shop

RSPCA (Richmond, Twickenham
& Barnes Branch)

RSPCA (Wimbledon & District)

Trinity Hospice

Wandsworth Housing Support Project

London W

Age Concern (Hammersmith & Fulham)

Octavia Hill Housing Trust

London WC

Imperial Cancer Research Fund

Lothian

Bethany Christian Trust

Cancer Research Campaign Scotland

Sue Ryder Foundation

Merseyside

Age Concern (Wirral)

Newton Visual Impaired Group

Southport & District Cerebral Palsy Association

Vincent Harkins Day Care Centre

Middlesex

British Red Cross Society

Hillingdon Community Furniture Recycling Project

Richmond Fellowship International

Norfolk

Centre 81

CSV Vocal Project

League of Friends – James Paget Hospital

Norfolk & Norwich Muscular Dystrophy Group

Norfolk & Norwich Scope

Norwich Community Workshop

Royal British Legion

North Yorkshire

Age Concern (Coleraine)

Age Concern (York)

Emmaus (Scarborough)

Network (Whitby Resource Centre)

St Leonard's Hospice

The Salvation Army

Selby District AVS Charity Shop

Northamptonshire

Daventry Contact

The Salvation Army

Northern Ireland

Age Action Ireland

Arthritis & Rheumatism Council (NI)

Barnardos (Belfast)

Emmaus Liberty Belfast

The Salvation Army Charity Shop

Voluntary Service (Belfast)

War on Want (NI)

Nottinghamshire

Age Concern (Nottinghamshire)

Beeston Volunteer Bureau

Croctal (Crochet & Other Handcrafts)

Eastwood Volunteer Bureau

Emmanuel House Day Centre

The Home Farm Trust

Kirby Volunteer Centre

Newark & Sherwood Play Support Group

RSPCA

Oxfordshire

Age Concern (Oxford)

Katharine House Hospice

Nuffield Orthopaedic Centre League of Friends

Oxfam

Powys

Replay

Shropshire

Knowle Sports Association

Shropshire & Mid Wales Hospice

Shropshire Children's Scrap Store

Somerset

Age Concern (Clevedon)

Age Concern (Somerset)

British Red Cross Somerset Branch

Imperial Cancer Research Fund

St Margaret's Somerset Hospice

Women's Royal Voluntary Service

South Glamorgan

Age Concern (South Glamorgan)

Track 2000

South Yorkshire

Age Concern (Rotherham)

Arthritis Research

Highway Tools & Crafts Centre

RSPCA (SYAC)

Salvation Army (Care & Share Shop)

Sheffield Family Services Unit

Staffordshire

Newcastle Play Council

RSPCA (North Staffs Branch)

Strathclyde

Enable (Scottish Society for the Mentally Handicapped)

Suffolk

Age Concern (Suffolk)

Arthritis & Rheumatism Council for Research

Home Farm Trust

St Louis Family Service

Tools with a Mission

Surrey

Age Concern (Sutton Borough (Shop))

Community Scrap Scheme

Disability Action Sutton

Epsom & Ewell Phab Club

Hydestile Wildlife Hospital

Hydon Hill Cheshire Home

Inner Wheel Club of Ewell

Mental Aid Projects

Mind in Croydon

Prader-Willi Syndrome Association (UK)

Prosa Foundation

Queen Elizabeth's Foundation for Disabled People

St Raphael's Hospice

SHCVS

Surrey Community Recycling and Play Project

Tayside

Brittle Bone Society

Montrose Scrapstore

Tyne & Wear

Age Concern (South Tyneside)

Community Furniture Service

St Oswald's Hospice

South Shields Ladies Lifeboat Comm

Warwickshire

Emmaus (Coventry & Warwickshire)

Oxfam

RACKS

Scope

West Midlands

Age Concern (Solihull)

Barnardos (West Retail Region)

Birmingham Play Resource Centre

Phoenix Sheltered Workshop

Stour Valley Cat Rescue

Walsall Gingerbread Advice Centre

West Sussex

Arthritis & Rheumatism Council for Research

British Red Cross

Guild Care

The Missions to Seamen

West Yorkshire

Age Concern (Bradford & District)

Age Concern (Calderdale)

Age Concern (Huddersfield & District)

Age Concern (North Kirklees)

Age Concern (Wakefield District)

Keighley Council for Voluntary Service

Kirkwood Hospice

RSPCA (Bradford & District Branch)

The Russell Street Project Limited

Wiltshire

Age Concern (Thamesdown)

RSPCA (Marlborough with Andover Branch)

RSPCA (Wiltshire North & Chippenham Branch)

Swindon Children's Scrapstore

Worcestershire

Malvern Churches Community Network

Magazines & comics

Avon

Age Concern (Bristol)

Service 9 – Bristol's Volunteer Bureau

Bedfordshire

Luton Day Centre for the Homeless

Women's Royal Voluntary Service

Berkshire

Age Concern (Reading)

Cambridgeshire

Newark Play Association

Central

Alloa Community Enterprises Limited

Cheshire

3C Teamwork

Age Concern (Cheshire)

Sue Ryder Foundation

Cumbria

Age Concern (Carlisle & District)

Age Concern (Northwest Cumbria)

Age Concern (South Lakeland)

Age Concern (Ulverston & District)

Derbyshire

Arthritis & Rheumatism Council

Salcare

Treetops Hospice

Devon

League of Friends – Plymouth Psychiatric Service

Seaton & District Hospital League of Friends

Dorset

Boscombe Salvation Army Charity Concern

East Sussex
Hove YMCA

Lewes Volunteer Bureau

Monday Club

Sussex Emmaus

East Yorkshire
Age Concern (East Riding of Yorkshire)

Essex
Barnardos (East Retail Region)

Farleigh (Mid-Essex Hospice)

St Helena Hospice

St Luke's Hospice

Grampian
Aberdeen Women's Aid

Voluntary Service (Aberdeen)

Greater Manchester
Age Concern (Manchester)

Barnardos (North Retail Region)

Wesley Community Project

Gwent
Wastesavers Recycling Association

Gwynedd
Age Concern (Gwynedd a Món)

Hampshire
Rehab – Basingstoke & Alton Cardiac Appeal

Hereford & Worcester
Community Chest

Hertfordshire
Base, Dacorum and St Albans Homeless Development Team

Friends of Danesbury

The Stort Trust

Isle of Wight
IW RCC (Wight Play Project)

Kent
Bexley Downs Syndrome Group

British Red Cross Margate Centre

St Cecilia's Cheshire Home

St Martin's Emmaus

Seven Springs Cheshire Home

Thanet Mind (Mental Health Day Centre)

Lancashire
Age Concern (Blackburn & District)

Age Concern (Blackpool)

Age Concern (Lytham St Anne's)

Emmaus (Greater Manchester)

Homeless in Blackpool

Queens Hall Help Committee

Leicester
Leicester Disabled Gardeners Club

Leicestershire Disabled Adventure Club

Leicestershire
Age Concern (Leicester)

Cat Action Trust

Loughborough Community Care

RSPCA (Leicestershire Branch)

Lincolnshire
Artlandish Limited

Bransby Home of Rest for Horses

Care Shop

St Barnabas Hospice Shops

Strut Limited

London E
Crisis

Hackney Pensioners' Association

London EC
Shelter, the National Campaign for Homeless People

London NW
Age Concern (Brent)

Age Concern (Westminster)

Mind in Camden Charity Shop

London SW
Age Concern England

RSPCA (Wimbledon & District)

London W
Age Concern (Hammersmith & Fulham)

Lothian
Bethany Christian Trust

Cancer Research Campaign Scotland

Sue Ryder Foundation

Merseyside
Newton Visual Impaired Group

Vincent Harkins Day Care Centre

Wirral Rehab T/AS Speaks Volumes

Middlesex
Aspire

Hillingdon Community Furniture Recycling Project

Norfolk
Centre 81

North Yorkshire
Age Concern (Coleraine)

Emmaus (Scarborough)

The Salvation Army

Northamptonshire
Daventry Contact

Northern Ireland
Age Action Ireland

Arthritis & Rheumatism Council (NI)

Barnardos (Belfast)

The Salvation Army Charity Shop

Voluntary Service (Belfast)

War on Want (NI)

....

Nottinghamshire

Age Concern (Nottinghamshire)

Croctal (Crochet & Other Handcrafts)

....

Oxfordshire

Age Concern (Oxford)

Oxfam

....

Powys

Replay

....

Shropshire

Knowle Sports Association

Shropshire & Mid Wales Hospice

....

Somerset

Imperial Cancer Research Fund

St Margaret's Somerset Hospice

West Somerset Council for Voluntary Service

....

South Glamorgan

Age Concern (South Glamorgan)

....

South Yorkshire

Bentley Association for Supportive Help

....

Staffordshire

RSPCA (North Staffs Branch)

....

Suffolk

Age Concern (Suffolk)

Arthritis & Rheumatism Council for Research

Home Farm Trust

....

Surrey

Disability Action Sutton

Feed the Minds

Hydon Hill Cheshire Home

Mental Aid Projects

Mind in Croydon

Royal National Mission To Deep Sea Fishermen

St Raphael's Hospice

Surrey Community Recycling and Play Project

....

Tyne & Wear

Community Furniture Service

Community Transport

....

Warwickshire

Emmaus (Coventry & Warwickshire)

RACKS

Rokeby Infant School PTFA

....

West Midlands

Age Concern (Solihull)

Barnardos (West Retail Region)

Birmingham Play Resource Centre

Phoenix Sheltered Workshop

Stour Valley Cat Rescue

Walsall Gingerbread Advice Centre

....

West Sussex

Arthritis & Rheumatism Council for Research

Guild Care

....

West Yorkshire

Age Concern (Huddersfield & District)

Age Concern (Wakefield District)

Keighley Council for Voluntary Service

Kirkwood Hospice

RSPCA (Bradford & District Branch)

....

Wiltshire

RSPCA (Marlborough with Andover Branch)

Musical instruments

Avon

Age Concern (Bedminster)

Age Concern (Bristol)

Age Concern (Clifton)

Age Concern (Knowle)

Age Concern (Weston-super-Mare)

....

Bedfordshire

Age Concern (Bedfordshire)

The Salvation Army

....

Berkshire

Age Concern (Reading)

Christian Community Action

Thames Valley Hospice

....

Buckinghamshire

Age Concern (Milton Keynes)

Age Concern (Bucks)

The National Society for Epilepsy

....

Cambridgeshire

Cambridge SOFA

Emmaus (Cambridge)

Newark Play Association

SOFA (Peterborough) Limited

Spaywatch

....

Central

Alloa Community Enterprises Limited

....

Cheshire

3C Teamwork

Age Concern (Cheshire)

Arthritis Research (Arthritis & Rheumatism Council)

PSS – Toy Library & Resource Centre

Sue Ryder Foundation

Cumbria
Age Concern (Carlisle & District)

Age Concern (Northwest Cumbria)

Age Concern (South Lakeland)

Derbyshire
Arthritis & Rheumatism Council

Salcare

Treetops Hospice

Devon
Acorn Furniture & Clothing Project

Age Concern (Exeter)

Age Concern (Paignton)

Age Concern (Torquay)

League of Friends – Plymouth Psychiatric Service

Seaton & District Hospital League of Friends

Dorset
Age Concern (Blandford Forum)

Age Concern (Boscombe)

Age Concern (Poole)

The Friends of Blandford Community Hospital

Pramacare

East Sussex
Eastbourne Playbus

Feline Foster

Hove YMCA

Lewes Volunteer Bureau

Monday Club

Peacehaven & Telscombe Volunteer Bureau

Seaford Volunteers

Sussex Emmaus

East Yorkshire
Age Concern (East Riding of Yorkshire)

Hull Resettlement Furniture Service

Essex
Barnardos (East Retail Region)

Farleigh (Mid-Essex Hospice)

The Friends of St Francis Hospice (Shops) Ltd

Hamelin Trust

St Helena Hospice

St Luke's Hospice

Scope in Colchester (Castlegate Centre)

Gloucestershire
Full House Furniture and Recycling Service

Grampian
Aberdeen Cyrenians

Voluntary Service (Aberdeen)

Greater Manchester
Age Concern (Manchester)

Age Concern (Metro Bury)

Barnardos (North Retail Region)

Bolton Community Transport

Manchester & Salford Methodist Mission

Manchester One Parent Family Advice Centre

The Salvation Army

Wesley Community Project

Gwynedd
Age Concern (Gwynedd a Món)

RSPCA (West Gwynedd Branch)

Hampshire
Oxford Mission

Rehab – Basingstoke & Alton Cardiac Appeal

Resettlement Project – South Hants

Hereford & Worcester
Arthritis Research Charity Shop

Community Chest

Full House Furniture & Recycling Service

Hertfordshire
Base, Dacorum and St Albans Homeless Development Team

Friends of Danesbury

National Animal Welfare Trust

The Stort Trust

Humberside
Age Concern (Hull)

Kent
Bexley Downs Syndrome Group

British Red Cross Margate Centre

Kent Red Cross Charity Shops

Lord Whisky Sanctuary Fund

RSPCA (Kent Rochester Branch)

St Cecilia's Cheshire Home

St George's Community Children's Project Limited

St Martin's Emmaus

Seven Springs Cheshire Home

Thanet Mind (Mental Health Day Centre)

Lancashire
Age Concern (Lytham St Anne's)

Age Concern (Preston & South Ribble)

Emmaus (Greater Manchester)

Homeless in Blackpool

Queens Hall Help Committee

Salvation Army

Save the Children

Leicester
Leicester Disabled Gardeners Club

Leicestershire Disabled Adventure Club

Leicestershire
British Red Cross

Loughborough Community Care

Work-Link Project

Lincolnshire
Care Shop

Strut Limited

London E
Immigration Welfare & Legal Advisory Services

Toynbee Hall

Walthamstow After School Club

London EC

Help the Aged

Shelter, the National Campaign for Homeless People

London NW

Age Concern (Brent)

Age Concern (Westminster)

Mind in Camden Charity Shop

London SE

St Christopher's Hospice

Shaftesbury Resources Centre

London SW

Age Concern England

Centre '70 Community Shop

The Homeless Furniture Project

Oasis Aids Support Centre

Trinity Hospice

Wandsworth Housing Support Project

London W

Age Concern (Hammersmith & Fulham)

London WC

The Children's Society

Imperial Cancer Research Fund

Lothian

Bethany Christian Trust

Cancer Research Campaign Scotland

The National Bible Society of Scotland

Sue Ryder Foundation

Merseyside

Age Concern (Wirral)

Southport & District Cerebral Palsy Association

Middlesex

British Red Cross Society

Hillingdon Community Furniture Recycling Project

Richmond Fellowship International

Norfolk

Centre 81

CSV Vocal Project

Dereham Gingerbread Club

Norfolk & Norwich Scope

North Yorkshire

Age Concern (Coleraine)

Age Concern (North West Yorkshire)

Emmaus (Scarborough)

St Leonard's Hospice

The Salvation Army

Selby District AVS Charity Shop

Northamptonshire

Caring & Sharing Trust

Northern Ireland

Age Action Ireland

Arthritis & Rheumatism Council (NI)

Barnardos (Belfast)

Emmaus Liberty Belfast

The Salvation Army Charity Shop

Voluntary Service (Belfast)

War on Want (NI)

Nottinghamshire

Age Concern (Nottinghamshire)

Emmanuel House Day Centre

Family First Limited

Kirby Volunteer Centre

Newark & Sherwood Play Support Group

Nottingham Mencap

RSPCA

Oxfordshire

Age Concern (Oxford)

Age Concern (Oxfordshire)

Katharine House Hospice

Oxfam

The Worldwide Fund for Nature (WWF)

Shropshire

Knowle Sports Association

Shropshire & Mid Wales Hospice

Somerset

Age Concern (Clevedon)

British Red Cross Somerset Branch

Imperial Cancer Research Fund

St Margaret's Somerset Hospice

South Glamorgan

Age Concern (South Glamorgan)

Track 2000

South Yorkshire

Arthritis Research

Salvation Army (Care & Share Shop)

Staffordshire

RSPCA (North Staffs Branch)

Strathclyde

David Livingstone International

The Salvation Army

Suffolk

Age Concern (Suffolk)

Arthritis & Rheumatism Council for Research

Home Farm Trust

Surrey

Age Concern (Sutton Borough (Shop))

Community Scrap Scheme

Disability Action Sutton

Epsom & Ewell Phab Club

Hydon Hill Cheshire Home

Mental Aid Projects

Mind in Croydon

Prosa Foundation

Queen Elizabeth's Foundation for Disabled People

St Raphael's Hospice

Tayside

Montrose Scrapstore

Tyne & Wear

Community Furniture Service

Community Transport

South Shields Ladies Lifeboat Comm

Warwickshire

Emmaus (Coventry & Warwickshire)

RACKS

Scope

West Midlands

Age Concern (Solihull)

Barnardos (West Retail Region)

Birmingham Play Resource Centre

Community Transport

Phoenix Sheltered Workshop

Stour Valley Cat Rescue

Walsall Gingerbread Advice Centre

West Sussex

Adur Furniture Network

Arthritis & Rheumatism Council for Research

Wallis Centre

West Yorkshire

Age Concern (Bradford & District)

Age Concern (Huddersfield & District)

Age Concern (Wakefield District)

Kirkwood Hospice

RSPCA (Bradford & District Branch)

The Russell Street Project Limited

Wiltshire

RSPCA (Marlborough with Andover Branch)

Worcestershire

Malvern Churches Community Network

Photographic equipment

Avon

Age Concern (Bristol)

The Home Farm Trust

Bedfordshire

Luton Day Centre for the Homeless

Berkshire

Age Concern (Reading)

Christian Community Action

Thames Valley Hospice

Buckinghamshire

Age Concern (Milton Keynes)

Age Concern (Bucks)

Cambridgeshire

Cambridge SOFA

Emmaus (Cambridge)

The Leonard Cheshire Foundation

SOFA (Peterborough) Limited

Central

Alloa Community Enterprises Limited

Cheshire

3C Teamwork

Age Concern (Cheshire)

Arthritis Research (Arthritis & Rheumatism Council)

Sue Ryder Foundation

Cumbria

Age Concern (Carlisle & District)

Age Concern (Northwest Cumbria)

Age Concern (South Lakeland)

Derbyshire

Salcare

Treetops Hospice

Devon

Arthritis & Rheumatism Council for Research

Dorset

Boscombe Salvation Army Charity Concern

The Friends of Blandford Community Hospital

Pramacare

East Sussex

Betts Memorial Heart Foundation

Hove YMCA

Lewes Volunteer Bureau

Seaford Volunteers

Sussex Emmaus

East Yorkshire

Age Concern (East Riding of Yorkshire)

Essex

Barnardos (East Retail Region)

Farleigh (Mid-Essex Hospice)

The Friends of St Francis Hospice (Shops) Ltd

Hamelin Trust

St Helena Hospice

St Luke's Hospice

Scope in Colchester (Castlegate Centre)

Gloucestershire

Full House Furniture and Recycling Service

Gloucestershire Resource Centre

Grampian

Aberdeen Cyrenians

Aberdeen Women's Aid

Voluntary Service (Aberdeen)

Greater Manchester

Age Concern (Manchester)

Age Concern (Metro Bury)

Barnardos (North Retail Region)

The Salvation Army

Wesley Community Project

Gwynedd

RSPCA (West Gwynedd Branch)

Hampshire

Rehab – Basingstoke & Alton Cardiac Appeal

Hereford & Worcester

Arthritis Research Charity Shop

Full House Furniture & Recycling Service

Hertfordshire

Base, Dacorum and St Albans Homeless Development Team

Friends of Danesbury

National Animal Welfare Trust

The Stort Trust

Kent

Bexley Downs Syndrome Group

British Red Cross Margate Centre

Kent Red Cross Charity Shops

RSPCA (Kent Rochester Branch)

St Cecilia's Cheshire Home

St Martin's Emmaus

Seven Springs Cheshire Home

Thanet Mind (Mental Health Day Centre)

Lancashire

Age Concern (Lytham St Anne's)

Age Concern (Preston & South Ribble)

Burnley Community Business & Resource Centre

Emmaus (Greater Manchester)

Homeless in Blackpool

Queens Hall Help Committee

Save the Children

Leicester

Leicester Disabled Gardeners Club

Leicestershire Disabled Adventure Club

Leicestershire

British Red Cross

Cat Action Trust

Loughborough Community Care

Lincolnshire

Artlandish Limited

St Barnabas Hospice Shops

Strut Limited

London E

Toynbee Hall

London EC

Help the Aged

Shelter, the National Campaign for Homeless People

London NW

Age Concern (Brent)

Age Concern (Westminster)

Brent Gingerbread

London SW

Age Concern England

The Homeless Furniture Project

Oasis Aids Support Centre

Trinity Hospice

London W

Age Concern (Hammersmith & Fulham)

London WC

The Children's Society

Imperial Cancer Research Fund

Lothian

Bethany Christian Trust

Cancer Research Campaign Scotland

Royal National Lifeboat Institution

Sue Ryder Foundation

Merseyside

Age Concern (Wirral)

Southport & District Cerebral Palsy Association

Middlesex

British Red Cross Society

Richmond Fellowship International

Norfolk

Centre 81

CSV Vocal Project

Norfolk & Norwich Scope

North Yorkshire

Age Concern (Coleraine)

Age Concern (North West Yorkshire)

Emmaus (Scarborough)

St Leonard's Hospice

Selby District AVS Charity Shop

Northampshire

Caring & Sharing Trust

Northern Ireland

Age Action Ireland

Barnardos (Belfast)

The Salvation Army Charity Shop

Voluntary Service (Belfast)

Nottinghamshire

Age Concern (Nottinghamshire)

Family First Limited

The Home Farm Trust

Kirby Volunteer Centre

RSPCA

Oxfordshire

Age Concern (Oxford)

Age Concern (Oxfordshire)

Katharine House Hospice

Oxfam

Shropshire

Knowle Sports Association

Shropshire & Mid Wales Hospice

Somerset

British Red Cross Somerset Branch

Imperial Cancer Research Fund

St Margaret's Somerset Hospice

Wellington Basins Project

South Glamorgan

Age Concern (South Glamorgan)

Track 2000

South Yorkshire

Arthritis Research

Salvation Army (Care & Share Shop)

Staffordshire

Alsager Animals in Need

RSPCA (North Staffs Branch)

Staffordshire Wildlife Trust

Strathclyde

David Livingstone International

Suffolk

Age Concern (Suffolk)

Arthritis & Rheumatism Council for Research

Home Farm Trust

Surrey

Age Concern (Sutton Borough (Shop))

Disability Action Sutton

Disabled Photographers' Society

Epsom & Ewell Phab Club

Feed the Minds

Hydon Hill Cheshire Home

Mental Aid Projects

Mind in Croydon

St Raphael's Hospice

Warwickshire

Emmaus (Coventry & Warwickshire)

RACKS

Scope

West Midlands

Age Concern (Solihull)

Barnardos (West Retail Region)

Birmingham Play Resource Centre

Community Transport

Phoenix Sheltered Workshop

Stour Valley Cat Rescue

West Yorkshire

Age Concern (Huddersfield & District)

Age Concern (Wakefield District)

Kirkwood Hospice

The Russell Street Project Limited

Wiltshire

Age Concern (Thamesdown)

RSPCA (Marlborough with Andover Branch)

RSPCA (Wiltshire North & Chippenham Branch)

Records & tapes

Avon

Age Concern (Bedminster)

Age Concern (Bristol)

Age Concern (Clifton)

Age Concern (Knowle)

Age Concern (Weston-super-Mare)

The Home Farm Trust

Service 9 – Bristol's Volunteer Bureau

Bedfordshire

Age Concern (Bedfordshire)

Friends of Biggleswade Hospital

Hospital Radio Bedford

Luton Day Centre for the Homeless

Berkshire

Age Concern (Reading)

Christian Community Action

Thames Valley Hospice

Berwickshire

Royal National Mission to Deep Sea Fishermen

Buckinghamshire

Age Concern (Milton Keynes)

Age Concern (Bucks)

The National Society for Epilepsy

Cambridgeshire

Cambridge SOFA

Emmaus (Cambridge)

SOFA (Peterborough) Limited

Central

Alloa Community Enterprises Limited

Cheshire

3C Teamwork

Age Concern (Cheshire)

Arthritis Research (Arthritis & Rheumatism Council)

Sue Ryder Foundation

Cumbria

Age Concern (Carlisle & District)

Age Concern (Northwest Cumbria)

Age Concern (South Lakeland)

Derbyshire

Age Concern (Derbyshire)

Arthritis & Rheumatism Council

Derby Furniture Project

Salcare

Treetops Hospice

Devon

Acorn Furniture & Clothing Project

Age Concern (Exeter)

Age Concern (Paignton)

Age Concern (Plymouth)

Age Concern (Torquay)

Arthritis & Rheumatism Council for Research

Exeter CVS Charity Shop

League of Friends – Plymouth Psychiatric Service

Seaton & District Hospital League of Friends

Dorset

Age Concern (Blandford Forum)

Age Concern (Boscombe)

Age Concern (Bournemouth)

Age Concern (Poole)

Boscombe Salvation Army Charity Concern

The Friends of Blandford Community Hospital

Gingerbread

Pramacare

Sheltered Work Opportunities Project

East Sussex

Betts Memorial Heart Foundation

Feline Foster

Friends of the Eastbourne Hospitals

The House Project Charity Shop

Hove YMCA

Lewes Volunteer Bureau

Peacehaven & Telscombe Volunteer Bureau

Sussex Emmaus

East Yorkshire

Age Concern (East Riding of Yorkshire)

RSPCA

Essex

Age Concern (Essex)

Barnardos (East Retail Region)

Farleigh (Mid-Essex Hospice)

The Friends of St Francis Hospice (Shops) Ltd

Hamelin Trust

St Helena Hospice

St Luke's Hospice

Scope in Colchester (Castlegate Centre)

Gloucestershire

Full House Furniture and Recycling Service

Grampian

Aberdeen Cyrenians

Aberdeen Women's Aid

Voluntary Service (Aberdeen)

Greater Manchester

Age Concern (Manchester)

Age Concern (Metro Bury)

Barnardos (North Retail Region)

The Salvation Army

Wesley Community Project

Gwynedd

Age Concern (Gwynedd a Món)

RSPCA (Meirionnydd Branch)

RSPCA (West Gwynedd Branch)

Hampshire

National Schizophrenia Fellowship

Rehab – Basingstoke & Alton Cardiac Appeal

Hereford & Worcester

Arthritis Research Charity Shop

Community Chest

Full House Furniture & Recycling Service

ME Association Hereford & Worcester Group

Hertfordshire

Base, Dacorum and St Albans Homeless Development Team

Dacorum Council for Voluntary Service

Friends of Danesbury

National Animal Welfare Trust

The Stort Trust

Humberside

Age Concern (Hull) .

Kent

Age Concern (Gillingham)

Bexley Downs Syndrome Group

British Red Cross Margate Centre

Dartford District Volunteer Bureau

Friends of Animals League

Hope Romania

Kent Red Cross Charity Shops

Lord Whisky Sanctuary Fund

RSPCA (Kent Rochester Branch)

St Cecilia's Cheshire Home

St Martin's Emmaus

Seven Springs Cheshire Home

Thanet Mind (Mental Health Day Centre)

Lancashire

Age Concern (Blackburn & District)

Age Concern (Blackpool)

Age Concern (Lytham St Anne's)

Age Concern (Preston & South Ribble)

Emmaus (Greater Manchester)

Homeless in Blackpool

Queens Hall Help Committee

Save the Children

Leicester

Leicester Disabled Gardeners Club

Leicestershire Disabled Adventure Club

Leicestershire

Cat Action Trust

Loughborough Community Care

RSPCA (Leicestershire Branch)

Work-Link Project

Lincolnshire

Care Shop

St Barnabas Hospice Shops

Strut Limited

London E

Hackney Pensioners' Association

Toynbee Hall

London EC

Friends of Moorfields Eye Hospital

Help the Aged

Shelter, the National Campaign for Homeless People.

London NW

Age Concern (Brent)

Age Concern (Westminster)

Brent Gingerbread

Mind in Camden Charity Shop

London SE

Elimination of Leukaemia Fund

League of Friends of Lewisham Hospital

St Christopher's Hospice

South Norwood Animal Rescue

London SW

Age Concern England

Age Concern (Wandsworth)

Centre '70 Community Shop

The Homeless Furniture Project

Oasis Aids Support Centre

RSPCA (Wimbledon & District)

Trinity Hospice

Wandsworth Housing Support Project

London W

Age Concern (Ealing Borough0

Age Concern (Hammersmith & Fulham)

Scoliosis Association (UK)

London WC

The Children's Society

Imperial Cancer Research Fund

Leukaemia Research Fund

Lothian

Age Concern Scotland

Bethany Christian Trust

Cancer Research Campaign Scotland

Sue Ryder Foundation

Merseyside

Age Concern (Wirral)

Newton Visual Impaired Group

Royal 945 AM

Southport & District Cerebral Palsy Association

Wirral Rehab T/AS Speaks Volumes

Middlesex

British Red Cross Society

Hillingdon Community Furniture Recycling Project

Richmond Fellowship International

Norfolk

Centre 81

CSV Vocal Project

League of Friends – James Paget Hospital

Norfolk & Norwich Scope

North Yorkshire

Age Concern (Coleraine)

Age Concern (North West Yorkshire)

Emmaus (Scarborough)

Network (Whitby Resource Centre)

St Leonard's Hospice

The Salvation Army

Selby District AVS Charity Shop

Northern Ireland

Age Action Ireland

Arthritis & Rheumatism Council (NI)

Barnardos (Belfast)

Emmaus Liberty Belfast

The Salvation Army Charity Shop

Voluntary Service (Belfast)

War on Want (NI)

Nottinghamshire

Age Concern (Nottinghamshire)

Family First Limited

The Home Farm Trust

Kirby Volunteer Centre

Living Room

Nottingham Mencap

RSPCA

Oxfordshire

Age Concern (Oxford)

Age Concern (Oxfordshire)

Nuffield Orthopaedic Centre League of Friends

Oxfam

Powys

Replay

Shropshire

Knowle Sports Association

Shropshire & Mid Wales Hospice

Somerset

Age Concern (Clevedon)

British Red Cross Somerset Branch

Imperial Cancer Research Fund

St Margaret's Somerset Hospice

West Somerset Council for Voluntary Service

South Glamorgan

Age Concern (South Glamorgan)

Track 2000

South Yorkshire

Age Concern (Rotherham)

Arthritis Research

RSPCA (SYAC)

Salvation Army (Care & Share Shop)

Sheffield Family Services Unit

Staffordshire

Alsager Animals in Need

RSPCA (North Staffs Branch)

Strathclyde

Dundee Voluntary Action

Suffolk

Age Concern (Suffolk)

Arthritis & Rheumatism Council for Research

Home Farm Trust

St Louis Family Service

Surrey

Age Concern (Sutton Borough (Shop))

British Red Cross

Community Scrap Scheme

Croydon Voluntary Action

Disability Action Sutton

Epsom & Ewell Phab Club

Feed the Minds

Hydestile Wildlife Hospital

Hydon Hill Cheshire Home

Mental Aid Projects

Mind in Croydon

Prosa Foundation

St Raphael's Hospice

Surrey Community Recycling and Play Project

Tayside

Montrose Scrapstore

Tyne & Wear

Age Concern (South Tyneside)

Community Furniture Service

Community Transport

St Oswald's Hospice

Warwickshire

Emmaus (Coventry & Warwickshire)

Oxfam

RACKS

Scope

West Midlands

Age Concern (Solihull)

Barnardos (West Retail Region)

Birmingham Play Resource Centre

Community Transport

Community Transport – Birmingham Project

Phoenix Sheltered Workshop

RSPCA (Birmingham & District Branch)

Stour Valley Cat Rescue

Walsall Gingerbread Advice Centre

West Sussex

Arthritis & Rheumatism Council for Research

Wallis Centre

West Yorkshire

Age Concern (Bradford & District)

Age Concern (Huddersfield & District)

Age Concern (North Kirklees)

Age Concern (Wakefield District)

Kirkwood Hospice

RSPCA (Bradford & District Branch)

Wiltshire

Age Concern (Thamesdown)

Devres & District PHAB

RSPCA (Marlborough with Andover Branch)

RSPCA (Wiltshire North & Chippenham Branch)

Worcestershire

Malvern Churches Community Network

Sports equipment

Avon

Age Concern (Bedminster)

Age Concern (Bristol)

Age Concern (Clifton)

Age Concern (Knowle)

Age Concern (Weston-super-Mare)

Bedfordshire

Luton Day Centre for the Homeless

Berkshire

Age Concern (Reading)

Christian Community Action

Thames Valley Hospice

Buckinghamshire

Age Concern (Milton Keynes)

Age Concern (Bucks)

Cambridgeshire

Cambridge SOFA

Emmaus (Cambridge)

Newark Play Association

SOFA (Peterborough) Limited

Central

Alloa Community Enterprises Limited

Cheshire

3C Teamwork

Age Concern (Cheshire)

Arthritis Research (Arthritis & Rheumatism Council)

PSS – Toy Library & Resource Centre

Sue Ryder Foundation

Cumbria

Age Concern (Carlisle & District)

Age Concern (Northwest Cumbria)

Age Concern (South Lakeland)

Derbyshire

Age Concern (Derbyshire)

Arthritis & Rheumatism Council

Salcare

Treetops Hospice

Devon

Acorn Furniture & Clothing Project

Age Concern (Exeter)

Age Concern (Paignton)

Age Concern (Torquay)

League of Friends – Plymouth Psychiatric Service

Seaton & District Hospital League of Friends

Dorset

Age Concern (Blandford Forum)

Age Concern (Boscombe)

Age Concern (Poole)

Boscombe Salvation Army Charity Concern

The Friends of Blandford Community Hospital

Gingerbread

Pramacare

East Sussex

Age Concern (Brighton)

Eastbourne Playbus

Hove YMCA

Lewes Volunteer Bureau

Sussex Emmaus

East Yorkshire

Age Concern (East Riding of Yorkshire)

Essex

Barnardos (East Retail Region)

Farleigh (Mid-Essex Hospice)

The Friends of St Francis Hospice (Shops) Ltd

Hamelin Trust

St Helena Hospice

St Luke's Hospice

Scope in Colchester (Castlegate Centre)

YMCA Day Camps

Gloucestershire

Full House Furniture and Recycling Service

Grampian

Aberdeen Cyrenians

Voluntary Service (Aberdeen)

Greater Manchester

Age Concern (Manchester)

Age Concern (Metro Bury)

Barnardos (North Retail Region)

Manchester & Salford Methodist Mission

Manchester One Parent Family Advice Centre

The Salvation Army

Wesley Community Project

Gwynedd

RSPCA (Meirionnydd Branch)

RSPCA (West Gwynedd Branch)

Hampshire

Rehab – Basingstoke & Alton Cardiac Appeal

Wessex Cancer Trust

Hereford & Worcester

Arthritis Research Charity Shop

Full House Furniture & Recycling Service

Hertfordshire

Friends of Danesbury

National Animal Welfare Trust

The Stort Trust

Humberside

Age Concern (Hull)

Isle of Wight

IW RCC (Wight Play Project)

Kent

Bexley Downs Syndrome Group

British Red Cross Margate Centre

Canterbury Women's Refuge

Kent Red Cross Charity Shops

St Cecilia's Cheshire Home

St George's Community Children's Project Limited

St Martin's Emmaus

Seven Springs Cheshire Home

Thanet Mind (Mental Health Day Centre)

Lancashire

Age Concern (Blackburn & District)

Age Concern (Blackpool)

Age Concern (Lytham St Anne's)

Age Concern (Preston & South Ribble)

Burnley Community Business & Resource Centre

Emmaus (Greater Manchester)

Homeless in Blackpool

Queens Hall Help Committee

Salvation Army

Save the Children

Leicester

Leicester Disabled Gardeners Club

Leicestershire Disabled Adventure Club

Leicestershire

Blaby & Whetstone Boys Club

Cat Action Trust

Loughborough Community Care

Lincolnshire

Care Shop

Strut Limited

London E

Toynbee Hall

Walthamstow After School Club

London EC

Help the Aged

Shelter, the National Campaign for Homeless People

London NW

Age Concern (Brent)

Age Concern (Westminster)

Brent Gingerbread

London SE

St Christopher's Hospice

Shaftesbury Resources Centre

London SW

Age Concern England

The Homeless Furniture Project

Oasis Aids Support Centre

Trinity Hospice

Wandsworth Housing Support Project

London W

Age Concern (Hammersmith & Fulham)

London WC

The Children's Society

Imperial Cancer Research Fund

Leukaemia Research Fund

Lothian

Bethany Christian Trust

Cancer Research Campaign Scotland

Royal National Lifeboat Institution

Sue Ryder Foundation

Merseyside

Age Concern (Wirral)

Southport & District Cerebral Palsy Association

Middlesex

British Red Cross Society

Hillingdon Community Furniture Recycling Project

Richmond Fellowship International

Norfolk

Centre 81

CSV Vocal Project

Dereham Gingerbread Club

Norfolk & Norwich Scope

North Yorkshire

Age Concern (Coleraine)

Age Concern (North West Yorkshire)

Emmaus (Scarborough)

Network (Whitby Resource Centre)

St Leonard's Hospice

The Salvation Army

Selby District AVS Charity Shop

Northampshire

Caring & Sharing Trust

Northern Ireland

Age Action Ireland

Arthritis & Rheumatism Council (NI)

Barnardos (Belfast)

Emmaus Liberty Belfast

The Salvation Army Charity Shop

Voluntary Service (Belfast)

War on Want (NI)

Nottinghamshire

Age Concern (Nottinghamshire)

Family First Limited

The Home Farm Trust

Kirby Volunteer Centre

Nottingham Mencap

RSPCA

Oxfordshire

Age Concern (Oxford)

Katharine House Hospice

Oxfam

Shropshire

Knowle Sports Association

Shropshire & Mid Wales Hospice

Shropshire Children's Scrap Store

Somerset

Age Concern (Clevedon)

British Red Cross Somerset Branch

Imperial Cancer Research Fund

St Margaret's Somerset Hospice

South Glamorgan

Age Concern (South Glamorgan)

Track 2000

South Yorkshire

Arthritis Research

RSPCA (SYAC)

Salvation Army (Care & Share Shop)

Sheffield Family Services Unit

Staffordshire

Newcastle Play Council

RSPCA (North Staffs Branch)

Strathclyde

Bethany House

Enable (Scottish Society for the Mentally Handicapped)

Suffolk

Age Concern (Suffolk)

Arthritis & Rheumatism Council for Research

Home Farm Trust

St Louis Family Service

Surrey

Age Concern (Sutton Borough (Shop))

Epsom & Ewell Phab Club

Hydon Hill Cheshire Home

Mental Aid Projects

Mind in Croydon

St Raphael's Hospice

Surrey Community Recycling and Play Project

Tayside

Montrose Scrapstore

Tyne & Wear

Age Concern (South Tyneside)

Community Furniture Service

Community Transport

Warwickshire

Emmaus (Coventry & Warwickshire)

Oxfam

RACKS

Scope

West Midlands

Age Concern (Solihull)

Barnardos (West Retail Region)

Birmingham Play Resource Centre

Community Transport

Community Transport – Birmingham Project

Phoenix Sheltered Workshop

RSPCA (Birmingham & District Branch)

Walsall Gingerbread Advice Centre

West Sussex

Wallis Centre

West Yorkshire

Age Concern (Huddersfield & District)

Age Concern (Wakefield District)

Keighley Council for Voluntary Service

Kirkwood Hospice

The Russell Street Project Limited

Wiltshire

RSPCA (Marlborough with Andover Branch)

Worcestershire

Malvern Churches Community Network

Toys & games

Avon

Age Concern (Bedminster)

Age Concern (Bristol)

Age Concern (Clifton)

Age Concern (Knowle)

Age Concern (Weston-super-Mare)

The Home Farm Trust

Service 9 – Bristol's Volunteer Bureau

Bedfordshire

Age Concern (Bedfordshire)

Bedford Refuge (part of Christian Family Care)

Luton Day Centre for the Homeless

Sandy Neighbourhood Centre (part of Christian Family Care)

Women's Royal Voluntary Service

Berkshire

Age Concern (Reading)

Christian Community Action

Thames Valley Hospice

Buckinghamshire

Age Concern (Milton Keynes)

Age Concern (Bucks)

Cambridgeshire

Cambridge SOFA

Emmaus (Cambridge)

Newark Play Association

St Theresa's House

SOFA (Peterborough) Limited

Central

Alloa Community Enterprises Limited

Cheshire

3C Teamwork

Age Concern (Cheshire)

Arthritis Research (Arthritis & Rheumatism Council)

PSS – Toy Library & Resource Centre

Sue Ryder Foundation

Cumbria

Age Concern (Carlisle & District)

Age Concern (Northwest Cumbria)

Age Concern (South Lakeland)

Age Concern (Ulverston & District)

Family Advice Centre

Jennifer Trust for SMA

Derbyshire

Age Concern (Derbyshire)

Arthritis & Rheumatism Council

Salcare

Treetops Hospice

Devon

Acorn Furniture & Clothing Project

Age Concern (Exeter)

Age Concern (Paignton)

Age Concern (Plymouth)

Age Concern (Torquay)

Exeter CVS Charity Shop

Seaton & District Hospital League of Friends

Dorset

Age Concern (Blandford Forum)

Age Concern (Boscombe)

Age Concern (Poole)

Boscombe Salvation Army Charity Concern

Christchurch Hospital League of Friends

The Friends of Blandford Community Hospital

Gingerbread

Pramacare

Durham

FRADE

East Sussex

Eastbourne Playbus

Friends of the Eastbourne Hospitals

The House Project Charity Shop

Hove YMCA

Lewes Volunteer Bureau

Peacehaven & Telscombe Volunteer Bureau

Seaford Volunteers

Sussex Emmaus

East Yorkshire

Age Concern (East Riding of Yorkshire)

RSPCA

Essex

Age Concern (Essex)

Barnardos (East Retail Region)

Farleigh (Mid-Essex Hospice)

The Friends of St Francis Hospice (Shops) Ltd

Friends of Wallace Kennels

Hamelin Trust

St Helena Hospice

St Luke's Hospice

Scope in Colchester (Castlegate Centre)

Gloucestershire

Full House Furniture and Recycling Service

Grampian

Aberdeen Women's Aid

Voluntary Service (Aberdeen)

Greater Manchester

Age Concern (Manchester)

Age Concern (Metro Bury)

Barnardos (North Retail Region)

Bolton Community Transport

Manchester & Salford Methodist Mission

Manchester One Parent Family Advice Centre

The Salvation Army

Wesley Community Project

Gwynedd

Age Concern (Gwynedd a Món)

RSPCA (Meirionnydd Branch)

RSPCA (West Gwynedd Branch)

Hampshire

Dorcas Project/Basics Bank

National Schizophrenia Fellowship

Rehab – Basingstoke & Alton Cardiac Appeal

Relate (Basingstoke & District)

Resettlement Project – South Hants

Wessex Cancer Trust

Hereford & Worcester

Arthritis Research Charity Shop

Community Chest

Full House Furniture & Recycling Service

ME Association Hereford & Worcester Group

Hertfordshire

Family Support Scheme Stotford & Arlesey (part of Christian Family Care)

Friends of Danesbury

National Animal Welfare Trust

The Stort Trust

Humberside

Age Concern (Hull)

Isle of Wight

IW RCC (Wight Play Project)

Kent

5th Dartford Scout Group

Age Concern (Gillingham)

Bexley Downs Syndrome Group

British Red Cross Margate Centre

Canterbury Women's Refuge

Cats Protection League (Bexley Branch)

Dartford District Volunteer Bureau

Friends of Animals League

Hope Romania

Kent Red Cross Charity Shops

Lord Whisky Sanctuary Fund

Medway Homes Refuge

RSPCA (Kent Rochester Branch)

St Cecilia's Cheshire Home

St George's Community Children's Project Limited

St Martin's Emmaus

Seven Springs Cheshire Home

Lancashire

Age Concern (Blackburn & District)

Age Concern (Blackpool)

Age Concern (Lytham St Anne's)

Age Concern (Preston & South Ribble)

Burnley Community Business & Resource Centre

Emmaus (Greater Manchester)

Homeless in Blackpool

Queens Hall Help Committee

Salvation Army

Save the Children

Leicester

Leicester Disabled Gardeners Club

Leicestershire Disabled Adventure Club

Leicestershire

Age Concern (Leicester)

Blaby & Whetstone Boys Club

British Red Cross

Cat Action Trust

The Gideons International

Loughborough Community Care

RSPCA (Leicestershire Branch)

Work-Link Project

Lincolnshire

Bransby Home of Rest for Horses

Care Shop

St Barnabas Hospice Shops

Strut Limited

London E

Crisis

Hackney Pensioners' Association

Immigration Welfare & Legal Advisory Services

Toynbee Hall

Walthamstow After School Club

London EC

Friends of Moorfields Eye Hospital

Help the Aged

Shelter, the National Campaign for Homeless People

London NW

Age Concern (Brent)

Age Concern (Westminster)

Brent Gingerbread

Mind in Camden Charity Shop

London SE

Friends of King's College Hospital

League of Friends of Lewisham Hospital

St Christopher's Hospice

Shaftesbury Resources Centre

London SW

Age Concern England

Cardinal Hume Centre for Young Homeless People

Centre '70 Community Shop

The Homeless Furniture Project

RSPCA (Wimbledon & District)

Wandsworth Housing Support Project

London W

Catholic Children's Society (Westminster)

London WC

The Children's Society

Imperial Cancer Research Fund

Leukaemia Research Fund

Lothian

Age Concern Scotland

Bethany Christian Trust

Cancer Research Campaign Scotland

Royal National Lifeboat Institution

Sue Ryder Foundation

Merseyside

Age Concern (Wirral)

Newton Visual Impaired Group

Southport & District Cerebral Palsy Association

Vincent Harkins Day Care Centre

Middlesex

Age Concern (Feltham, Hanworth & Bedfont)

British Red Cross Society

Hillingdon Community Furniture Recycling Project

Hounslow Community Transport Furniture Project

Richmond Fellowship International

Norfolk

Centre 81

Dereham Gingerbread Club

League of Friends – James Paget Hospital

Norfolk & Norwich Scope

North Yorkshire

Age Concern (Coleraine)

Age Concern (North West Yorkshire)

Age Concern (York)

Emmaus (Scarborough)

Network (Whitby Resource Centre)

St Leonard's Hospice

The Salvation Army

Selby District AVS Charity Shop

Northamptonshire

Daventry Contact

Northern Ireland

Age Action Ireland

Arthritis & Rheumatism Council (NI)

Barnardos (Belfast)

Emmaus Liberty Belfast

The Salvation Army Charity Shop

Voluntary Service (Belfast)

War on Want (NI)

Nottinghamshire

Age Concern (Nottinghamshire)

Beeston Volunteer Bureau

Emmanuel House Day Centre

Family First Limited

The Furniture Project

The Home Farm Trust

Kirby Volunteer Centre

Newark & Sherwood Play Support Group

Nottingham Mencap

RSPCA

Oxfordshire

Age Concern (Oxford)

Age Concern (Oxfordshire)

The Blue Cross

Hearing Dogs for the Deaf

Oxfam

Powys

Replay

Shropshire

Knowle Sports Association

Shropshire & Mid Wales Hospice

Somerset

Age Concern (Clevedon)

Age Concern (Somerset)

British Red Cross Somerset Branch

Imperial Cancer Research Fund

NCH Action for Children

St Margaret's Somerset Hospice

West Somerset Council for Voluntary Service

South Glamorgan

Age Concern (South Glamorgan)

Track 2000

South Yorkshire

Age Concern (Rotherham)

Arthritis Research

Bentley Association for Supportive Help

Cot-Age – Child Safety & Nursery Equipment

RSPCA (SYAC)

Salvation Army (Care & Share Shop)

Sheffield Family Services Unit

Staffordshire

Alsager Animals in Need

Newcastle Play Council

RSPCA (North Staffs Branch)

Strathclyde

Drumchapel Furnishaid Project

Dundee Voluntary Action

Enable (Scottish Society for the Mentally Handicapped)

The Salvation Army

Suffolk

Age Concern (Suffolk)

Arthritis & Rheumatism Council for Research

Home Farm Trust

St Louis Family Service

Surrey

Age Concern (Sutton Borough (Shop))

British Red Cross

Cats in Care

Christian Family Concern

Community Scrap Scheme

Croydon Voluntary Action

Disability Action Sutton

Epsom & Ewell Phab Club

Hydestile Wildlife Hospital

Hydon Hill Cheshire Home

Mental Aid Projects

Mind in Croydon

St Raphael's Hospice

SHCVS

Surrey Community Recycling and Play Project

Tayside

Brittle Bone Society

Montrose Scrapstore

Tayside Furniture Project

Tyne & Wear

Age Concern (South Tyneside)

Community Furniture Service

Community Transport

St Oswald's Hospice

South Shields Ladies Lifeboat Comm

Wearside Women in Need

Warwickshire

Emmaus (Coventry & Warwickshire)

Oxfam

RACKS

Scope

West Midlands

Age Concern (Solihull)

Barnardos (West Retail Region)

Birmingham Play Resource Centre

Community Transport

Community Transport – Birmingham Project

Phoenix Sheltered Workshop

Stour Valley Cat Rescue

Walsall Gingerbread Advice Centre

West Sussex

Arthritis & Rheumatism Council for Research

Guild Care

St Bridget's Cheshire Home

Wallis Centre

West Yorkshire

Age Concern (Bradford & District)

Age Concern (Huddersfield & District)

Age Concern (North Kirklees)

Age Concern (Wakefield District)

Batley Family & Community Centre, Community Furniture Service

Keighley Council for Voluntary Service

Kirkwood Hospice

RSPCA (Bradford & District Branch)

St George's Crypt

Wiltshire

Age Concern (Thamesdown)

Devres & District PHAB

RSPCA (Marlborough with Andover Branch)

RSPCA (Swindon Branch)

RSPCA (Wiltshire North & Chippenham Branch)

Swindon Children's Scrapstore

Worcestershire

Malvern Churches Community Network

Video/computer games

Avon

Age Concern (Bedminster)

Age Concern (Bristol)

Age Concern (Clifton)

Age Concern (Knowle)

Age Concern (Weston-super-Mare)

Service 9 – Bristol's Volunteer Bureau

Berkshire

Age Concern (Reading)

Thames Valley Hospice

Buckinghamshire

Age Concern (Milton Keynes)

Age Concern (Bucks)

Cambridgeshire

Cambridge SOFA

Emmaus (Cambridge)

Central

Alloa Community Enterprises Limited

Cheshire

3C Teamwork

Age Concern (Cheshire)

Arthritis Research (Arthritis & Rheumatism Council)

PSS – Toy Library & Resource Centre

Cumbria

Age Concern (Northwest Cumbria)

Age Concern (South Lakeland)

Jennifer Trust for SMA

Derbyshire

Salcare

Devon

Age Concern (Exeter)

Age Concern (Paignton)

Age Concern (Torquay)

Dorset

Age Concern (Blandford Forum)

Age Concern (Boscombe)

Age Concern (Poole)

Boscombe Salvation Army Charity Concern

The Friends of Blandford Community Hospital

Gingerbread

East Sussex

Betts Memorial Heart Foundation

Hove YMCA

Lewes Volunteer Bureau

Sussex Emmaus

East Yorkshire

Age Concern (East Riding of Yorkshire)

Essex

Barnardos (East Retail Region)

Farleigh (Mid-Essex Hospice)

The Friends of St Francis Hospice (Shops) Ltd

Hamelin Trust

St Helena Hospice

St Luke's Hospice

Gloucestershire

Full House Furniture and Recycling Service

Grampian

Aberdeen Cyrenians

Aberdeen Women's Aid

Voluntary Service (Aberdeen)

Greater Manchester

Age Concern (Manchester)

Age Concern (Metro Bury)

Barnardos (North Retail Region)

The Salvation Army

Wesley Community Project

Hampshire

Rehab – Basingstoke & Alton Cardiac Appeal

Hereford & Worcester

Full House Furniture & Recycling Service

ME Association Hereford & Worcester Group

Hertfordshire

Base, Dacorum and St Albans Homeless Development Team

Dacorum Council for Voluntary Service

National Animal Welfare Trust

The Stort Trust

Humberside

Age Concern (Hull)

Isle of Wight

IW RCC (Wight Play Project)

Kent

Age Concern (Gillingham)

Bexley Downs Syndrome Group

British Red Cross Margate Centre

Canterbury Women's Refuge

Kent Red Cross Charity Shops

St George's Community Children's Project Limited

Seven Springs Cheshire Home

Lancashire

Age Concern (Blackburn & District)

Age Concern (Lytham St Anne's)

Age Concern (Preston & South Ribble)

Emmaus (Greater Manchester)

Homeless in Blackpool

Queens Hall Help Committee

Save the Children

Leicester

Leicester Disabled Gardeners Club

Leicestershire Disabled Adventure Club

Leicestershire

Blaby & Whetstone Boys Club

Cat Action Trust

RSPCA (Leicestershire Branch)

Lincolnshire

Care Shop

Strut Limited

London E

Immigration Welfare & Legal Advisory Services

Toynbee Hall

Walthamstow After School Club

London EC

Help the Aged

Shelter, the National Campaign for Homeless People

London NW

Age Concern (Brent)

Age Concern (Westminster)

Brent Gingerbread

Mind in Camden Charity Shop

London SE

African Foundation for Development (Afford)

League of Friends of Lewisham Hospital

London SW

Age Concern England

The Homeless Furniture Project

Oasis Aids Support Centre

Trinity Hospice

Wandsworth Housing Support Project

London W

Age Concern (Hammersmith & Fulham)

London WC

Imperial Cancer Research Fund

Leukaemia Research Fund

Lothian

Royal National Lifeboat Institution

Sue Ryder Foundation

Merseyside

Age Concern (Wirral)

Newton Visual Impaired Group

Southport & District Cerebral Palsy Association

Middlesex

British Red Cross Society

Hounslow Community Transport Furniture Project

Richmond Fellowship International

Norfolk

Centre 81

CSV Vocal Project

Norfolk & Norwich Scope

North Yorkshire

Age Concern (North West Yorkshire)

Emmaus (Scarborough)

The Salvation Army

Selby District AVS Charity Shop

Northern Ireland

Age Action Ireland

Barnardos (Belfast)

Emmaus Liberty Belfast

War on Want (NI)

Nottinghamshire

Family First Limited

The Home Farm Trust

Kirby Volunteer Centre

Oxfordshire

Age Concern (Oxford)

Age Concern (Oxfordshire)

Hearing Dogs for the Deaf

Oxfam

Shropshire

Knowle Sports Association

Somerset

Age Concern (Clevedon)

Furnicare

St Margaret's Somerset Hospice

South Glamorgan

Age Concern (South Glamorgan)

Track 2000

South Yorkshire

Arthritis Research

Bentley Association for Supportive Help

RSPCA (SYAC)

Salvation Army (Care & Share Shop)

Staffordshire

RSPCA (North Staffs Branch)

Strathclyde

Bethany House

David Livingstone International

Enable (Scottish Society for the Mentally Handicapped)

Suffolk

Age Concern (Suffolk)

Arthritis & Rheumatism Council for Research

St Louis Family Service

Surrey

Community Scrap Scheme

Disability Action Sutton

Epsom & Ewell Phab Club

Hydestile Wildlife Hospital

Hydon Hill Cheshire Home

Mental Aid Projects

Mind in Croydon

Queen Elizabeth's Foundation for Disabled People

St Raphael's Hospice

Surrey Community Recycling and Play Project

Tayside

Tayside Furniture Project

Tyne & Wear

Community Furniture Service

Community Transport

South Shields Ladies Lifeboat Comm

Warwickshire

Emmaus (Coventry & Warwickshire)

RACKS

Scope

West Midlands

Age Concern (Solihull)

Barnardos (West Retail Region)

Birmingham Play Resource Centre

Phoenix Sheltered Workshop

Walsall Gingerbread Advice Centre

West Sussex

Wallis Centre

West Yorkshire

Age Concern (Huddersfield & District)

Age Concern (Wakefield District)

Kirkwood Hospice

RSPCA (Bradford & District Branch)

The Russell Street Project Limited

Wiltshire

RSPCA (Marlborough with Andover Branch)

Worcestershire

Malvern Churches Community Network

Memorabilia

Antique post cards

Avon

Age Concern (Bedminster)

Age Concern (Bristol)

Age Concern (Clifton)

Age Concern (Knowle)

Age Concern (Weston-super-Mare)

Service 9 – Bristol's Volunteer Bureau

Bedfordshire

Friends of Biggleswade Hospital

Berkshire

Age Concern (Reading)

Christian Community Action

The Guide Dogs for the Blind Association

Thames Valley Hospice

Berwickshire

Royal National Mission to Deep Sea Fishermen

Buckinghamshire

Age Concern (Bucks)

Cambridgeshire

Emmaus (Cambridge)

SOFA (Peterborough) Limited

Spaywatch

Central

Alloa Community Enterprises Limited

Cheshire

Age Concern (Cheshire)

Arthritis Research (Arthritis & Rheumatism Council)

Sue Ryder Foundation

Cumbria

Age Concern (Northwest Cumbria)

Age Concern (South Lakeland)

Derbyshire

Salcare

Treetops Hospice

Devon

Age Concern (Exeter)

Age Concern (Paignton)

Age Concern (Torquay)

Seaton & District Hospital League of Friends

Dorset

Age Concern (Blandford Forum)

Age Concern (Boscombe)

Age Concern (Bournemouth)

Age Concern (Poole)

Boscombe Salvation Army Charity Concern

Christchurch Hospital League of Friends

Gingerbread

Guide Dogs for the Blind – Poole & District Branch

Pramacare

East Sussex

Age Concern (Brighton)

Betts Memorial Heart Foundation

Bexhill & District Diabetic Group

Feline Foster

Friends of the Eastbourne Hospitals

The House Project Charity Shop

Lewes Volunteer Bureau

Royal National Lifeboat Institution

Seaford Volunteers

Sussex Emmaus

East Yorkshire

Age Concern (East Riding of Yorkshire)

Essex

Age Concern (Essex)

Barnardos (East Retail Region)

Farleigh (Mid-Essex Hospice)

The Friends of St Francis Hospice (Shops) Ltd

St Helena Hospice

St Luke's Hospice

Scope in Colchester (Castlegate Centre)

Sudan Church Association

Gloucestershire

Full House Furniture and Recycling Service

Grampian

Voluntary Service (Aberdeen)

Greater Manchester

Age Concern (Manchester)

Barnardos (North Retail Region)

Manchester & Salford Methodist Mission

Royal National Lifeboat Institution

The Salvation Army

Gwynedd

Age Concern (Gwynedd a Món)

RSPCA (Meirionnydd Branch)

Hampshire

British Kidney Patient Association

Marwell Zoological Society

Rehab – Basingstoke & Alton Cardiac Appeal

Teg Down Residents' Association

Totton & Eling Community Association

Hereford & Worcester

Arthritis Research Charity Shop

Hertfordshire

Friends of Danesbury

National Animal Welfare Trust

Royal Veterinary College Animal Care Trust

The Stort Trust

Humberside

Age Concern (Hull)

Kent

Age Concern (Gillingham)

Bexley Downs Syndrome Group

Friends of Animals League

Kent Red Cross Charity Shops

RSPCA (Kent Rochester Branch)

St Cecilia's Cheshire Home

St Martin's Emmaus

Seven Springs Cheshire Home

Thanet Phobic Group

Lancashire

Age Concern (Blackburn & District)

Age Concern (Blackpool)

Age Concern (Lytham St Anne's)

Age Concern (Preston & South Ribble)

Emmaus (Greater Manchester)

Homeless in Blackpool

Horses & Ponies Protection Association

Queens Hall Help Committee

Salvation Army

Save the Children

Zaire Evangelistic Mission

Leicester

Leicester Disabled Gardeners Club

Leicestershire Disabled Adventure Club

Leicestershire

British Red Cross

RSPCA (Leicestershire Branch)

Lincolnshire

Artlandish Limited

Care Shop

St Barnabas Hospice Shops

London EC

Shelter, the National Campaign for Homeless People

London NW

Age Concern (Brent)

Age Concern (Westminster)

Inland Waterways Association

London SE

St Christopher's Hospice

Shaftesbury Resources Centre

South Norwood Animal Rescue

London SW

Age Concern England

The Homeless Furniture Project

Marie Curie Cancer Care

Oasis Aids Support Centre

RSPCA (Richmond, Twickenham & Barnes Branch)

Scout Holiday Homes Trust

Trinity Hospice

London W

Age Concern (Hammersmith & Fulham)

Royal National Mission to Deep Sea Fishermen

London WC

The Children's Society

Imperial Cancer Research Fund

Leukaemia Research Fund

Lothian

Bethany Christian Trust

Cancer Research Campaign Scotland

The National Bible Society of Scotland

Royal National Lifeboat Institution

Sue Ryder Foundation

Merseyside

Age Concern (Wirral)

Newton Visual Impaired Group

Southport & District Cerebral Palsy Association

Wirral Rehab T/AS Speaks Volumes

Middlesex

British Red Cross Society

Enfield Preservation Society

League of Friends of Teddington Memorial Hospital

Norfolk

Centre 81

The Norfolk Society

North Yorkshire

Age Concern (Coleraine)

Age Concern (North West Yorkshire)

Emmaus (Scarborough)

St Leonard's Hospice

Northern Ireland

Age Action Ireland

Barnardos (Belfast)

The Salvation Army Charity Shop

Nottinghamshire

Age Concern (Nottinghamshire)

Croctal (Crochet & Other Handcrafts)

Living Room

Nottingham Mencap

RSPCA

Oxfordshire

Age Concern (Oxford)

Age Concern (Oxfordshire)

The Blue Cross

Oxfam

Shropshire

Knowle Sports Association

Somerset

Age Concern (Clevedon)

Age Concern (Somerset)

British Red Cross Somerset Branch

Imperial Cancer Research Fund

St Margaret's Somerset Hospice

South Glamorgan

Age Concern (South Glamorgan)

Track 2000

South Yorkshire

Age Concern (Rotherham)

Bentley Association for Supportive Help

Suffolk

Age Concern (Suffolk)

Arthritis & Rheumatism Council for Research

Surrey

Age Concern (Sutton Borough (Shop))

Disability Action Sutton

Hydestile Wildlife Hospital

Hydon Hill Cheshire Home

Mental Aid Projects

Mind in Croydon

St Raphael's Hospice

Tyne & Wear

British Lung Foundation (Breathe North)

Warwickshire

Emmaus (Coventry & Warwickshire)

Oxfam

RACKS

Scope

West Midlands

Age Concern (Solihull)

Barnardos (West Retail Region)

Stour Valley Cat Rescue

Walsall Gingerbread Advice Centre

West Sussex

Arthritis & Rheumatism Council for Research

The Cats Protection League

St Bridget's Cheshire Home

West Yorkshire

Age Concern (Bradford & District)

Age Concern (Wakefield District)

Kirkwood Hospice

Pet Animals Welfare Society (PAWS)

RSPCA (Bradford & District Branch)

Wiltshire

Age Concern (Thamesdown)

Marie Curie Cancer Care

Prospect Hospice

RSPCA (Marlborough with Andover Branch)

RSPCA (Wiltshire North & Chippenham Branch)

Worcestershire

Malvern Churches Community Network

Coins foreign

Avon

Age Concern (Bedminster)

Age Concern (Bristol)

Age Concern (Clifton)

Age Concern (Knowle)

Age Concern (Weston-super-Mare)

Bedfordshire

The Salvation Army

Berkshire

Age Concern (Reading)

Berkshire Multiple Sclerosis Therapy Centre

Christian Community Action

The Guide Dogs for the Blind Association

Thames Valley Hospice

Berwickshire

Royal National Mission to Deep Sea Fishermen

Buckinghamshire

Age Concern (Bucks)

Cambridgeshire

Emmaus (Cambridge)

Spaywatch

Cheshire

Arthritis Research (Arthritis & Rheumatism Council)

Sue Ryder Foundation

Cumbria

Age Concern (Northwest Cumbria)

Age Concern (South Lakeland)

Derbyshire

Arthritis & Rheumatism Council

Salcare

Treetops Hospice

Devon

Age Concern (Exeter)

Age Concern (Paignton)

Age Concern (Torquay)

Dorset

Age Concern (Blandford Forum)

Age Concern (Boscombe)

Age Concern (Bournemouth)

Age Concern (Poole)

Boscombe Salvation Army Charity Concern

The Friends of Blandford Community Hospital

Gingerbread

Guide Dogs for the Blind – Poole & District Branch

Pramacare

East Sussex

Age Concern (East Sussex)

Bexhill & District Diabetic Group

Feline Foster

Lewes Volunteer Bureau

Monday Club

Royal National Lifeboat Institution

Seaford Volunteers

Sussex Emmaus

Essex

Age Concern (Essex)

Barnardos (East Retail Region)

Farleigh (Mid-Essex Hospice)

The Friends of St Francis Hospice (Shops) Ltd

Hamelin Trust

St Helena Hospice

St Luke's Hospice

Scope in Colchester (Castlegate Centre)

Gloucestershire

Full House Furniture and Recycling Service

National Meningitis Trust

Grampian

Voluntary Service (Aberdeen)

Greater Manchester

Age Concern (Manchester)

Barnardos (North Retail Region)

Manchester & Salford Methodist Mission

Royal National Lifeboat Institution

The Salvation Army

Gwynedd

Age Concern (Gwynedd a Món)

RSPCA (Meirionnydd Branch)

Hampshire

British Kidney Patient Association

Moorlands Community Association

National Schizophrenia Fellowship

Rehab – Basingstoke & Alton Cardiac Appeal

Hereford & Worcester

Arthritis Research Charity Shop

ME Association Hereford & Worcester Group

Hertfordshire

Friends of Danesbury

National Animal Welfare Trust

Royal Veterinary College Animal Care Trust

The Stort Trust

Humberside

Age Concern (Hull)

Kent

Bexley Downs Syndrome Group

British Red Cross Margate Centre

Friends of Animals League

Kent Red Cross Charity Shops

Lord Whisky Sanctuary Fund

St Cecilia's Cheshire Home

St Martin's Emmaus

Seven Springs Cheshire Home

Lancashire

Age Concern (Blackpool)

Age Concern (Lytham St Anne's)

Emmaus (Greater Manchester)

Homeless in Blackpool

Horses & Ponies Protection Association

Save the Children

Leicester

Leicester Disabled Gardeners Club

Leicestershire Disabled Adventure Club

Leicestershire

Blaby & Whetstone Boys Club

British Red Cross

The National Trust

RSPCA (Leicestershire Branch)

Lincolnshire

Arthritis Care

Care Shop

London EC

Friends of Moorfields Eye Hospital

Shelter, the National Campaign for Homeless People

London NW

Age Concern (Brent)

Inland Waterways Association

RSPCA (Mayhew Animal Home)

London SE

Elimination of Leukaemia Fund

Iris Fund for Prevention of Blindness

St Christopher's Hospice

Shaftesbury Resources Centre

London SW

Age Concern England

Age Concern (Wandsworth)

Cancer Prevention Research Trust

The Homeless Furniture Project

Marie Curie Cancer Care

Oasis Aids Support Centre

RSPCA (Richmond, Twickenham & Barnes Branch)

Scout Holiday Homes Trust

Trinity Hospice

London W

Age Concern (Hammersmith & Fulham)

Cancer Relief Macmillan Fund

Catholic Children's Society (Westminster)

Royal National Mission to Deep Sea Fishermen

Scoliosis Association (UK)

London WC

The Children's Society

Imperial Cancer Research Fund

Leukaemia Research Fund

Lothian

Bethany Christian Trust

Cancer Research Campaign Scotland

The National Bible Society of Scotland

Royal National Lifeboat Institution

Sue Ryder Foundation

Merseyside

Newton Visual Impaired Group

Middlesex

British Red Cross Society

League of Friends of Teddington Memorial Hospital

Norfolk

Centre 81

Norfolk & Norwich Muscular Dystrophy Group

North Yorkshire

Age Concern (Coleraine)

Emmaus (Scarborough)

St Leonard's Hospice

Northern Ireland

Age Action Ireland

Arthritis & Rheumatism Council (NI)

Barnardos (Belfast)

The Salvation Army Charity Shop

Nottinghamshire

Age Concern (Nottinghamshire)

Living Room

Nottingham Mencap

Oxfordshire

Age Concern (Oxford)

Age Concern (Oxfordshire)

Hearing Dogs for the Deaf

Imperial Cancer Research Fund

Katharine House Hospice

Oxfam

The Worldwide Fund for Nature (WWF)

Shropshire

Knowle Sports Association

Somerset

Age Concern (Clevedon)

Age Concern (Somerset)

British Red Cross Somerset Branch

Imperial Cancer Research Fund

St Margaret's Somerset Hospice

South Glamorgan

Age Concern (South Glamorgan)

Royal National Lifeboat Institution

Track 2000

South Yorkshire

Arthritis Research

Bentley Association for Supportive Help

Staffordshire

Alsager Animals in Need

Suffolk

Age Concern (Suffolk)

Arthritis & Rheumatism Council for Research

Surrey

Age Concern (Sutton Borough (Shop))

British Red Cross

Disability Action Sutton

Hydestile Wildlife Hospital

Hydon Hill Cheshire Home

Mind in Croydon

St Raphael's Hospice

SHCVS

Tyne & Wear

British Lung Foundation (Breathe North)

Warwickshire

Emmaus (Coventry & Warwickshire)

Oxfam

Scope

West Midlands

Age Concern (Solihull)

Barnardos (West Retail Region)

Phoenix Sheltered Workshop

Walsall Gingerbread Advice Centre

West Sussex

Arthritis & Rheumatism Council for Research

British Red Cross

The Missions to Seamen

St Bridget's Cheshire Home

West Yorkshire

Guide Dogs for the Blind Association

Kirkwood Hospice

RSPCA (Bradford & District Branch)

Wiltshire

Age Concern (Thamesdown)

Marie Curie Cancer Care

Prospect Hospice

RSPCA (Marlborough with Andover Branch)

Coins old

Avon

Age Concern (Bedminster)

Age Concern (Bristol)

Age Concern (Clifton)

Age Concern (Knowle)

Age Concern (Weston-super-Mare)

Bedfordshire

The Salvation Army

Berkshire

Age Concern (Reading)

Christian Community Action

The Guide Dogs for the Blind Association

Thames Valley Hospice

Berwickshire

Royal National Mission to Deep Sea Fishermen

Buckinghamshire

Age Concern (Bucks)

Cambridgeshire

Emmaus (Cambridge)

Spaywatch

Cheshire

Arthritis Research (Arthritis & Rheumatism Council)

Sue Ryder Foundation

Cumbria

Age Concern (Northwest Cumbria)

Age Concern (South Lakeland)

Derbyshire

Arthritis & Rheumatism Council

Salcare

Treetops Hospice

Devon

Age Concern (Exeter)

Age Concern (Paignton)

Age Concern (Torquay)

Dorset

Age Concern (Blandford Forum)

Age Concern (Boscombe)

Age Concern (Poole)

Boscombe Salvation Army Charity Concern

The Friends of Blandford Community Hospital

Gingerbread

Guide Dogs for the Blind – Poole & District Branch

Pramacare

East Sussex

Age Concern (Brighton)

Bexhill & District Diabetic Group

Lewes Volunteer Bureau

Monday Club

Royal National Lifeboat Institution

Seaford Volunteers

Sussex Emmaus

Essex

Age Concern (Essex)

Farleigh (Mid-Essex Hospice)

The Friends of St Francis Hospice (Shops) Ltd

Hamelin Trust

St Helena Hospice

St Luke's Hospice

Scope in Colchester (Castlegate Centre)

Gloucestershire

Full House Furniture and Recycling Service

Grampian

Voluntary Service (Aberdeen)

Greater Manchester

Age Concern (Manchester)

Manchester & Salford Methodist Mission

Royal National Lifeboat Institution

The Salvation Army

Gwynedd

Age Concern (Gwynedd a Món)

RSPCA (Meirionnydd Branch)

Hampshire

British Kidney Patient Association

Moorlands Community Association

National Schizophrenia Fellowship

Rehab – Basingstoke & Alton Cardiac Appeal

Hereford & Worcester

Arthritis Research Charity Shop

ME Association Hereford & Worcester Group

Hertfordshire

Friends of Danesbury

National Animal Welfare Trust

Royal Veterinary College Animal Care Trust

The Stort Trust

Humberside

Age Concern (Hull)

Kent

Age Concern (Gillingham)

Bexley Downs Syndrome Group

British Red Cross Margate Centre

Friends of Animals League

Kent Red Cross Charity Shops

Lord Whisky Sanctuary Fund

St Cecilia's Cheshire Home

St Martin's Emmaus

Seven Springs Cheshire Home

Lancashire

Age Concern (Blackpool)

Age Concern (Lytham St Anne's)

Age Concern (Preston & South Ribble)

Emmaus (Greater Manchester)

Homeless in Blackpool

Horses & Ponies Protection Association

Save the Children

Leicester

Leicester Disabled Gardeners Club

Leicestershire Disabled Adventure Club

Leicestershire

British Red Cross

The National Trust

RSPCA (Leicestershire Branch)

Lincolnshire

Care Shop

London EC

Shelter, the National Campaign for Homeless People

London NW

Age Concern (Brent)

Inland Waterways Association

RSPCA (Mayhew Animal Home)

London SE

Iris Fund for Prevention of Blindness

St Christopher's Hospice

Shaftesbury Resources Centre

London SW

Age Concern England

Age Concern (Wandsworth)

The Homeless Furniture Project

Marie Curie Cancer Care

Oasis Aids Support Centre

RSPCA (Richmond, Twickenham & Barnes Branch)

Scout Holiday Homes Trust

Trinity Hospice

London W

Age Concern (Hammersmith & Fulham)

Cancer Relief Macmillan Fund

Catholic Children's Society (Westminster)

Royal National Mission to Deep Sea Fishermen

Scoliosis Association (UK)

London WC

The Children's Society

Imperial Cancer Research Fund

Leukaemia Research Fund

Lothian

Bethany Christian Trust

Cancer Research Campaign Scotland

The National Bible Society of Scotland

Royal National Lifeboat Institution

Sue Ryder Foundation

Merseyside

Newton Visual Impaired Group

Middlesex

British Red Cross Society

League of Friends of Teddington Memorial Hospital

Norfolk

Centre 81

North Yorkshire

Age Concern (Coleraine)

Emmaus (Scarborough)

St Leonard's Hospice

Northern Ireland

Age Action Ireland

Arthritis & Rheumatism Council (NI)

The Salvation Army Charity Shop

Nottinghamshire

Age Concern (Nottinghamshire)

Nottingham Mencap

Oxfordshire

Age Concern (Oxford)

Age Concern (Oxfordshire)

Hearing Dogs for the Deaf

Imperial Cancer Research Fund

Katharine House Hospice

Oxfam

The Worldwide Fund for Nature (WWF)

Shropshire

Knowle Sports Association

Somerset

Age Concern (Clevedon)

Age Concern (Somerset)

British Red Cross Somerset Branch

Imperial Cancer Research Fund

St Margaret's Somerset Hospice

South Glamorgan

Age Concern (South Glamorgan)

Royal National Lifeboat Institution

Track 2000

South Yorkshire

Arthritis Research

Bentley Association for Supportive Help

Staffordshire

Alsager Animals in Need

Suffolk

Age Concern (Suffolk)

Arthritis & Rheumatism Council for Research

Surrey

Age Concern (Sutton Borough (Shop))

Disability Action Sutton

Hydestile Wildlife Hospital

Hydon Hill Cheshire Home

Mind in Croydon

St Raphael's Hospice

Tyne & Wear

British Lung Foundation (Breathe North)

Warwickshire

Emmaus (Coventry & Warwickshire)

Oxfam

Scope

West Midlands

Age Concern (Solihull)

Phoenix Sheltered Workshop

Walsall Gingerbread Advice Centre

West Sussex

Arthritis & Rheumatism Council for Research

British Red Cross

The Missions to Seamen

St Bridget's Cheshire Home

West Yorkshire

Age Concern (Wakefield District)

Guide Dogs for the Blind Association

Kirkwood Hospice

Pet Animals Welfare Society (PAWS)

RSPCA (Bradford & District Branch)

Wiltshire

Age Concern (Thamesdown)

Marie Curie Cancer Care

Prospect Hospice

RSPCA (Marlborough with Andover Branch)

Medals

Avon
Age Concern (Bedminster)
Age Concern (Bristol)
Age Concern (Clifton)
Age Concern (Knowle)
Age Concern (Weston-super-Mare)

Bedfordshire
Luton Day Centre for the Homeless
The Salvation Army

Berkshire
Age Concern (Reading)
Christian Community Action
Thames Valley Hospice

Berwickshire
Royal National Mission to Deep Sea Fishermen

Buckinghamshire
Age Concern (Bucks)

Cambridgeshire
Emmaus (Cambridge)
Spaywatch

Central
Alloa Community Enterprises Limited

Cheshire
Arthritis Research (Arthritis & Rheumatism Council)
Sue Ryder Foundation

Cumbria
Age Concern (Northwest Cumbria)
Age Concern (South Lakeland)

Derbyshire
Salcare
Treetops Hospice

Devon
Age Concern (Exeter)
Age Concern (Paignton)
Age Concern (Torquay)
Arthritis & Rheumatism Council for Research

Dorset
Age Concern (Blandford Forum)
Age Concern (Boscombe)
Age Concern (Poole)
Boscombe Salvation Army Charity Concern
Gingerbread
Pramacare

East Sussex
Bexhill & District Diabetic Group
Lewes Volunteer Bureau
Royal National Lifeboat Institution
Seaford Volunteers
Sussex Emmaus

Essex
Age Concern (Essex)
Barnardos (East Retail Region)
Farleigh (Mid-Essex Hospice)
The Friends of St Francis Hospice (Shops) Ltd
Hamelin Trust
St Helena Hospice
St Luke's Hospice
Scope in Colchester (Castlegate Centre)

Gloucestershire
Full House Furniture and Recycling Service

Grampian
Voluntary Service (Aberdeen)

Greater Manchester
Age Concern (Manchester)
Barnardos (North Retail Region)
Manchester & Salford Methodist Mission

Royal National Lifeboat Institution
The Salvation Army

Gwynedd
Age Concern (Gwynedd a Món)

Hampshire
British Kidney Patient Association
National Schizophrenia Fellowship
Rehab – Basingstoke & Alton Cardiac Appeal
Teg Down Residents' Association

Hereford & Worcester
Arthritis Research Charity Shop

Hertfordshire
Friends of Danesbury
National Animal Welfare Trust
The Stort Trust

Humberside
Age Concern (Hull)

Kent
Age Concern (Gillingham)
Bexley Downs Syndrome Group
British Red Cross Margate Centre
Friends of Animals League
Kent Red Cross Charity Shops
Lord Whisky Sanctuary Fund
St Cecilia's Cheshire Home
St Martin's Emmaus
Seven Springs Cheshire Home

Lancashire
Age Concern (Blackpool)
Age Concern (Lytham St Anne's)
Age Concern (Preston & South Ribble)
Emmaus (Greater Manchester)
Homeless in Blackpool

Horses & Ponies Protection Association

Salvation Army

Save the Children

Leicester

Leicester Disabled Gardeners Club

Leicestershire Disabled Adventure Club

Leicestershire

British Red Cross

RSPCA (Leicestershire Branch)

Lincolnshire

Care Shop

London EC

Shelter, the National Campaign for Homeless People

London NW

Age Concern (Brent)

Inland Waterways Association

London SE

Iris Fund for Prevention of Blindness

St Christopher's Hospice

Shaftesbury Resources Centre

London SW

Age Concern England

Centre '70 Community Shop

The Homeless Furniture Project

Marie Curie Cancer Care

Oasis Aids Support Centre

Scout Holiday Homes Trust

Trinity Hospice

London W

Age Concern (Hammersmith & Fulham)

Royal National Mission to Deep Sea Fishermen

London WC

The Children's Society

Imperial Cancer Research Fund

Lothian

Bethany Christian Trust

Cancer Research Campaign Scotland

The National Bible Society of Scotland

Royal National Lifeboat Institution

Sue Ryder Foundation

Merseyside

Age Concern (Wirral)

Newton Visual Impaired Group

Middlesex

British Red Cross Society

League of Friends of Teddington Memorial Hospital

Norfolk

Centre 81

Royal British Legion

North Yorkshire

Age Concern (Coleraine)

Emmaus (Scarborough)

St Leonard's Hospice

Northern Ireland

Age Action Ireland

Barnardos (Belfast)

The Salvation Army Charity Shop

Nottinghamshire

Age Concern (Nottinghamshire)

Nottingham Mencap

RSPCA

Oxfordshire

Age Concern (Oxford)

Age Concern (Oxfordshire)

Oxfam

The Worldwide Fund for Nature (WWF)

Shropshire

Knowle Sports Association

Somerset

Age Concern (Clevedon)

Age Concern (Somerset)

British Red Cross Somerset Branch

Imperial Cancer Research Fund

St Margaret's Somerset Hospice

South Glamorgan

Age Concern (South Glamorgan)

Track 2000

South Yorkshire

Bentley Association for Supportive Help

Staffordshire

Alsager Animals in Need

Suffolk

Age Concern (Suffolk)

Arthritis & Rheumatism Council for Research

Surrey

Age Concern (Sutton Borough (Shop))

Disability Action Sutton

Hydon Hill Cheshire Home

Mental Aid Projects

Mind in Croydon

St Raphael's Hospice

Tyne & Wear

British Lung Foundation (Breathe North)

Warwickshire

Emmaus (Coventry & Warwickshire)

Oxfam

West Midlands

Age Concern (Solihull)

Barnardos (West Retail Region)

Stour Valley Cat Rescue

West Sussex

Arthritis & Rheumatism Council for Research

West Yorkshire

Age Concern (Bradford & District)

Age Concern (Wakefield District)

Kirkwood Hospice

Pet Animals Welfare Society (PAWS)

RSPCA (Bradford & District Branch)

Wiltshire

Age Concern (Thamesdown)

Marie Curie Cancer Care

Prospect Hospice

RSPCA (Marlborough with Andover Branch)

RSPCA (Wiltshire North & Chippenham Branch)

Stamps British

Avon

Age Concern (Bedminster)

Age Concern (Bristol)

Age Concern (Clifton)

Age Concern (Knowle)

Age Concern (Weston-super-Mare)

Bedfordshire

Bedford Refuge (part of Christian Family Care)

Luton Day Centre for the Homeless

The Royal Society for the Protection of Birds

The Salvation Army

Berkshire

Age Concern (Reading)

Berkshire Multiple Sclerosis Therapy Centre

Christian Community Action

The Guide Dogs for the Blind Association

Thames Valley Hospice

Berwickshire

Royal National Mission to Deep Sea Fishermen

Buckinghamshire

Age Concern (Bucks)

Cambridgeshire

Emmaus (Cambridge)

The Leonard Cheshire Foundation

Cheshire

Arthritis Research (Arthritis & Rheumatism Council)

Raynaud's & Scleroderma Association

Sue Ryder Foundation

Cumbria

Age Concern (Northwest Cumbria)

Age Concern (South Lakeland)

Derbyshire

Arthritis & Rheumatism Council

Salcare

Treetops Hospice

Devon

Age Concern (Exeter)

Age Concern (Paignton)

Age Concern (Torquay)

Dorset

Age Concern (Blandford Forum)

Age Concern (Boscombe)

Age Concern (Bournemouth)

Age Concern (Poole)

Boscombe Salvation Army Charity Concern

Christchurch Hospital League of Friends

Gingerbread

Guide Dogs for the Blind – Poole & District Branch

Pramacare

East Sussex

Bexhill & District Diabetic Group

Feline Foster

Friends of the Eastbourne Hospitals

Lewes Volunteer Bureau

Monday Club

Seaford Volunteers

Sussex Emmaus

East Yorkshire

RSPCA

Essex

Age Concern (Essex)

Farleigh (Mid-Essex Hospice)

St Helena Hospice

St Luke's Hospice

Scope in Colchester (Castlegate Centre)

Grampian

Aberdeen Cyrenians

Voluntary Service (Aberdeen)

Greater Manchester

Manchester & Salford Methodist Mission

Royal National Lifeboat Institution

The Salvation Army

Gwynedd

RSPCA (Meirionnydd Branch)

Hampshire

British Kidney Patient Association

Moorlands Community Association

National Schizophrenia Fellowship

Oxford Mission

Rehab – Basingstoke & Alton Cardiac Appeal

Relate (Basingstoke & District)

Teg Down Residents' Association

Totton & Eling Community Association

Hereford & Worcester

Arthritis Research Charity Shop

ME Association Hereford & Worcester Group

Worcestershire Association for the Blind

Hertfordshire

Base, Dacorum and St Albans Homeless Development Team

National Animal Welfare Trust

Royal Veterinary College Animal Care Trust

The Stort Trust

Humberside

Age Concern (Hull)

Kent

5th Dartford Scout Group

Bexley Downs Syndrome Group

British Red Cross Margate Centre

Cats Protection League (Bexley Branch)

Epilepsy Network Gravesend

Friends of Animals League

Hope Romania

Kent Red Cross Charity Shops

Lord Whisky Sanctuary Fund

St Cecilia's Cheshire Home

Seven Springs Cheshire Home

Sidcup Torch Fellowship for the Blind

Thanet Phobic Group

Lancashire

Age Concern (Lytham St Anne's)

Age Concern (Preston & South Ribble)

Emmaus (Greater Manchester)

Horses & Ponies Protection Association

Preston Animal Welfare Society

Save the Children

Zaire Evangelistic Mission

Leicester

Leicester Disabled Gardeners Club

Leicestershire Disabled Adventure Club

Leicestershire

The Gideons International

The National Trust

RSPCA (Leicestershire Branch)

Lincolnshire

Bransby Home of Rest for Horses

Care Shop

London E

Hackney Pensioners' Association

London EC

Shelter, the National Campaign for Homeless People

London N

WWF UK North London Office

London NW

Inland Waterways Association

RSPCA (Mayhew Animal Home)

London SE

Iris Fund for Prevention of Blindness

St Christopher's Hospice

Shaftesbury Resources Centre

South Norwood Animal Rescue

London SW

Age Concern England

Cancer Prevention Research Trust

The Homeless Furniture Project

Marie Curie Cancer Care

Scout Holiday Homes Trust

London W

Age Concern (Hammersmith & Fulham)

Cancer Relief Macmillan Fund

Royal National Mission to Deep Sea Fishermen

London WC

The Children's Society

Leukaemia Research Fund

Lothian

Bethany Christian Trust

Cancer Research Campaign Scotland

The National Bible Society of Scotland

Royal National Lifeboat Institution

Sue Ryder Foundation

Merseyside

Newton Visual Impaired Group

Middlesex

British Red Cross Society

League of Friends of Teddington Memorial Hospital

Norfolk

Centre 81

Norfolk & Norwich Muscular Dystrophy Group

Royal British Legion

North Yorkshire

Age Concern (Coleraine)

Emmaus (Scarborough)

St Leonard's Hospice

Northern Ireland

Arthritis & Rheumatism Council (NI)

The Salvation Army Charity Shop

Nottinghamshire

Age Concern (Nottinghamshire)

Beeston Volunteer Bureau

Oxfordshire

Age Concern (Oxford)

Hearing Dogs for the Deaf

Katharine House Hospice

National Organisation for Counselling Adoptees and Parents (NORCAP)

Oxfam

The Worldwide Fund for Nature (WWF)

Shropshire

Knowle Sports Association

Shropshire Children's Scrap Store

Somerset

Age Concern (Clevedon)

Age Concern (Somerset)

British Red Cross Somerset Branch

Ferne Animal Sanctuary

Imperial Cancer Research Fund

St Margaret's Somerset Hospice

Wellington Basins Project

West Somerset Council for Voluntary Service

South Glamorgan

Royal National Lifeboat Institution

Track 2000

South Yorkshire

Arthritis Research

RSPCA (SYAC)

Staffordshire

Alsager Animals in Need

Staffordshire Wildlife Trust

Strathclyde

Enable (Scottish Society for the Mentally Handicapped)

Suffolk

Age Concern (Suffolk)

Arthritis & Rheumatism Council for Research

Surrey

Age Concern (Sutton Borough (Shop))

Disability Action Sutton

Epsom & Ewell Phab Club

Hydon Hill Cheshire Home

Inner Wheel Club of Ewell

Mental Aid Projects

Mind in Croydon

Prader-Willi Syndrome Association (UK)

Queen Elizabeth's Foundation for Disabled People

Religious Society of Friends

Royal National Mission To Deep Sea Fishermen

St Raphael's Hospice

SHCVS

Tayside

Brittle Bone Society

Tyne & Wear

British Lung Foundation (Breathe North)

Warwickshire

Emmaus (Coventry & Warwickshire)

Oxfam

West Midlands

Age Concern (Solihull)

Phoenix Sheltered Workshop

RSPCA (Birmingham & District Branch)

Stour Valley Cat Rescue

Walsall Gingerbread Advice Centre

West Sussex

Arthritis & Rheumatism Council for Research

British Red Cross

The Cats Protection League

The Missions to Seamen

West Yorkshire

Age Concern (Wakefield District)

Guide Dogs for the Blind Association

Kirkwood Hospice

Wiltshire

Age Concern (Thamesdown)

Devres & District PHAB

Marie Curie Cancer Care

Prospect Hospice

RSPCA (Marlborough with Andover Branch)

RSPCA (Wiltshire North & Chippenham Branch)

Worcestershire

Malvern Churches Community Network

Stamps foreign

Avon
Age Concern (Bedminster)

Age Concern (Bristol)

Age Concern (Clifton)

Age Concern (Knowle)

Age Concern (Weston-super-Mare)

Bedfordshire
Bedford Refuge (part of Christian Family Care)

Luton Day Centre for the Homeless

The Royal Society for the Protection of Birds

The Salvation Army

Berkshire
Age Concern (Reading)

Berkshire Multiple Sclerosis Therapy Centre

Christian Community Action

The Guide Dogs for the Blind Association

Thames Valley Hospice

Berwickshire
Royal National Mission to Deep Sea Fishermen

Buckinghamshire
Age Concern (Bucks)

Cambridgeshire
Emmaus (Cambridge)

The Leonard Cheshire Foundation

Spaywatch

Cheshire
Arthritis Research (Arthritis & Rheumatism Council)

Raynaud's & Scleroderma Association

Sue Ryder Foundation

Cumbria
Age Concern (Northwest Cumbria)

Age Concern (South Lakeland)

Derbyshire
Arthritis & Rheumatism Council

Salcare

Treetops Hospice

Devon
Age Concern (Exeter)

Age Concern (Paignton)

Age Concern (Torquay)

Dorset
Age Concern (Blandford Forum)

Age Concern (Boscombe)

Age Concern (Bournemouth)

Age Concern (Poole)

Boscombe Salvation Army Charity Concern

Christchurch Hospital League of Friends

Gingerbread

Guide Dogs for the Blind – Poole & District Branch

Pramacare

East Sussex
Bexhill & District Diabetic Group

Feline Foster

Friends of the Eastbourne Hospitals

Lewes Volunteer Bureau

Monday Club

Seaford Volunteers

Sussex Emmaus

East Yorkshire
RSPCA

Essex
Age Concern (Essex)

Farleigh (Mid-Essex Hospice)

St Helena Hospice

St Luke's Hospice

Scope in Colchester (Castlegate Centre)

Grampian
Aberdeen Cyrenians

Voluntary Service (Aberdeen)

Greater Manchester
Age Concern (Manchester)

Royal National Lifeboat Institution

The Salvation Army

Gwynedd
RSPCA (Meirionnydd Branch)

Hampshire
British Kidney Patient Association

Moorlands Community Association

National Schizophrenia Fellowship

Oxford Mission

Rehab – Basingstoke & Alton Cardiac Appeal

Relate (Basingstoke & District)

Teg Down Residents' Association

Totton & Eling Community Association

Hereford & Worcester
Arthritis Research Charity Shop

ME Association Hereford & Worcester Group

Worcestershire Association for the Blind

Hertfordshire
Base, Dacorum and St Albans Homeless Development Team

National Animal Welfare Trust

Royal Veterinary College Animal Care Trust

The Stort Trust

Humberside
Age Concern (Hull)

Kent
5th Dartford Scout Group

Bexley Downs Syndrome Group

British Red Cross Margate Centre

Cats Protection League (Bexley Branch)

Epilepsy Network Gravesend

Friends of Animals League

Hope Romania

Kent Red Cross Charity Shops

Lord Whisky Sanctuary Fund

St Cecilia's Cheshire Home

Seven Springs Cheshire Home

Sidcup Torch Fellowship for the Blind

Thanet Phobic Group

Lancashire

Age Concern (Lytham St Anne's)

Age Concern (Preston & South Ribble)

Emmaus (Greater Manchester)

Horses & Ponies Protection Association

Preston Animal Welfare Society

Save the Children

Zaire Evangelistic Mission

Leicester

Leicester Disabled Gardeners Club

Leicestershire Disabled Adventure Club

Leicestershire

The Gideons International

The National Trust

RSPCA (Leicestershire Branch)

Lincolnshire

Bransby Home of Rest for Horses

Care Shop

London E

Hackney Pensioners' Association

London EC

Shelter, the National Campaign for Homeless People

London N

WWF UK North London Office

London NW

Inland Waterways Association

RSPCA (Mayhew Animal Home)

London SE

Iris Fund for Prevention of Blindness

St Christopher's Hospice

Shaftesbury Resources Centre

South Norwood Animal Rescue

London SW

Age Concern England

Cancer Prevention Research Trust

The Homeless Furniture Project

Marie Curie Cancer Care

RSPCA (Richmond, Twickenham & Barnes Branch)

Scout Holiday Homes Trust

Trinity Hospice

London W

Age Concern (Hammersmith & Fulham)

Cancer Relief Macmillan Fund

Royal National Mission to Deep Sea Fishermen

Scoliosis Association (UK)

London WC

The Children's Society

Leukaemia Research Fund

Lothian

Bethany Christian Trust

Cancer Research Campaign Scotland

The National Bible Society of Scotland

Royal National Lifeboat Institution

Sue Ryder Foundation

Merseyside

Newton Visual Impaired Group

Middlesex

British Red Cross Society

League of Friends of Teddington Memorial Hospital

Norfolk

Centre 81

Norfolk & Norwich Muscular Dystrophy Group

Royal British Legion

North Yorkshire

Age Concern (Coleraine)

Emmaus (Scarborough)

St Leonard's Hospice

Northern Ireland

Arthritis & Rheumatism Council (NI)

The Salvation Army Charity Shop

Nottinghamshire

Age Concern (Nottinghamshire)

Oxfordshire

Age Concern (Oxford)

Hearing Dogs for the Deaf

Katharine House Hospice

National Organisation for Counselling Adoptees and Parents (NORCAP)

Oxfam

The Worldwide Fund for Nature (WWF)

Shropshire

Knowle Sports Association

Shropshire Children's Scrap Store

Somerset

Age Concern (Clevedon)

Age Concern (Somerset)

British Red Cross Somerset Branch

Ferne Animal Sanctuary

Imperial Cancer Research Fund

St Margaret's Somerset Hospice

Wellington Basins Project

West Somerset Council for Voluntary Service

South Glamorgan

Royal National Lifeboat Institution

Track 2000

South Yorkshire

Arthritis Research

Staffordshire

Alsager Animals in Need

Staffordshire Wildlife Trust

Strathclyde

Enable (Scottish Society for the Mentally Handicapped)

Suffolk

Age Concern (Suffolk)

Arthritis & Rheumatism Council for Research

Surrey

Cats in Care

Disability Action Sutton

Epsom & Ewell Phab Club

Feed the Minds

Hydon Hill Cheshire Home

Inner Wheel Club of Ewell

Mental Aid Projects

Mind in Croydon

Prader-Willi Syndrome Association (UK)

Queen Elizabeth's Foundation for Disabled People

Religious Society of Friends

Royal National Mission To Deep Sea Fishermen

St Raphael's Hospice

SIM International (UK)

Tayside

Brittle Bone Society

Tyne & Wear

British Lung Foundation (Breathe North)

Warwickshire

Emmaus (Coventry & Warwickshire)

Oxfam

West Midlands

Age Concern (Solihull)

Phoenix Sheltered Workshop

RSPCA (Birmingham & District Branch)

Stour Valley Cat Rescue

Walsall Gingerbread Advice Centre

West Sussex

Arthritis & Rheumatism Council for Research

British Red Cross

The Cats Protection League

The Missions to Seamen

St Bridget's Cheshire Home

West Yorkshire

Age Concern (Wakefield District)

Guide Dogs for the Blind Association

Kirkwood Hospice

Wiltshire

Age Concern (Thamesdown)

Devres & District PHAB

Marie Curie Cancer Care

Prospect Hospice

RSPCA (Marlborough with Andover Branch)

RSPCA (Wiltshire North & Chippenham Branch)

Worcestershire

Malvern Churches Community Network

Recycling

Aluminium

Berkshire

Berkshire Multiple Sclerosis Therapy Centre

Christian Community Action

The Guide Dogs for the Blind Association

Cambridgeshire

Emmaus (Cambridge)

SOFA (Peterborough) Limited

Central

Alloa Community Enterprises Limited

Cheshire

3C Teamwork

Cheshire Wildlife Trust

Cumbria

Age Concern (Northwest Cumbria)

Derbyshire

Arthritis & Rheumatism Council

Dorset

Guide Dogs for the Blind – Poole & District Branch

East Sussex

Hove YMCA

Magpie Recycling Co-op Limited

Sussex Emmaus

East Yorkshire

RSPCA

Greater Manchester

Wesley Community Project

Gwent

Wastesavers Recycling Association

Gwynedd

RSPCA (West Gwynedd Branch)

Hertfordshire

Friends of Danesbury

Royal Veterinary College Animal Care Trust

Humberside

Age Concern (Hull)

Kent

St Martin's Emmaus

Lancashire

Burnley Community Business & Resource Centre

Emmaus (Greater Manchester)

Leicestershire

Blaby & Whetstone Boys Club

Cat Action Trust

The National Trust

RSPCA (Leicestershire Branch)

London E

Walthamstow After School Club

Waste Not Recycling

London EC

Islington Age Concern

London NW

Inland Waterways Association

Mind in Camden Charity Shop

London SE

South Norwood Animal Rescue

London SW

The Homeless Furniture Project

London W

Age Concern (Hammersmith & Fulham)

Middlesex

Aspire

Norfolk

Centre 81

Royal British Legion

North Yorkshire

Network (Whitby Resource Centre)

Northern Ireland

Bryson House

Emmaus Liberty Belfast

Orkney

Age Concern (Orkney)

Oxfordshire

Imperial Cancer Research Fund

Oxfam

Powys

Replay

Shropshire

Knowle Sports Association

League of Friends of the Shrewsbury Hospitals

Shropshire & Mid Wales Hospice

Shropshire Children's Scrap Store

Somerset

1st Taunton (Wilton) Scout Group

Imperial Cancer Research Fund

South Yorkshire

RSPCA (SYAC)

Staffordshire

RSPCA (Burton-on-Trent & District Branch)

Staffordshire Wildlife Trust

Surrey

Hydon Hill Cheshire Home

Surrey Community Recycling and Play Project

Tyne & Wear

Wearside Women in Need

Warwickshire

Emmaus (Coventry & Warwickshire)

Oxfam

Rokeby Infant School PTFA

West Midlands

Phoenix Sheltered Workshop

West Sussex

British Red Cross

West Yorkshire

Cash from Trash in Aid of Charities

Guide Dogs for the Blind Association

RSPCA (Bradford & District Branch)

Wiltshire

Prospect Hospice

RSPCA (Swindon Branch)

Childrens play/ craft scrap

Cambridgeshire

SOFA (Peterborough) Limited

Cheshire

3C Teamwork

Devon

South Devon Play and Resource Centre Scrapstore (SPARC)

East Sussex

Eastbourne Playbus

Sussex Emmaus

Essex

Scope in Colchester (Castlegate Centre)

YMCA Day Camps

Gloucestershire

Gloucestershire Resource Centre

Gwent

The Community Furniture Project

Isle of Wight

IW RCC (Wight Play Project)

Lancashire

Burnley Community Business & Resource Centre

Emmaus (Greater Manchester)

Lincolnshire

Artlandish Limited

London E

Walthamstow After School Club

London NW

Brent Gingerbread

London W

Age Concern (Hammersmith & Fulham)

Merseyside

St Helen's Opportunity for Play

Norfolk

Dereham Gingerbread Club

Mini-Scrapbox

Nottinghamshire

Kirby Volunteer Centre

Newark & Sherwood Play Support Group

Powys

Replay

Staffordshire

Newcastle Play Council

Surrey

Surrey Community Recycling and Play Project

Tayside

Montrose Scrapstore

Warwickshire

Emmaus (Coventry & Warwickshire)

West Midlands

Birmingham Play Resource Centre

Walsall Gingerbread Advice Centre

West Sussex

British Red Cross

Wiltshire

Swindon Children's Scrapstore

Worcestershire

Malvern Churches Community Network

Christmas cards

Cambridgeshire

SOFA (Peterborough) Limited

East Sussex

Age Concern (East Sussex)

Essex

Farleigh (Mid-Essex Hospice)

Scope in Colchester (Castlegate Centre)

Greater Manchester

Manchester & Salford Methodist Mission

Gwynedd

RSPCA (Meirionnydd Branch)

Kent

British Red Cross Margate Centre

St Martin's Emmaus

Thanet Mind (Mental Health Day Centre)

Lancashire

Emmaus (Greater Manchester)

Preston Animal Welfare Society

Lincolnshire

Strut Limited

London W

Age Concern (Hammersmith & Fulham)

London WC

Leukaemia Research Fund

Middlesex

Aspire

Norfolk

Royal British Legion

North Yorkshire

Network (Whitby Resource Centre)

Shropshire

Knowle Sports Association

Shropshire Children's Scrap Store

South Yorkshire

Highway Tools & Crafts Centre

Surrey

Disability Action Sutton

Hydon Hill Cheshire Home

Tayside

Montrose Scrapstore

Tyne & Wear

South Shields Ladies Lifeboat Comm

Warwickshire

Emmaus (Coventry & Warwickshire)

Rokeby Infant School PTFA

West Midlands

Birmingham Play Resource Centre

Walsall Gingerbread Advice Centre

Wiltshire

Swindon Children's Scrapstore

Glass

Central

Alloa Community Enterprises
Limited

East Sussex

Sussex Emmaus

Humberside

Age Concern (Hull)

Kent

Bexley Downs Syndrome Group

Kent Red Cross Charity Shops

Norfolk

Norwich Community Workshop

North Yorkshire

Emmaus (Scarborough)

Orkney

Age Concern (Orkney)

Shropshire

Knowle Sports Association

Tyne & Wear

South Shields Ladies Lifeboat
Comm

Warwickshire

Emmaus (Coventry &
Warwickshire)

Rokeby Infant School PTFA

Milk bottle tops

Bedfordshire

Luton Day Centre for the
Homeless

Berkshire

Christian Community Action

The Guide Dogs for the Blind
Association

Cambridgeshire

SOFA (Peterborough) Limited

Cheshire

Cheshire Wildlife Trust

Dorset

Guide Dogs for the Blind –
Poole & District Branch

East Sussex

Eastbourne Playbus

Magpie Recycling Co-op Limited

Monday Club

Sussex Emmaus

East Yorkshire

RSPCA

Essex

Uttlesford Council for Voluntary
Service

Hampshire

Teg Down Residents'
Association

Hertfordshire

Royal Veterinary College
Animal Care Trust

Lancashire

Burnley Community Business &
Resource Centre

Emmaus (Greater Manchester)

Leicestershire

Cat Action Trust

The National Trust

RSPCA (Leicestershire Branch)

London NW

Inland Waterways Association

Mind in Camden Charity Shop

Lothian

Sue Ryder Foundation

Merseyside

Newton Visual Impaired Group

Norfolk

Royal British Legion

Nottinghamshire

Newark & Sherwood Play
Support Group

Oxfordshire

Oxfam

Surrey

Community Scrap Scheme

Surrey Community Recycling
and Play Project

Tayside

Montrose Scrapstore

Warwickshire

Emmaus (Coventry &
Warwickshire)

Oxfam

Rokeby Infant School PTFA

West Sussex

British Red Cross

West Yorkshire

Cash from Trash in Aid of
Charities

Guide Dogs for the Blind
Association

Other metals

Bedfordshire

Luton Day Centre for the Homeless

Berkshire

Christian Community Action

Cambridgeshire

Emmaus (Cambridge)

SOFA (Peterborough) Limited

Central

Alloa Community Enterprises Limited

Cheshire

3C Teamwork

Derbyshire

Derby Furniture Project

East Sussex

Magpie Recycling Co-op Limited

Sussex Emmaus

East Yorkshire

RSPCA

Gwent

Wastesavers Recycling Association

Kent

St Martin's Emmaus

Lancashire

Emmaus (Greater Manchester)

London NW

Inland Waterways Association

Lothian

Sue Ryder Foundation

North Yorkshire

Network (Whitby Resource Centre)

Shropshire

Knowle Sports Association

Warwickshire

Emmaus (Coventry & Warwickshire)

Rokeby Infant School PTFA

Plastics

Cambridgeshire

SOFA (Peterborough) Limited

Cheshire

NiPlas Recycling

Devon

South Devon Play and Resource Centre Scrapstore (SPARC)

East Sussex

Sussex Emmaus

Gloucestershire

Gloucestershire Resource Centre

Hampshire

Southampton Scrap Store

Humberside

Age Concern (Hull)

Isle of Wight

IW RCC (Wight Play Project)

Lancashire

Emmaus (Greater Manchester)

Nottinghamshire

Newark & Sherwood Play Support Group

Shropshire

Shropshire Children's Scrap Store

Surrey

Community Scrap Scheme

Warwickshire

Emmaus (Coventry & Warwickshire)

West Midlands

Birmingham Play Resource Centre

Postcards used

Berkshire

Age Concern (Reading)

Christian Community Action

The Guide Dogs for the Blind Association

Derbyshire

Salcare

Dorset

Guide Dogs for the Blind – Poole & District Branch

East Sussex

Bexhill & District Diabetic Group

Friends of the Eastbourne Hospitals

Seaford Volunteers

Essex

Farleigh (Mid-Essex Hospice)

Sudan Church Association

Greater Manchester

Age Concern (Manchester)

Royal National Lifeboat Institution

Gwynedd

RSPCA (Meirionnydd Branch)

Hampshire

Moorlands Community Association

Rehab – Basingstoke & Alton Cardiac Appeal

Teg Down Residents' Association

Hertfordshire

Royal Veterinary College Animal Care Trust

The Stort Trust

Kent

Kent Red Cross Charity Shops

St Cecilia's Cheshire Home

St Martin's Emmaus

Seven Springs Cheshire Home

Thanet Mind (Mental Health Day Centre)

Lancashire

Age Concern (Preston & South Ribble)

Emmaus (Greater Manchester)

Zaire Evangelistic Mission

Leicestershire

The National Trust

Lincolnshire

Artlandish Limited

London NW

Inland Waterways Association

London SE

South Norwood Animal Rescue

London SW

Marie Curie Cancer Care

London W

Royal National Mission to Deep Sea Fishermen

London WC

The Children's Society

Leukaemia Research Fund

Lothian

The National Bible Society of Scotland

Merseyside

Wirral Rehab T/AS Speaks Volumes

Middlesex

Enfield Preservation Society

Norfolk

Royal British Legion

North Yorkshire

Emmaus (Scarborough)

Northern Ireland

The Salvation Army Charity Shop

War on Want (NI)

Oxfordshire

Oxfam

Shropshire

Knowle Sports Association

Somerset

Wellington Basins Project

West Somerset Council for Voluntary Service

Strathclyde

Enable (Scottish Society for the Mentally Handicapped)

Surrey

Cats in Care

Disability Action Sutton

Hydon Hill Cheshire Home

Mind in Croydon

Tyne & Wear

British Lung Foundation (Breathe North)

Warwickshire

Emmaus (Coventry & Warwickshire)

Oxfam

RACKS

West Midlands

Birmingham Play Resource Centre

Stour Valley Cat Rescue

Wiltshire

Swindon Children's Scrapstore

Worcestershire

Malvern Churches Community Network

Rags

Berkshire

Christian Community Action

Cambridgeshire

SOFA (Peterborough) Limited

Central

Alloa Community Enterprises Limited

Cumbria

Age Concern (Northwest Cumbria)

Derbyshire

Treetops Hospice

Devon

Age Concern (Plymouth)

Dorset

Age Concern (Bournemouth)

East Sussex

Hove YMCA

Magpie Recycling Co-op Limited

Sussex Emmaus

Essex

Farleigh (Mid-Essex Hospice)

Grampian

Voluntary Service (Aberdeen)

Gwent

Wastesavers Recycling Association

Hereford & Worcester

Arthritis Research Charity Shop

Humberside

Age Concern (Hull)

Isle of Wight

IW RCC (Wight Play Project)

Kent

St Martin's Emmaus

Lancashire

Age Concern (Lytham St Anne's)

Emmaus (Greater Manchester)

Homeless in Blackpool

Lincolnshire

St Barnabas Hospice Shops

Strut Limited

London NW

Age Concern (Brent)

London SW

Age Concern England

Oasis Aids Support Centre

Lothian

Sue Ryder Foundation

Norfolk

Norwich Community Workshop

Northamptonshire

The Salvation Army

Northern Ireland

Age Action Ireland

The Salvation Army Charity Shop

Nottinghamshire

Age Concern (Nottinghamshire)

Newark & Sherwood Play Support Group

Orkney

Age Concern (Orkney)

Oxfordshire

Oxfam

Powys

Replay

Shropshire

Knowle Sports Association

Shropshire & Mid Wales Hospice

Shropshire Children's Scrap Store

Somerset

St Margaret's Somerset Hospice

South Glamorgan

Track 2000

South Yorkshire

Age Concern (Rotherham)

RSPCA (SYAC)

Salvation Army (Care & Share Shop)

Strathclyde

The Salvation Army

Suffolk

Home Farm Trust

St Louis Family Service

Surrey

Mind in Croydon

Surrey Community Recycling and Play Project

Warwickshire

Emmaus (Coventry & Warwickshire)

Rokeby Infant School PTFA

West Midlands

Birmingham Play Resource Centre

Phoenix Sheltered Workshop

Walsall Gingerbread Advice Centre

West Yorkshire

Bradford Gingerbread Centre

Kirkwood Hospice

St George's Crypt

Silver paper & aluminium foil

Bedfordshire

Luton Day Centre for the Homeless

Women's Royal Voluntary Service

Berkshire

Christian Community Action

The Guide Dogs for the Blind Association

Cambridgeshire

Emmaus (Cambridge)

SOFA (Peterborough) Limited

Cheshire

Cheshire Wildlife Trust

Dorset

Guide Dogs for the Blind – Poole & District Branch

East Sussex

Eastbourne Playbus

Magpie Recycling Co-op Limited

Monday Club

Sussex Emmaus

East Yorkshire

RSPCA

Essex

Uttlesford Council for Voluntary Service

Hampshire

Southampton Scrap Store

Teg Down Residents' Association

Hertfordshire

Royal Veterinary College Animal Care Trust

Isle of Wight

IW RCC (Wight Play Project)

Lancashire

Burnley Community Business & Resource Centre

Emmaus (Greater Manchester)

Leicestershire

Cat Action Trust

The National Trust

RSPCA (Leicestershire Branch)

Lincolnshire

Artlandish Limited

London E

Walthamstow After School Club

London NW

Inland Waterways Association

Mind in Camden Charity Shop

London W

Age Concern (Hammersmith & Fulham)

Merseyside

Newton Visual Impaired Group

Norfolk

Royal British Legion

Nottinghamshire

Newark & Sherwood Play Support Group

Oxfordshire

Oxfam

Powys

Replay

Shropshire

Shropshire & Mid Wales Hospice

Shropshire Children's Scrap Store

South Yorkshire

Bentley Association for Supportive Help

Surrey

Community Scrap Scheme

Surrey Community Recycling and Play Project

Tayside

Montrose Scrapstore

Warwickshire

Emmaus (Coventry & Warwickshire)

Oxfam

Rokeby Infant School PTFA

West Midlands

Birmingham Play Resource Centre

West Sussex

British Red Cross

West Yorkshire

Cash from Trash in Aid of Charities

Guide Dogs for the Blind Association

Wiltshire

Swindon Children's Scrapstore

Telephone cards

Berkshire

Age Concern (Reading)

Christian Community Action

The Guide Dogs for the Blind Association

Cumbria

Age Concern (Northwest Cumbria)

Derbyshire

Treetops Hospice

Dorset

Guide Dogs for the Blind – Poole & District Branch

East Sussex

Bexhill & District Diabetic Group

Sussex Emmaus

Essex

Scope in Colchester (Castlegate Centre)

Sudan Church Association

Greater Manchester

Age Concern (Manchester)

Royal National Lifeboat Institution

Hampshire

British Kidney Patient Association

Rehab – Basingstoke & Alton Cardiac Appeal

Hertfordshire

Base, Dacorum and St Albans Homeless Development Team

The Stort Trust

Kent

St Cecilia's Cheshire Home

Thanet Phobic Group

Lancashire

Emmaus (Greater Manchester)

Save the Children

Leicestershire

The National Trust

RSPCA (Leicestershire Branch)

Lincolnshire

Bransby Home of Rest for Horses

London SE

Iris Fund for Prevention of Blindness

South Norwood Animal Rescue

London SW

Marie Curie Cancer Care

Oasis Aids Support Centre

Scout Holiday Homes Trust

London WC

The Children's Society

Leukaemia Research Fund

Lothian

The National Bible Society of Scotland

Royal National Lifeboat Institution

Norfolk

Norfolk & Norwich Muscular Dystrophy Group

Northern Ireland

The Salvation Army Charity Shop

Oxfordshire

Hearing Dogs for the Deaf

Oxfam

Shropshire

Knowle Sports Association

South Glamorgan

Age Concern (South Glamorgan)

Surrey

Hydon Hill Cheshire Home

Warwickshire

Emmaus (Coventry & Warwickshire)

Oxfam

West Midlands

Birmingham Play Resource Centre

Walsall Gingerbread Advice Centre

West Sussex

The Cats Protection League

West Yorkshire

RSPCA (Bradford & District Branch)

Worcestershire

Malvern Churches Community Network

Waste paper

Bedfordshire

Sandy Neighbourhood Centre
(part of Christian Family Care)

Berkshire

Berkshire Multiple Sclerosis
Therapy Centre

The Guide Dogs for the Blind
Association

Cambridgeshire

SOFA (Peterborough) Limited

Devon

South Devon Play and Resource
Centre Scrapstore (SPARC)

East Sussex

Eastbourne Playbus

Magpie Recycling Co-op Limited

Sussex Emmaus

Essex

Farleigh (Mid-Essex Hospice)

Uttlesford Council for Voluntary
Service

Gloucestershire

Gloucestershire Resource Centre

Gwent

Wastesavers Recycling
Association

Hampshire

Marwell Zoological Society

Southampton Scrap Store

Hertfordshire

Base, Dacorum and St Albans
Homeless Development Team

Royal Veterinary College
Animal Care Trust

Humberside

Age Concern (Hull)

Isle of Wight

IW RCC (Wight Play Project)

Kent

5th Dartford Scout Group

Age Concern (Gillingham)

Catholic Fund for Overseas
Development (Cafod)
Southwark

Dartford District Volunteer
Bureau

Friends of Animals League

St George's Community
Children's Project Limited

St Martin's Emmaus

Seven Springs Cheshire Home

Lancashire

Emmaus (Greater Manchester)

Lincolnshire

St Barnabas Hospice Shops

Middlesex

Aspire

Norfolk

Mini-Scrapbox

Norwich Community Workshop

Royal British Legion

Northern Ireland

War on Want (NI)

Nottinghamshire

Newark & Sherwood Play
Support Group

Oxfordshire

Imperial Cancer Research Fund

Powys

Replay

Shropshire

Knowle Sports Association

League of Friends of the
Shrewsbury Hospitals

Shropshire & Mid Wales Hospice

Shropshire Children's Scrap
Store

Somerset

1st Taunton (Wilton) Scout
Group

South Yorkshire

RSPCA (SYAC)

Staffordshire

Burton YMCA

Surrey

Feed the Minds

Hydestile Wildlife Hospital

Hydon Hill Cheshire Home

Mind in Croydon

Surrey Community Recycling
and Play Project

Warwickshire

Emmaus (Coventry &
Warwickshire)

Rokeby Infant School PTFA

West Midlands

Birmingham Play Resource
Centre

Phoenix Sheltered Workshop

West Yorkshire

Cash from Trash in Aid of
Charities

Imperial Cancer Research Fund

Vouchers, Coupons, Tokens

Air miles

Bedfordshire

The Royal Society for the Protection of Birds

Berkshire

Age Concern (Reading)

Christian Community Action

The Guide Dogs for the Blind Association

Thames Valley Hospice

Cambridgeshire

The Leonard Cheshire Foundation

Cheshire

Arthritis Research (Arthritis & Rheumatism Council)

Derbyshire

Arthritis & Rheumatism Council

Treetops Hospice

Dorset

Boscombe Salvation Army Charity Concern

Pramacare

East Sussex

Betts Memorial Heart Foundation

Sussex Emmaus

Essex

Farleigh (Mid-Essex Hospice)

St Helena Hospice

St Luke's Hospice

Grampian

Aberdeen Cyrenians

Aberdeen Women's Aid

Greater Manchester

Age Concern (Manchester)

Manchester & Salford Methodist Mission

Hampshire

British Kidney Patient Association

Moorlands Community Association

National Schizophrenia Fellowship

Rehab – Basingstoke & Alton Cardiac Appeal

Wessex Cancer Trust

Hereford & Worcester

Arthritis Research Charity Shop

Hertfordshire

National Animal Welfare Trust

The Stort Trust

Humberside

Age Concern (Hull)

Kent

Bexley Downs Syndrome Group

Epilepsy Network Gravesend

Friends of Animals League

Hope Romania

Seven Springs Cheshire Home

Lancashire

Emmaus (Greater Manchester)

Horses & Ponies Protection Association

Preston Animal Welfare Society

Salvation Army

Save the Children

Zaire Evangelistic Mission

Leicestershire

Blaby & Whetstone Boys Club

The Gideons International

The National Trust

RSPCA (Leicestershire Branch)

Lincolnshire

Arthritis Care

London E

Walthamstow After School Club

London N

WWF UK North London Office

London NW

Inland Waterways Association

RSPCA (Mayhew Animal Home)

London SE

Elimination of Leukaemia Fund

Iris Fund for Prevention of Blindness

St Christopher's Hospice

Shaftesbury Resources Centre

London SW

Cardinal Hume Centre for Young Homeless People

Marie Curie Cancer Care

Oasis Aids Support Centre

London W

Cancer Relief Macmillan Fund

Family Holiday Association

London WC

The Children's Society

Imperial Cancer Research Fund

Leukaemia Research Fund

Lothian

Cancer Research Campaign Scotland

The National Bible Society of Scotland

Sue Ryder Foundation

Middlesex

Aspire

British Red Cross Society

Richmond Fellowship International

Norfolk

Centre 81

CSV Vocal Project

Norfolk & Norwich Scope

North Yorkshire

St Leonard's Hospice

Northern Ireland

Arthritis & Rheumatism Council (NI)

Conservation Volunteers Northern Ireland

War on Want (NI)

Nottinghamshire

Age Concern (Nottinghamshire)

Nottingham Mencap

RSPCA

Oxfordshire

Age Concern (Oxford)

Hearing Dogs for the Deaf

Imperial Cancer Research Fund

Oxfam

The Worldwide Fund for Nature (WWF)

Shropshire

Shropshire & Mid Wales Hospice

Somerset

Imperial Cancer Research Fund

St Margaret's Somerset Hospice

South Glamorgan

Age Concern (South Glamorgan)

Track 2000

South Yorkshire

RSPCA (SYAC)

Suffolk

Age Concern (Suffolk)

Arthritis & Rheumatism Council for Research

Surrey

Cats in Care

Disability Action Sutton

Feed the Minds

Hydestile Wildlife Hospital

Hydon Hill Cheshire Home

Inner Wheel Club of Ewell

Prader-Willi Syndrome Association (UK)

Prosa Foundation

St Raphael's Hospice

SHCVS

SIM International (UK)

Warwickshire

Oxfam

West Midlands

Stour Valley Cat Rescue

Walsall Gingerbread Advice Centre

West Sussex

Arthritis & Rheumatism Council for Research

The Cats Protection League

West Yorkshire

Age Concern (Wakefield District)

Cash from Trash in Aid of Charities

Imperial Cancer Research Fund

Kirkwood Hospice

Pet Animals Welfare Society (PAWS)

Wiltshire

Prospect Hospice

Money-off coupons

Berkshire

Age Concern (Reading)

Christian Community Action

The Guide Dogs for the Blind Association

Thames Valley Hospice

Cambridgeshire

Emmaus (Cambridge)

St Theresa's House

Cheshire

Arthritis Research (Arthritis & Rheumatism Council)

Derbyshire

Arthritis & Rheumatism Council

Dorset

Boscombe Salvation Army Charity Concern

Gingerbread

Pramacare

Sheltered Work Opportunities Project

East Sussex

Betts Memorial Heart Foundation

Sussex Emmaus

Essex

Farleigh (Mid-Essex Hospice)

St Luke's Hospice

Grampian

Aberdeen Cyrenians

Aberdeen Women's Aid

Greater Manchester

Age Concern (Manchester)

Hampshire

British Kidney Patient Association

National Schizophrenia Fellowship

Rehab – Basingstoke & Alton Cardiac Appeal

Hertfordshire

Base, Dacorum and St Albans Homeless Development Team

Dacorum Council for Voluntary Service

National Animal Welfare Trust

The Stort Trust

Humberside

Age Concern (Hull)

Kent

Bexley Downs Syndrome Group

Epilepsy Network Gravesend

Friends of Animals League

Seven Springs Cheshire Home

Lancashire

Age Concern (Blackpool)

Emmaus (Greater Manchester)

Save the Children

Leicestershire

Cat Action Trust

The Gideons International

The National Trust

RSPCA (Leicestershire Branch)

Lincolnshire

Arthritis Care

Bransby Home of Rest for Horses

Strut Limited

London NW

Brent Gingerbread

RSPCA (Mayhew Animal Home)

London SE

St Christopher's Hospice

Shaftesbury Resources Centre

South Norwood Animal Rescue

London SW

Cardinal Hume Centre for Young Homeless People

Oasis Aids Support Centre

Scout Holiday Homes Trust

London W

Family Holiday Association

London WC

The Children's Society

Lothian

Sue Ryder Foundation

Merseyside

Newton Visual Impaired Group

Middlesex

Aspire

Norfolk

CSV Vocal Project

Dereham Gingerbread Club

North Yorkshire

St Leonard's Hospice

Northamptonshire

Caring & Sharing Trust

Northern Ireland

Arthritis & Rheumatism Council (NI)

Nottinghamshire

Age Concern (Nottinghamshire)

RSPCA

Oxfordshire

Imperial Cancer Research Fund

Oxfam

The Worldwide Fund for Nature (WWF)

Shropshire

Shropshire Children's Scrap Store

Somerset

NCH Action for Children

St Margaret's Somerset Hospice

West Somerset Council for
Voluntary Service

South Glamorgan

Track 2000

South Yorkshire

Arthritis Research

Suffolk

Age Concern (Suffolk)

Arthritis & Rheumatism Council
for Research

Surrey

Disability Action Sutton

Hydestile Wildlife Hospital

Hydon Hill Cheshire Home

Mind in Croydon

Prader-Willi Syndrome
Association (UK)

St Raphael's Hospice

SHCVS

Warwickshire

Oxfam

West Midlands

Phoenix Sheltered Workshop

Stour Valley Cat Rescue

Walsall Gingerbread Advice
Centre

West Sussex

Arthritis & Rheumatism Council
for Research

The Cats Protection League

West Yorkshire

Age Concern (Bradford &
District)

Age Concern (Wakefield
District)

Kirkwood Hospice

Pet Animals Welfare Society
(PAWS)

Wiltshire

Devres & District PHAB

Prospect Hospice

Swindon Gingerbread

Petrol vouchers

Bedfordshire

The Royal Society for the
Protection of Birds

Berkshire

Age Concern (Reading)

Berkshire Multiple Sclerosis
Therapy Centre

Christian Community Action

The Guide Dogs for the Blind
Association

Thames Valley Hospice

Buckinghamshire

Age Concern (Bucks)

Cambridgeshire

The Leonard Cheshire
Foundation

Cheshire

3C Teamwork

Arthritis Research (Arthritis &
Rheumatism Council)

Raynaud's & Scleroderma
Association

Cumbria

Age Concern (South Lakeland)

Jennifer Trust for SMA

Derbyshire

Arthritis & Rheumatism Council

Treetops Hospice

Dorset

Age Concern (Bournemouth)

Boscombe Salvation Army
Charity Concern

Gingerbread

Pramacare

Sheltered Work Opportunities
Project

East Sussex

Betts Memorial Heart
Foundation

Sussex Emmaus

East Yorkshire
RSPCA

Essex
Epping Forest Field Centre

Farleigh (Mid-Essex Hospice)

St Helena Hospice

St Luke's Hospice

Grampian
Aberdeen Women's Aid

Greater Manchester
Age Concern (Manchester)

Hampshire
British Kidney Patient Association

Marwell Zoological Society

Moorlands Community Association

National Schizophrenia Fellowship

Rehab – Basingstoke & Alton Cardiac Appeal

Totton & Eling Community Association

Wessex Cancer Trust

Hereford & Worcester
Arthritis Research Charity Shop

ME Association Hereford & Worcester Group

Hertfordshire
Base, Dacorum and St Albans Homeless Development Team

Dacorum Council for Voluntary Service

National Animal Welfare Trust

The Stort Trust

Humberside
Age Concern (Hull)

Kent
5th Dartford Scout Group

Bexley Downs Syndrome Group

Epilepsy Network Gravesend

Friends of Animals League

St Cecilia's Cheshire Home

Seven Springs Cheshire Home

Lancashire
Emmaus (Greater Manchester)

Horses & Ponies Protection Association

Save the Children

Zaire Evangelistic Mission

Leicestershire
Cat Action Trust

The Gideons International

The National Trust

RSPCA (Leicestershire Branch)

Lincolnshire
Arthritis Care

Bransby Home of Rest for Horses

Strut Limited

London E
Crisis

Walthamstow After School Club

London NW
Inland Waterways Association

RSPCA (Mayhew Animal Home)

London SE
Elimination of Leukaemia Fund

St Christopher's Hospice

Shaftesbury Resources Centre

South Norwood Animal Rescue

London SW
Marie Curie Cancer Care

Oasis Aids Support Centre

Scout Holiday Homes Trust

London W
Age Concern (Hammersmith & Fulham)

Cancer Relief Macmillan Fund

Family Holiday Association

London WC
The Children's Society

Imperial Cancer Research Fund

Leukaemia Research Fund

Lothian
Cancer Research Campaign Scotland

Sue Ryder Foundation

Merseyside
Newton Visual Impaired Group

Middlesex
Aspire

British Red Cross Society

Richmond Fellowship International

Norfolk
CSV Vocal Project

Dereham Gingerbread Club

Norfolk & Norwich Muscular Dystrophy Group

North Yorkshire
St Leonard's Hospice

Northampshire
Caring & Sharing Trust

Northern Ireland
Arthritis & Rheumatism Council (NI)

Conservation Volunteers Northern Ireland

War on Want (NI)

Nottinghamshire
Age Concern (Nottinghamshire)

RSPCA

Oxfordshire
Imperial Cancer Research Fund

Katharine House Hospice

National Organisation for Counselling Adoptees and Parents (NORCAP)

Oxfam

The Worldwide Fund for Nature (WWF)

Shropshire

Shropshire & Mid Wales Hospice

Somerset

St Margaret's Somerset Hospice

West Somerset Council for Voluntary Service

South Glamorgan

Track 2000

South Yorkshire

Arthritis Research

Cot-Age – Child Safety & Nursery Equipment

RSPCA (SYAC)

Staffordshire

Staffordshire Wildlife Trust

Strathclyde

Enable (Scottish Society for the Mentally Handicapped)

Suffolk

Age Concern (Suffolk)

Arthritis & Rheumatism Council for Research

Surrey

Disability Action Sutton

Feed the Minds

Hydestile Wildlife Hospital

Hydon Hill Cheshire Home

Mind in Croydon

Prader-Willi Syndrome Association (UK)

Queen Elizabeth's Foundation for Disabled People

St Raphael's Hospice

SHCVS

Tyne & Wear

British Lung Foundation (Breathe North)

St Oswald's Hospice

Warwickshire

Oxfam

West Midlands

Phoenix Sheltered Workshop

Stour Valley Cat Rescue

Walsall Gingerbread Advice Centre

West Sussex

Arthritis & Rheumatism Council for Research

British Red Cross

The Cats Protection League

St Bridget's Cheshire Home

Wallis Centre

West Yorkshire

Age Concern (Wakefield District)

Imperial Cancer Research Fund

Kirkwood Hospice

Pet Animals Welfare Society (PAWS)

Wiltshire

Devres & District PHAB

Prospect Hospice

RSPCA (Swindon Branch)

RSPCA (Wiltshire North & Chippenham Branch)

Swindon Gingerbread

Trading stamps

Berkshire

Age Concern (Reading)

Christian Community Action

The Guide Dogs for the Blind Association

Buckinghamshire

Age Concern (Bucks)

Cambridgeshire

The Leonard Cheshire Foundation

St Theresa's House

Cheshire

Arthritis Research (Arthritis & Rheumatism Council)

Raynaud's & Scleroderma Association

Sue Ryder Foundation

Cumbria

Age Concern (South Lakeland)

Jennifer Trust for SMA

Derbyshire

Arthritis & Rheumatism Council

Dorset

Boscombe Salvation Army Charity Concern

Pramacare

East Sussex

Betts Memorial Heart Foundation

Sussex Emmaus

Essex

St Helena Hospice

St Luke's Hospice

Greater Manchester

Age Concern (Manchester)

Hampshire

British Kidney Patient Association

Marwell Zoological Society

Moorlands Community Association

National Schizophrenia Fellowship

Rehab – Basingstoke & Alton Cardiac Appeal

Totton & Eling Community Association

Hereford & Worcester

Arthritis Research Charity Shop

Hertfordshire

Base, Dacorum and St Albans Homeless Development Team

National Animal Welfare Trust

The Stort Trust

Humberside

Age Concern (Hull)

Kent

Bexley Downs Syndrome Group

Epilepsy Network Gravesend

Friends of Animals League

St Cecilia's Cheshire Home

St Martin's Emmaus

Seven Springs Cheshire Home

Lancashire

Age Concern (Blackpool)

Emmaus (Greater Manchester)

Horses & Ponies Protection Association

Save the Children

Zaire Evangelistic Mission

Leicestershire

Cat Action Trust

The Gideons International

The National Trust

RSPCA (Leicestershire Branch)

Lincolnshire

Arthritis Care

Bransby Home of Rest for Horses

Strut Limited

London NW

Inland Waterways Association

RSPCA (Mayhew Animal Home)

London SE

Elimination of Leukaemia Fund

Iris Fund for Prevention of Blindness

St Christopher's Hospice

Shaftesbury Resources Centre

South Norwood Animal Rescue

London SW

Marie Curie Cancer Care

Oasis Aids Support Centre

Scout Holiday Homes Trust

London W

Cancer Relief Macmillan Fund

Family Holiday Association

London WC

The Children's Society

Leukaemia Research Fund

Lothian

Sue Ryder Foundation

Merseyside

Newton Visual Impaired Group

Middlesex

Aspire

British Red Cross Society

Norfolk

CSV Vocal Project

North Yorkshire

St Leonard's Hospice

Northamptonshire

Caring & Sharing Trust

Northern Ireland

Arthritis & Rheumatism Council (NI)

Nottinghamshire

Age Concern (Nottinghamshire)

RSPCA

Oxfordshire

Imperial Cancer Research Fund

National Organisation for Counselling Adoptees and Parents (NORCAP)

Oxfam

The Worldwide Fund for Nature (WWF)

Shropshire

Knowle Sports Association

Somerset

Imperial Cancer Research Fund

St Margaret's Somerset Hospice

West Somerset Council for Voluntary Service

South Glamorgan

Track 2000

South Yorkshire

Arthritis Research

RSPCA (SYAC)

Strathclyde

Enable (Scottish Society for the Mentally Handicapped)

Suffolk

Age Concern (Suffolk)

Arthritis & Rheumatism Council for Research

Surrey

Cats in Care

Disability Action Sutton

Epsom & Ewell Phab Club

Hydestile Wildlife Hospital

Hydon Hill Cheshire Home

Mind in Croydon

Prader-Willi Syndrome Association (UK)

Prosa Foundation

St Raphael's Hospice

SHCVS

Tyne & Wear

St Oswald's Hospice

Warwickshire

Oxfam

West Midlands

Phoenix Sheltered Workshop

Stour Valley Cat Rescue

Walsall Gingerbread Advice Centre

West Sussex

Arthritis & Rheumatism Council for Research

The Cats Protection League

St Bridget's Cheshire Home

West Yorkshire

Age Concern (Wakefield District)

Imperial Cancer Research Fund

Kirkwood Hospice

Pet Animals Welfare Society (PAWS)

Wiltshire

Devres & District PHAB

Prospect Hospice

RSPCA (Wiltshire North & Chippenham Branch)

PART TWO

Alphabetical list of organisations

This section gives the details of the individual organisations in alphabetical order

■ 1st Taunton (Wilton) Scout Group

ADDRESS 7 Wilton Close, Taunton, Somerset
TA1 4EZ

TELEPHONE 01823 331058

CATEGORY Aluminium *drinks cans* ● Bric-a-brac
● Used toner cartridges ● Waste paper *monthly collection*

COLLECTION SERVICE No

■ 3C Teamwork

ADDRESS St Paul's Community Resource Centre,
Hightown Crewe, Cheshire CW1 3BY

TELEPHONE 01270 586186

FAX 01270 250683

CATEGORY Aluminium ● Arts & crafts equipment
● Baby equipment ● Bed linen and mattresses
● Bicycles ● Books hardback ● Books paperback
● Bric-a-brac ● Children's play/craft scrap ● Clocks
● Computer hardware and software ● Diy
equipment ● Furniture ● Gardening equipment
● Household items *ironing boards etc* ● Knitting,
crochet and sewing equipment ● Knitting wool
● Magazines & comics ● Musical instruments
● Office equipment and stationery ● Other metals
domestic appliances & metal furniture ● Petrol
vouchers ● Pets' equipment ● Photographic
equipment ● Records & tapes ● Sports equipment
● Toys & games ● Video/computer games

COLLECTION SERVICE Yes

■ 5th Dartford Scout Group

ADDRESS c/o 17 Mitchell Close, Dartford, Kent
DA1 1PJ

TELEPHONE 01322 221384

CATEGORY Arts & crafts equipment ● Books
paperback ● Fabric remnants ● Knitting wool
● Non perishable foods ● Petrol vouchers
● Stamps British ● Stamps foreign ● Toiletries
● Toys & games ● Waste paper *newspaper only*

COLLECTION SERVICE No

■ Aberdeen Cyrenians

ADDRESS Palmerston House, 3rd Floor, 221 Market
Street, Aberdeen, Grampian AB11 5PT

TELEPHONE 01224 572877

FAX 01224 572785

CATEGORY Air miles ● Arts & crafts equipment ● Bed
linen and mattresses ● Bicycles ● Books hardback
● Books paperback ● Clothing adults' *winter coats,
jackets & warm clothes* ● Computer hardware and
software ● Household items *ironing boards etc*
● Money-off coupons ● Musical instruments
● Non perishable foods ● Office equipment and
stationery ● Photographic equipment ● Records &
tapes ● Sports equipment ● Stamps British
● Stamps foreign ● Toiletries ● Video/computer
games

COLLECTION SERVICE Yes

■ Aberdeen Women's Aid

ADDRESS 66 The Green, Aberdeen, Grampian
AB11 6PE

TELEPHONE 01224 591577

CATEGORY Air miles ● Bed linen and mattresses
● Bicycles ● Books hardback ● Books paperback
● Bric-a-brac ● Clocks ● Clothing adults'
● Clothing children's ● Computer hardware and
software ● Diy equipment ● Furniture
● Gardening equipment ● Household items
ironing boards etc ● Jewellery ● Knitting, crochet
and sewing equipment ● Knitting wool
● Magazines & comics ● Money-off coupons
● Non perishable foods ● Office equipment and
stationery ● Petrol vouchers ● Photographic
equipment ● Records & tapes ● Toiletries ● Toys
& games ● Video/computer games ● Watches

COLLECTION SERVICE No

■ Acorn Furniture & Clothing Project

ADDRESS 18a Octagon Street, Plymouth, Devon
PL1 1TZ

TELEPHONE 01752 672876

CATEGORY Baby equipment ● Bed linen and
mattresses *mattresses must comply with 1988 fire
safety regulations* ● Bicycles ● Books hardback
● Books paperback ● Bric-a-brac ● Clocks
● Clothing adults' ● Clothing children's ● Diy
equipment ● Fabric remnants ● Fur coats
● Furniture *excluding non-fire-resistant three
piece suites, etc* ● Gardening equipment
● Household items *ironing boards etc* ● Knitting,
crochet and sewing equipment ● Knitting wool
● Musical instruments ● Office equipment and
stationery ● Records & tapes ● Sports equipment
● Toys & games

COLLECTION SERVICE Yes

■ Actionaid National Recycling Unit

ADDRESS Carlton Chambers, 23–25 Baldwins Street,
Bristol, Avon BS1 1NF

TELEPHONE 0117-929 8818

FAX 0117-925 2339

CATEGORY Used toner cartridges

COLLECTION SERVICE Yes

■ Adur Furniture Network

ADDRESS 80 High Street, Shoreham-by-Sea,
W Sussex BN43 5DB

TELEPHONE 01273 441700

CATEGORY Baby equipment ● Bed linen and
mattresses ● Furniture ● Household items *ironing
boards etc* ● Musical instruments

COLLECTION SERVICE Yes

■ African Foundation for Development (Afford)

ADDRESS 54 Camberwell Road (Methodist Mission), London SE5 0EN

TELEPHONE 0171-703 0653

CATEGORY Computer hardware and software • Office equipment and stationery • Video/computer games

COLLECTION SERVICE No

■ Age Action Ireland

ADDRESS 30–31 Lower Camden Street, Dublin 2, Ireland

TELEPHONE 003531 4785060

CATEGORY Antique post cards • Baby equipment • Bed linen and mattresses *bed linen only* • Bicycles • Books hardback • Books paperback • Bric-a-brac • Clocks • Clothing adults' • Clothing children's • Coins foreign • Coins old • Computer hardware and software • Fabric remnants • Fur coats • Furniture *not large bulky items* • Household items *ironing boards etc* • Jewellery • Knitting, crochet and sewing equipment • Knitting wool • Magazines & comics • Medals • Musical instruments • Office equipment and stationery • Photographic equipment • Rags • Records & tapes • Spectacles • Sports equipment • Toiletries • Toys & games • Used toner cartridges • Video/computer games • Watches

COLLECTION SERVICE No

■ Age Concern (Bedfordshire)

ADDRESS No1 Staff House, The Moat House, Conduit Road, Beds MK40 1EQ

TELEPHONE 01234 360510

CATEGORY Books hardback • Books paperback • Bric-a-brac • Clothing adults' • Clothing children's • Jewellery • Musical instruments • Records & tapes • Toys & games • Watches

COLLECTION SERVICE No

■ Age Concern (Bedminster)

ADDRESS 2 Imperial Arcade, East Street, Bedminster, Bristol, Avon BS3 4HH

TELEPHONE 01179 532745

CATEGORY Antique post cards • Arts & crafts equipment • Bed linen and mattresses *no mattresses* • Books hardback • Books paperback • Bric-a-brac • Clocks • Clothing adults' • Clothing children's • Coins foreign • Coins old • Fabric remnants • Household items *ironing boards etc* • Jewellery • Knitting, crochet and sewing equipment • Knitting wool • Medals • Musical instruments • Records & tapes • Sports equipment • Stamps British • Stamps foreign • Toiletries • Toys & games • Video/computer games • Wedding clothes for hire

COLLECTION SERVICE Yes

■ Age Concern (Blackburn & District)

ADDRESS 4 King Street, Blackburn, Lancs BB2 2DH

TELEPHONE 01254 664242

FAX 01254 664248

CATEGORY Antique post cards • Arts & crafts equipment • Bed linen and mattresses *linen only, which must be in good clean resaleable condition* • Books hardback • Books paperback • Bric-a-brac *must be of resaleable quality* • Clocks *must be in working order* • Clothing adults' *must be of good clean resaleable quality* • Clothing children's *must be of good clean relsaleable quality* • Fabric remnants *clean and in resaleable condition* • Furniture *must be in resaleable condition, however please note upholstered furniture manufactured prior to 1988 is not acceptable* • Gardening equipment *not electrical* • Household items *ironing boards etc must be in working order, clean and in good condition* • Jewellery • Knitting, crochet and sewing equipment • Knitting wool • Magazines & comics • Non perishable foods • Records & tapes *in resaleable condition* • Sports equipment *in resaleable condition* • Toiletries • Toys & games *in resaleable condition* • Video/computer games *must be in resaleable condition* • Watches *must be in working order*

COLLECTION SERVICE Yes

■ Age Concern (Blackpool)

ADDRESS 3 Cookson Street, Blackpool, Lancs FY1 3EF

TELEPHONE 01253 751747

FAX 01253 751252

CATEGORY Antique post cards • Arts & crafts equipment • Baby equipment • Bed linen and mattresses *not mattresses* • Books hardback • Books paperback • Bric-a-brac • Clocks • Clothing adults' *no real fur* • Clothing children's *no shoes* • Coins foreign • Coins old • Diy equipment • Fabric remnants • Furniture *wooden – small only* • Gardening equipment • Household items *ironing boards etc* • Jewellery • Knitting, crochet and sewing equipment • Knitting wool • Magazines & comics • Medals • Money-off coupons • Office equipment and stationery • Records & tapes • Spectacles • Sports equipment • Toiletries • Toys & games • Trading stamps • Watches

COLLECTION SERVICE Yes

■ Age Concern (Blandford Forum)

ADDRESS 73 East Street, Blandford Forum, Dorset DT11 7DX

TELEPHONE 01258 451522

CATEGORY Antique post cards • Arts & crafts equipment • Bed linen and mattresses *no mattresses* • Books hardback • Books paperback • Bric-a-brac • Clocks • Clothing adults' • Clothing children's • Coins foreign • Coins old • Fabric remnants • Household items *ironing boards etc* • Jewellery • Knitting, crochet and sewing equipment • Knitting wool • Medals • Musical instruments • Records & tapes • Sports equipment • Stamps British • Stamps foreign •

Toiletries • Toys & games • Video/computer games • Wedding clothes for hire

COLLECTION SERVICE Yes

■ Age Concern (Boscombe)

ADDRESS 617 Christchurch Road, Boscombe, Bournemouth, Dorset BH1 1HP

TELEPHONE 01202 392742

CATEGORY Antique post cards • Arts & crafts equipment • Bed linen and mattresses *no mattresses* • Books hardback • Books paperback • Bric-a-brac • Clocks • Clothing adults' • Clothing children's • Coins foreign • Coins old • Fabric remnants • Household items *ironing boards etc* • Jewellery • Knitting, crochet and sewing equipment • Knitting wool • Medals • Musical instruments • Records & tapes • Sports equipment • Stamps British • Stamps foreign • Toiletries • Toys & games • Video/computer games • Wedding clothes for hire

COLLECTION SERVICE Yes

■ Age Concern (Bournemouth)

ADDRESS 700 Wimborne Road, Winton, Bournemouth, Dorset BH9 2EG

TELEPHONE 01202 530530

FAX 01202 530530

CATEGORY Antique post cards • Books hardback • Books paperback • Bric-a-brac • Clothing adults' • Clothing children's • Coins foreign • Fabric remnants • Jewellery • Knitting, crochet and sewing equipment • Knitting wool • Petrol vouchers • Rags • Records & tapes • Stamps British • Stamps foreign

COLLECTION SERVICE No

■ Age Concern (Bradford & District)

ADDRESS 19–25 Sunbridge Road, Bradford, W Yorks BD1 2AY

TELEPHONE 01274 395144

CATEGORY Antique post cards • Arts & crafts equipment • Bed linen and mattresses *not mattresses* • Books hardback • Books paperback • Bric-a-brac • Clocks • Clothing adults' • Clothing children's • Fabric remnants • Household items *ironing boards etc* • Jewellery • Knitting, crochet and sewing equipment • Knitting wool • Medals • Money-off coupons • Musical instruments • Records & tapes • Toiletries • Toys & games • Watches

COLLECTION SERVICE No

■ Age Concern (Brent)

ADDRESS 120 Craven Park Road, Harlesden, London NW10 8QD

TELEPHONE 0181-965 5975

FAX 0181-961 8976

CATEGORY Antique post cards • Arts & crafts equipment • Baby equipment • Bed linen and mattresses *bed linen but not mattresses* • Bicycles

just children's • Books hardback • Books paperback • Bric-a-brac • Clocks • Clothing adults' • Clothing children's • Coins foreign • Coins old • Diy equipment *only small items* • Fabric remnants • Fur coats • Furniture *only small items* • Gardening equipment *only small items* • Household items *ironing boards etc only small items* • Jewellery • Knitting, crochet and sewing equipment • Knitting wool • Magazines & comics • Medals • Musical instruments • Office equipment and stationery *small items* • Pets equipment • Photographic equipment *small items* • Rags • Records & tapes • Sports equipment *small items* • Toiletries *unopen, not used items* • Toys & games • Video/computer games • Watches • Wedding clothes for hire *but we will sell them rather than hire them out*

COLLECTION SERVICE Yes

■ Age Concern (Brighton)

ADDRESS 57 Ditchling Road, Brighton, E Sussex BN1 4SD

TELEPHONE 01273 570732

FAX 01273 624196

CATEGORY Antique post cards • Arts & crafts equipment • Books hardback • Books paperback • Bric-a-brac • Clothing adults' • Clothing children's • Coins old • Jewellery • Knitting wool • Sports equipment • Watches • Wedding clothes for hire

COLLECTION SERVICE No

■ Age Concern (Bristol)

ADDRESS Canningford House, Victoria Street, Bristol, Avon BS1 6BY

TELEPHONE 0117-922 1933

FAX 0117-922 1911

CATEGORY Antique post cards • Baby equipment • Books hardback • Books paperback • Bric-a-brac • Clocks • Clothing adults' • Clothing children's • Coins foreign • Coins old • Computer hardware and software • Diy equipment • Fabric remnants • Gardening equipment • Jewellery • Knitting, crochet and sewing equipment • Knitting wool • Magazines & comics • Medals • Musical instruments • Office equipment and stationery • Photographic equipment • Records & tapes • Sports equipment • Stamps British • Stamps foreign • Toys & games • Video/computer games • Watches

COLLECTION SERVICE No

■ Age Concern (Bristol)

ADDRESS 85 Regent Street, Kingswood, Bristol, Avon BS15 2LJ

TELEPHONE 01179 478080

CATEGORY Antique post cards • Arts & crafts equipment • Bed linen and mattresses *no mattresses* • Books hardback • Books paperback • Bric-a-brac • Clocks • Clothing adults' • Clothing children's • Coins foreign • Coins old • Fabric remnants • Household items *ironing boards etc* • Jewellery • Knitting, crochet and sewing equipment • Knitting wool • Medals • -

Musical instruments • Records & tapes • Sports equipment • Stamps British • Stamps foreign • Toiletries • Toys & games • Video/computer games • Wedding clothes for hire

COLLECTION SERVICE Yes

■ Age Concern (Bucks)

ADDRESS 146 Meadowcroft, Aylesbury, Bucks HP19 3HH

TELEPHONE 01296 431127

FAX 01296 330783

CATEGORY Antique post cards • Arts & crafts equipment • Baby equipment • Bed linen and mattresses • Books hardback • Books paperback • Bric-a-brac • Clocks • Clothing adults' • Clothing children's • Coins foreign • Coins old • Diy equipment • Fur coats • Furniture *small items* • Gardening equipment *small items* • Household items *ironing boards etc* • Jewellery • Knitting, crochet and sewing equipment • Knitting wool • Medals • Musical instruments • Office equipment and stationery • Petrol vouchers • Photographic equipment • Records & tapes • Sports equipment • Stamps British • Stamps foreign • Toiletries • Toys & games • Trading stamps • Video/computer games • Watches

COLLECTION SERVICE No

■ Age Concern (Calderdale)

ADDRESS 10 Ward's End, Halifax, W Yorks HX1 1BX

TELEPHONE 01422 359086

FAX 01422 342951

CATEGORY Arts & crafts equipment • Books paperback • Bric-a-brac • Clocks • Clothing adults' *in good condition* • Clothing children's *in good condition* • Fabric remnants • Jewellery • Knitting, crochet and sewing equipment • Knitting wool • Watches

COLLECTION SERVICE Yes

■ Age Concern (Carlisle & District)

ADDRESS 20 Spencer Street, Carlisle, Cumbria CA1 1BG

TELEPHONE 01228 36673

FAX 01228 597039

CATEGORY Arts & crafts equipment • Baby equipment • Bed linen and mattresses *no mattresses* • Books hardback • Books paperback • Bric-a-brac • Clocks • Clothing adults' • Clothing children's • Fabric remnants • Furniture • Gardening equipment • Household items *ironing boards etc* • Jewellery *no earrings for pierced ears* • Knitting, crochet and sewing equipment • Knitting wool • Magazines & comics • Musical instruments • Non perishable foods • Photographic equipment • Records & tapes • Spectacles • Sports equipment • Toiletries • Toys & games • Watches

COLLECTION SERVICE Yes

■ Age Concern (Cheshire)

ADDRESS 67b Chester Road, Northwich, Cheshire CW8 1HG

TELEPHONE 01606 781406

FAX 01606 783778

CATEGORY Antique post cards • Arts & crafts equipment • Books hardback • Books paperback • Bric-a-brac • Clocks • Clothing adults' • Clothing children's • Diy equipment • Fabric remnants • Gardening equipment • Household items *ironing boards etc* • Jewellery • Knitting, crochet and sewing equipment • Knitting wool • Magazines & comics • Musical instruments • Pets equipment • Photographic equipment • Records & tapes • Sports equipment • Toiletries • Toys & games • Video/computer games • Watches

COLLECTION SERVICE Yes

■ Age Concern (Clevedon)

ADDRESS 4 The Triangle Centre, Clevedon, Somerset BS21 6NG

TELEPHONE 01275 342247

CATEGORY Antique post cards • Arts & crafts equipment • Bed linen and mattresses *no mattresses* • Books hardback • Books paperback • Bric-a-brac • Clocks • Clothing adults' • Clothing children's • Coins foreign • Coins old • Fabric remnants • Household items *ironing boards etc* • Jewellery • Knitting, crochet and sewing equipment • Knitting wool • Medals • Musical instruments • Records & tapes • Sports equipment • Stamps British • Stamps foreign • Toiletries • Toys & games • Video/computer games • Wedding clothes for hire

COLLECTION SERVICE Yes

■ Age Concern (Clifton)

ADDRESS 60 Whiteladies Road, Clifton, Bristol, Avon BS8 2LY

TELEPHONE 01179 737869

CATEGORY Antique post cards • Arts & crafts equipment • Bed linen and mattresses *no mattresses* • Books hardback • Books paperback • Bric-a-brac • Clocks • Clothing adults' • Clothing children's • Coins foreign • Coins old • Fabric remnants • Household items *ironing boards etc* • Jewellery • Knitting, crochet and sewing equipment • Knitting wool • Medals • Musical instruments • Records & tapes • Sports equipment • Stamps British • Stamps foreign • Toiletries • Toys & games • Video/computer games • Wedding clothes for hire

COLLECTION SERVICE Yes

■ Age Concern (Coleraine)

ADDRESS 1 Waterside, Coleraine, Londonderry BT51 3DP

TELEPHONE 01265 57966

CATEGORY Antique post cards • Arts & crafts equipment • Bed linen and mattresses *not*

mattresses ● Books hardback ● Books paperback ● Bric-a-brac ● Clocks ● Clothing adults' ● Clothing children's ● Coins foreign ● Coins old ● Fabric remnants ● Fur coats ● Household items *ironing boards etc* ● Jewellery ● Knitting, crochet and sewing equipment ● Knitting wool ● Magazines & comics ● Medals ● Musical instruments ● Photographic equipment ● Records & tapes ● Sports equipment ● Stamps British ● Stamps foreign ● Toiletries ● Toys & games

COLLECTION SERVICE No

■ Age Concern (Derbyshire)

ADDRESS Shops Division, Unit 6, Leacroft Court, Leacroft Road, Derby, Derbys DE23 8HU

TELEPHONE 01332 296197

FAX 01332 296197

CATEGORY Baby equipment ● Books hardback ● Books paperback ● Bric-a-brac ● Clocks ● Clothing adults' ● Clothing children's ● Fabric remnants ● Household items *ironing boards etc* ● Jewellery ● Knitting, crochet and sewing equipment ● Knitting wool ● Records & tapes ● Sports equipment ● Toiletries ● Toys & games ● Watches

COLLECTION SERVICE No

■ Age Concern (Ealing Borough)

ADDRESS 135 Uxbridge Road, London W13 9AU

TELEPHONE 0181-567 8017

FAX 0181-566 5696

CATEGORY Books hardback *in Ealing only* ● Books paperback *in Ealing only* ● Clothing adults' *Ealing Borough only* ● Clothing children's *Ealing Borough only* ● Fur coats *Ealing Borough only* ● Furniture *small items only, Ealing Borough only* ● Jewellery *Ealing Borough only* ● Records & tapes *Ealing Borough only* ● Watches *Ealing Borough only*

COLLECTION SERVICE No

■ Age Concern (East Riding of Yorkshire)

ADDRESS Morley's Cottage, Morley's Yard, Walkergate, Beverley, E Yorks HU17 9BY

TELEPHONE 01482 869181/867383

FAX 01482 861065

CATEGORY Antique post cards ● Arts & crafts equipment ● Baby equipment ● Bed linen and mattresses ● Books hardback ● Books paperback ● Bric-a-brac ● Clocks *not free standing ones* ● Clothing adults' ● Clothing children's ● Diy equipment ● Fabric remnants ● Gardening equipment ● Household items *ironing boards etc* ● Jewellery ● Knitting, crochet and sewing equipment ● Knitting wool ● Magazines & comics ● Musical instruments ● Photographic equipment ● Records & tapes ● Sports equipment ● Toiletries ● Toys & games ● Video/computer games ● Watches

COLLECTION SERVICE No

■ Age Concern (East Sussex)

ADDRESS 54 Cliffe High Street, Lewes, E Sussex BN7 2AN

TELEPHONE 01273 476704

CATEGORY Christmas cards *any other greetings cards, not Christmas* ● Coins foreign ● Clothing adults' *good quality only* ● Clothing children's *good quality only* ● Jewellery ● Watches *working*

COLLECTION SERVICE No

■ Age Concern England

ADDRESS Astral House, 1268 London Road, Norbury, London SW16 4ER

TELEPHONE 0181-679 8000

FAX 0181-679 6069

CATEGORY Antique post cards ● Arts & crafts equipment ● Baby equipment *if BS kitemarked* ● Bed linen and mattresses ● Bicycles ● Books hardback ● Books paperback ● Bric-a-brac ● Clocks ● Clothing adults' ● Clothing children's ● Coins foreign ● Coins old ● Computer hardware and software ● Diy equipment ● Furniture *generally small items only* ● Gardening equipment ● Household items *ironing boards etc* ● Jewellery ● Knitting, crochet and sewing equipment ● Knitting wool ● Magazines & comics ● Medals ● Musical instruments ● Pets equipment ● Photographic equipment ● Rags ● Records & tapes ● Sports equipment ● Stamps British ● Stamps foreign ● Toys & games ● Video/computer games ● Watches

COLLECTION SERVICE No

■ Age Concern (Essex)

ADDRESS 112 Springfield Road, Chelmsford, Essex CM2 6LF

TELEPHONE 01245 264499

FAX 01245 346107

E-MAIL bg@acsx.demon.co.uk

CATEGORY Antique post cards ● Bric-a-brac ● Clothing adults' ● Clothing children's ● Coins foreign ● Coins old ● Jewellery ● Medals ● Records & tapes ● Stamps British ● Stamps foreign ● Toys & games

COLLECTION SERVICE No

■ Age Concern (Exeter)

ADDRESS 23 Paris Street, Exeter, Devon EX1 2JB

TELEPHONE 01392 218500

CATEGORY Antique post cards ● Arts & crafts equipment ● Bed linen and mattresses *no mattresses* ● Books hardback ● Books paperback ● Bric-a-brac ● Clocks ● Clothing adults' ● Clothing children's ● Coins foreign ● Coins old ● Fabric remnants ● Household items *ironing boards etc* ● Jewellery ● Knitting, crochet and sewing equipment ● Knitting wool ● Medals ● Musical instruments ● Records & tapes ● Sports equipment ● Stamps British ● Stamps foreign ●

Toiletries • Toys & games • Video/computer games • Wedding clothes for hire

COLLECTION SERVICE Yes

■ Age Concern (Exeter)

ADDRESS 138 Cowick Street, Exeter, Devon EX4 1HS

TELEPHONE 01392 218300

FAX 01392 490796

CATEGORY Bric-a-brac • Clothing adults' *good quality only* • Clothing children's *good quality only* • Jewellery • Knitting wool • Musical instruments

COLLECTION SERVICE Yes

■ Age Concern (Feltham, Hanworth & Bedfont)

ADDRESS Feltham Lodge, Harlington Road, Feltham, Middx TW14 0JJ

TELEPHONE 0181-751 5829

CATEGORY Arts & crafts equipment • Bed linen and mattresses *clean condition* • Books hardback • Books paperback • Bric-a-brac • Clocks *working* • Clothing adults' *good resaleable condition* • Clothing children's *good resaleable condition* • Fabric remnants • Gardening equipment • Jewellery • Knitting, crochet and sewing equipment • Non perishable foods • Office equipment and stationery • Toiletries *unused* • Toys & games • Watches *saleable condition*

COLLECTION SERVICE Yes

■ Age Concern (Gillingham)

ADDRESS The Mackenney Centre, Woodlands Road, Gillingham, Kent ME7 2BX

TELEPHONE 01634 572616

CATEGORY Antique post cards • Arts & crafts equipment • Baby equipment • Bed linen and mattresses • Books paperback • Bric-a-brac • Clocks • Clothing adults' • Clothing children's • Coins old • Diy equipment • Fabric remnants • Fur coats • Gardening equipment • Hearing aids • Household items *ironing boards etc* • Jewellery • Knitting, crochet and sewing equipment • Knitting wool • Medals • Office equipment and stationery • Pets equipment • Records & tapes • Toiletries • Toys & games • Video/computer games • Waste paper • Watches

COLLECTION SERVICE Yes

■ Age Concern (Gwynedd a Món)

ADDRESS Ffordd Santes Helen, Caernarfon, Gwynedd LL55 2YD

TELEPHONE 01286 677711

FAX 01286 674389

CATEGORY Antique post cards • Books hardback • Books paperback • Bric-a-brac • Clocks • Clothing adults' • Clothing children's • Coins foreign • Coins old • Diy equipment • Furniture • Gardening equipment • Household items

ironing boards etc • Jewellery • Magazines & comics • Medals • Musical instruments *small instruments only – no pianos, etc* • Office equipment and stationery • Records & tapes • Toys & games • Watches

COLLECTION SERVICE No

■ Age Concern (Hammersmith & Fulham)

ADDRESS 105 Greyhound Road, London W6 8NJ

TELEPHONE 0171-386 9085

FAX 0171-386 5740

CATEGORY Aluminium • Antique post cards • Arts & crafts equipment • Baby equipment • Bicycles • Books hardback • Books paperback • Bric-a-brac • Childrens play/craft scrap • Christmas cards *unused only* • Clocks • Clothing adults' • Clothing children's • Coins foreign • Coins old • Computer hardware and software • Diy equipment • Fabric remnants • Gardening equipment *domestic only* • Jewellery • Knitting, crochet and sewing equipment • Knitting wool • Magazines & comics • Medals • Musical instruments • Office equipment and stationery • Petrol vouchers • Photographic equipment • Records & tapes • Silver paper & aluminium foil • Sports equipment • Stamps British • Stamps foreign • Toiletries • Video/computer games • Watches

COLLECTION SERVICE No

■ Age Concern (Huddersfield & District)

ADDRESS 24 Cross Church Street, Huddersfield, W Yorks HD1 2PT

TELEPHONE 01484 535994

CATEGORY Bed linen and mattresses *only bed linen* • Books hardback • Books paperback • Bric-a-brac • Clocks • Clothing adults' • Clothing children's • Fabric remnants • Jewellery • Knitting, crochet and sewing equipment • Knitting wool • Magazines & comics • Musical instruments • Non perishable foods • Photographic equipment • Records & tapes • Sports equipment • Toiletries • Toys & games • Video/computer games • Watches

COLLECTION SERVICE No

■ Age Concern (Hull)

ADDRESS 44 Portland Street, Hull, Humberside HU2 8JX

TELEPHONE 01482 324644

FAX 01482 226176

CATEGORY Air miles • Aluminium • Antique post cards • Arts & crafts equipment • Baby equipment • Bed linen and mattresses • Bicycles • Books hardback • Books paperback • Bric-a-brac • Clocks • Clothing adults' • Clothing children's • Coins foreign • Coins old • Computer hardware and software • Diy equipment • Fabric remnants • Furniture • Gardening equipment • Glass *green, brown, clear* • Household items *ironing boards etc* • Jewellery • Knitting, crochet and sewing equipment • Knitting wool • Medals • Money-off coupons • Musical instruments •

Non perishable foods • Office equipment and stationery • Petrol vouchers • Plastics • Rags • Records & tapes • Sports equipment • Stamps British • Stamps foreign • Toiletries • Toys & games • Trading stamps • Video/computer games • Waste paper • Watches • Wedding clothes for hire

COLLECTION SERVICE Yes

■ Age Concern (Knowle)

ADDRESS 4 Broad Walk, Knowle, Bristol, Avon BS4 2QU

TELEPHONE 01179 770205

CATEGORY Antique post cards • Arts & crafts equipment • Bed linen and mattresses *no mattresses* • Books hardback • Books paperback • Bric-a-brac • Clocks • Clothing adults' • Clothing children's • Coins foreign • Coins old • Fabric remnants • Household items *ironing boards etc* • Jewellery • Knitting, crochet and sewing equipment • Knitting wool • Medals • Musical instruments • Records & tapes • Sports equipment • Stamps British • Stamps foreign • Toiletries • Toys & games • Video/computer games • Wedding clothes for hire

COLLECTION SERVICE Yes

■ Age Concern (Leicester)

ADDRESS Clarence House, 46 Humberstone Gate, Leicester, Leics LE1 3PJ

TELEPHONE 0116-262 4104

FAX 0116-251 4601

CATEGORY Books hardback • Books paperback • Bric-a-brac • Clothing adults' • Clothing children's • Jewellery • Knitting wool • Magazines & comics • Toiletries • Toys & games • Watches

COLLECTION SERVICE No

■ Age Concern (Lytham St Anne's)

ADDRESS 7 St George's Road, Lytham St Anne's, Lancs FY8 2AE

TELEPHONE 01253 725563

FAX 01253 781193

CATEGORY Antique post cards • Arts & crafts equipment • Baby equipment • Bed linen and mattresses • Bicycles • Books hardback • Books paperback • Bric-a-brac • Clocks • Clothing adults' • Clothing children's • Coins foreign • Coins old • Computer hardware and software • Diy equipment • Fabric remnants • Furniture • Gardening equipment • Household items *ironing boards etc* • Jewellery • Knitting, crochet and sewing equipment • Knitting wool • Magazines & comics • Medals • Musical instruments • Non perishable foods • Office equipment and stationery • Photographic equipment • Rags • Records & tapes • Spectacles • Sports equipment • Stamps British • Stamps foreign • Toiletries • Toys & games • Video/computer games • Watches • Wedding clothes for hire

COLLECTION SERVICE Yes

■ Age Concern (Manchester)

ADDRESS Corpus Christi Centre, Varley Street, Manchester M40 8EE

TELEPHONE 0161-205 9770

FAX 0161-205 7504

CATEGORY Air miles • Antique post cards • Arts & crafts equipment • Baby equipment • Bed linen and mattresses • Bicycles • Books hardback • Bric-a-brac • Clocks • Clothing adults' • Clothing children's • Coins foreign • Coins old • Computer hardware and software • Diy equipment • Fabric remnants • Furniture • Gardening equipment • Household items *ironing boards etc* • Jewellery • Knitting, crochet and sewing equipment • Magazines & comics • Medals • Money-off coupons • Musical instruments • Office equipment and stationery • Petrol vouchers • Pets equipment • Photographic equipment • Postcards used • Records & tapes • Sports equipment • Stamps foreign • Telephone cards • Toiletries • Toys & games • Trading stamps • Used toner cartridges *in original packaging* • Video/computer games • Watches

COLLECTION SERVICE Yes

■ Age Concern (Metro Bury)

ADDRESS 132 The Rock, Bury, Gtr Manchester BL9 0PP

TELEPHONE 0161-761 5895

FAX 0161-761 2715

CATEGORY Arts & crafts equipment • Baby equipment • Bed linen and mattresses • Bicycles • Books hardback • Books paperback • Bric-a-brac • Clocks • Clothing adults' • Clothing children's • Diy equipment • Furniture • Gardening equipment • Household items *ironing boards etc* • Jewellery • Knitting, crochet and sewing equipment • Musical instruments • Photographic equipment • Records & tapes • Sports equipment • Toys & games • Video/computer games • Watches

COLLECTION SERVICE Yes

■ Age Concern (Metropolitan Rochdale)

ADDRESS 12 South Parade, Rochdale, Gtr Manchester OL16 1LR

TELEPHONE 01706 712515

CATEGORY Books hardback • Books paperback • Clothing adults' *clean* • Clothing children's *clean* • Fur coats *clean* • Knitting wool

COLLECTION SERVICE No

■ Age Concern (Milton Keynes)

ADDRESS 6 Burners Lane, Kiln Farm, Milton Keynes, Bucks MK11 3HB

TELEPHONE 01908 261268

FAX 01908 260255

CATEGORY Baby equipment • Bed linen and mattresses *in good condition* • Bicycles • Books hardback • **Books** paperback • Bric-a-brac • Clocks • Clothing adults' • Clothing children's • Diy equipment • Furniture *foam must meet safety standards* • Gardening equipment • Household items *ironing boards etc* • Jewellery • Knitting, crochet and sewing equipment • Knitting wool • Musical instruments • Photographic equipment • Records & tapes • Sports equipment • Toys & games *must meet safety standards* • Video/computer games

COLLECTION SERVICE Yes

■ Age Concern (North Kirklees)

ADDRESS 3–5 Bradford Road, Cleckheaton, W Yorks BD19 5AG

TELEPHONE 01274 871328

FAX 01274 852130

CATEGORY Bed linen and mattresses *bed linen only* • Books hardback • Books paperback • Bric-a-brac • Clothing adults' • Clothing children's • Jewellery • Knitting wool • Records & tapes • Toiletries • Toys & games

COLLECTION SERVICE No

■ Age Concern (North West Yorkshire)

ADDRESS 5 Station Bridge, Harrogate, N Yorks HG1 1SS

TELEPHONE 01423 507903

CATEGORY Antique post cards • Arts & crafts equipment • Bed linen and mattresses • Books hardback • Books paperback • Bric-a-brac • Clocks • Clothing adults' • Clothing children's • Hearing aids • Household items *ironing boards etc* • Jewellery • Musical instruments • Photographic equipment • Records & tapes • Sports equipment • Toys & games • Video/computer games • Watches

COLLECTION SERVICE No

■ Age Concern (North West Yorkshire)

ADDRESS 128 High Street, Northallerton, N Yorks DL7 8PQ

TELEPHONE 01609 771624

CATEGORY Antique post cards • Arts & crafts equipment • Bed linen and mattresses • Books hardback • Books paperback • Bric-a-brac • Clocks • Clothing adults' • Clothing children's • Hearing aids • Household items *ironing boards etc* • Jewellery • Musical instruments • Photographic equipment • Records & tapes • Sports equipment • Toys & games • Video/computer games • Watches

COLLECTION SERVICE No

■ Age Concern (Northwest Cumbria)

ADDRESS The Old Customs House, West Strand, Whitehaven, Cumbria CA28 7LR

TELEPHONE 01946 66669

FAX 01946 591182

CATEGORY Aluminium • Antique post cards • Arts & crafts equipment • Baby equipment • Bed linen and mattresses *must comply with fire regulations* • Bicycles • Books hardback • Books paperback • Bric-a-brac • Clocks • Clothing adults' • Clothing children's • Coins foreign • Coins old • Computer hardware and software • Diy equipment • Fabric remnants • Furniture • Gardening equipment • Household items *ironing boards etc* • Jewellery • Knitting, crochet and sewing equipment • Knitting wool • Magazines & comics • Medals • Musical instruments • Non perishable foods • Office equipment and stationery • Photographic equipment • Rags • Records & tapes • Spectacles • Sports equipment • Stamps British • Stamps foreign • Telephone cards • Toiletries • Toys & games • Video/computer games • Watches

COLLECTION SERVICE Yes

■ Age Concern (Nottinghamshire)

ADDRESS Woodland Chambers, 52a Long Row, Notts NG1 6JB

TELEPHONE 01159 475892

FAX 01159 502418

CATEGORY Air miles • Antique post cards • Arts & crafts equipment • Baby equipment • Bed linen and mattresses • Bicycles • Books hardback • Bric-a-brac • Clocks • Clothing adults' • Clothing children's • Coins foreign • Coins old • Diy equipment *non-electrical* • Fabric remnants • Furniture *small* • Gardening equipment • Household items *ironing boards etc* • Jewellery • Knitting, crochet and sewing equipment • Knitting wool • Magazines & comics • Medals • Money-off coupons • Musical instruments • Office equipment and stationery • Petrol vouchers • Photographic equipment • Rags • Records & tapes • Sports equipment • Stamps British • Stamps foreign • Toiletries • Toys & games • Trading stamps • Used toner cartridges • Watches • Wedding clothes for hire

COLLECTION SERVICE Yes

■ Age Concern (Orkney)

ADDRESS Anchor Buildings, 6 Bridge Street, Kirkwall, Orkney KW15 1TN

TELEPHONE 01856 872438

FAX 01856 873167

CATEGORY Aluminium • Bric-a-brac • Clothing adults' • Clothing children's • Diy equipment • Fabric remnants • Furniture • Gardening equipment • Glass • Household items *ironing boards etc* • Jewellery • Rags

COLLECTION SERVICE No

■ Age Concern (Oxford)

ADDRESS 45 Upper Barr, Templers Square, Cowley, Oxon OX4 3UX

TELEPHONE 01865 771517

CATEGORY Air miles ● Antique post cards ● Arts & crafts equipment ● Baby equipment ● Bed linen and mattresses ● Bicycles ● Books hardback ● Books paperback ● Bric-a-brac ● Clocks ● Coins foreign ● Coins old ● Computer hardware and software ● Diy equipment ● Furniture ● Gardening equipment ● Hearing aids ● Household items *ironing boards etc* ● Jewellery ● Knitting, crochet and sewing equipment ● Knitting wool ● Magazines & comics ● Medals ● Musical instruments ● Office equipment and stationery ● Photographic equipment ● Records & tapes ● Spectacles ● Sports equipment ● Stamps British ● Stamps foreign ● Toiletries ● Toys & games ● Used toner cartridges ● Video/computer games ● Watches ● Wedding clothes for hire

COLLECTION SERVICE No

■ Age Concern (Oxfordshire)

ADDRESS Age Concern Shop, 21–22 St Clements, Oxford, Oxon OX4 1AB

TELEPHONE 01865 722898

CATEGORY Antique post cards ● Arts & crafts equipment ● Books hardback ● Books paperback ● Bric-a-brac ● Clocks ● Clothing adults' ● Clothing children's ● Coins foreign ● Coins old ● Household items *ironing boards etc not electrical* ● Jewellery ● Knitting, crochet and sewing equipment ● Medals ● Musical instruments ● Photographic equipment ● Records & tapes ● Toiletries ● Toys & games ● Video/computer games ● Watches

COLLECTION SERVICE Yes

■ Age Concern (Paignton)

ADDRESS 34 Hyde Road, Paignton, Devon PQ4 7DB

TELEPHONE 01803 521269

CATEGORY Antique post cards ● Arts & crafts equipment ● Bed linen and mattresses *no mattresses* ● Books hardback ● Books paperback ● Bric-a-brac ● Clocks ● Clothing adults' ● Clothing children's ● Coins foreign ● Coins old ● Fabric remnants ● Household items *ironing boards etc* ● Jewellery ● Knitting, crochet and sewing equipment ● Knitting wool ● Medals ● Musical instruments ● Records & tapes ● Sports equipment ● Stamps British ● Stamps foreign ● Toiletries ● Toys & games ● Video/computer games ● Wedding clothes for hire

COLLECTION SERVICE Yes

■ Age Concern (Plymouth)

ADDRESS Elspeth Sitters House, Hoegate Street, Plymouth, Devon PL1 2JB

TELEPHONE 01752 665424

FAX 01752 251618

CATEGORY Arts & crafts equipment ● Bed linen and mattresses *no mattresses* ● Books hardback ● Books paperback ● Bric-a-brac ● Clocks ● Clothing adults' ● Clothing children's ● Fabric remnants ● Furniture *non-upholstered* ● Jewellery ● Knitting, crochet and sewing equipment ● Knitting wool ● Rags ● Records & tapes ● Toys & games

COLLECTION SERVICE No

■ Age Concern (Poole)

ADDRESS 83 High Street, Poole, Dorset BH15 1AH

TELEPHONE 01202 660590

CATEGORY Antique post cards ● Arts & crafts equipment ● Bed linen and mattresses *no mattresses* ● Books hardback ● Books paperback ● Bric-a-brac ● Clocks ● Clothing adults' ● Clothing children's ● Coins foreign ● Coins old ● Fabric remnants ● Household items *ironing boards etc* ● Jewellery ● Knitting, crochet and sewing equipment ● Knitting wool ● Medals ● Musical instruments ● Records & tapes ● Sports equipment ● Stamps British ● Stamps foreign ● Toiletries ● Toys & games ● Video/computer games ● Wedding clothes for hire

COLLECTION SERVICE Yes

■ Age Concern (Preston & South Ribble)

ADDRESS Arkwright House, Stoneygate, Preston, Lancs PR1 3XT

TELEPHONE 01772 253079

FAX 01772 561705

CATEGORY Antique post cards ● Books hardback ● Books paperback ● Bric-a-brac ● Clocks ● Clothing adults' ● Clothing children's ● Coins old ● Computer hardware and software ● Diy equipment ● Fabric remnants ● Furniture ● Gardening equipment ● Household items *ironing boards etc* ● Jewellery ● Knitting, crochet and sewing equipment ● Knitting wool ● Medals ● Musical instruments ● Office equipment and stationery ● Photographic equipment ● Postcards used ● Records & tapes ● Sports equipment ● Stamps British ● Stamps foreign ● Toiletries ● Toys & games ● Video/computer games

COLLECTION SERVICE Yes

■ Age Concern (Reading)

ADDRESS 302 Oxford Road, Reading, Berks RG30 1AD

TELEPHONE 01734 508866

CATEGORY Air miles ● Antique post cards ● Arts & crafts equipment ● Baby equipment ● Bed linen and mattresses *not mattresses* ● Books hardback ● Books paperback ● Bric-a-brac ● Clocks ●

Clothing adults' • Clothing children's • Coins foreign • Coins old • Diy equipment • Fabric remnants • Furniture *small pieces only* • Gardening equipment • Household items *ironing boards etc* • Jewellery • Knitting, crochet and sewing equipment • Knitting wool • Magazines & comics • Medals • Money-off coupons • Musical instruments • Non perishable foods *not out of date* • Office equipment and stationery • Petrol vouchers • Pets equipment • Photographic equipment • Postcards used • Records & tapes • Sports equipment • Stamps British • Stamps foreign • Telephone cards • Toiletries • Toys & games • Trading stamps • Video/computer games • Watches

COLLECTION SERVICE Yes

■ Age Concern (Rotherham)

ADDRESS 49–53 St Ann's Road, Rotherham, S Yorks S66 1PF

TELEPHONE 01709 829621

FAX 01709 835195

CATEGORY Antique post cards • Arts & crafts equipment • Baby equipment *no baby cot mattresses* • Bed linen and mattresses *no mattresses* • Books hardback • Books paperback • Bric-a-brac • Clocks • Clothing adults' • Clothing children's • Furniture *will not collect furniture which is not fire resistant* • Household items *ironing boards etc* • Jewellery • Knitting wool • Non perishable foods • Office equipment and stationery • Rags • Records & tapes • Toys & games *particularly jigsaws for our lending library* • Watches

COLLECTION SERVICE Yes

■ Age Concern Scotland

ADDRESS 113 Rose Street, Edinburgh, Lothian EH2 3DT

TELEPHONE 0131-220 3345

FAX 0131-220 2779

CATEGORY Bicycles *children's only* • Books hardback • Books paperback • Bric-a-brac • Clocks • Clothing adults' • Clothing children's • Fur coats • Jewellery • Records & tapes • Spectacles • Toys & games • Watches

COLLECTION SERVICE No

■ Age Concern (Solihull)

ADDRESS Alice House, 10 Homer Road, Solihull, W Midlands B91 3QQ

TELEPHONE 0121-705 9128

CATEGORY Antique post cards • Arts & crafts equipment • Baby equipment • Bed linen and mattresses *bed linen only* • Bicycles • Books hardback • Books paperback • Bric-a-brac • Clocks • Clothing adults' • Clothing children's • Coins foreign • Coins old • Diy equipment • Jewellery • Knitting, crochet and sewing equipment • Knitting wool • Magazines & comics • Medals • Musical instruments • Pets equipment • Photographic equipment • Records & tapes • Sports equipment • Stamps British • Stamps

foreign • Toiletries • Toys & games • Video/ computer games • Watches • Wedding clothes for hire

COLLECTION SERVICE No

■ Age Concern (Somerset)

ADDRESS The Market House, Fore Street, Taunton, Somerset TA1 1JD

TELEPHONE 01823 322113

FAX 01823 324128

CATEGORY Antique post cards • Bed linen and mattresses *no mattresses* • Books hardback • Books paperback • Bric-a-brac • Clocks • Clothing adults' • Clothing children's • Coins foreign • Coins old • Fabric remnants • Jewellery • Knitting, crochet and sewing equipment • Knitting wool • Medals • Stamps British • Stamps foreign • Toys & games • Watches

COLLECTION SERVICE Yes

■ Age Concern (South Glamorgan)

ADDRESS 91/93 Caerphilly Road, Birchgrove, Cardiff, S Glamorgan CF4 4AE

TELEPHONE 01222 521052

FAX 01222 520357

CATEGORY Air miles • Antique post cards • Arts & crafts equipment • Baby equipment • Bed linen and mattresses *not mattresses* • Bicycles • Books hardback • Books paperback • Bric-a-brac • Clocks • Clothing adults' *no fur coats* • Clothing children's • Coins foreign • Coins old • Gardening equipment *not lawnmowers* • Household items *ironing boards etc* • Jewellery • Knitting, crochet and sewing equipment *not knitting machines* • Knitting wool • Magazines & comics • Medals • Musical instruments • Photographic equipment • Records & tapes • Sports equipment *not large items* • Telephone cards • Toiletries *only if unopened* • Toys & games • Video/computer games • Watches

COLLECTION SERVICE Yes

■ Age Concern (South Lakeland)

ADDRESS Furniture Saleroom, Entry Lane, Kendal, Cumbria LA9 4NQ

TELEPHONE 01539 740657

CATEGORY Antique post cards • Arts & crafts equipment • Baby equipment • Bed linen and mattresses • Bicycles • Books hardback • Books paperback • Bric-a-brac • Clocks • Clothing adults' *only collected in large quantity* • Clothing children's *only collected in large quantity* • Coins foreign • Coins old • Diy equipment • Fabric remnants • Furniture • Gardening equipment • Household items *ironing boards etc* • Jewellery • Knitting, crochet and sewing equipment • Knitting wool • Magazines & comics • Medals • Musical instruments *including pianos* • Office equipment and stationery • Petrol vouchers • Photographic equipment • Records & tapes • Sports equipment • Stamps British • Stamps foreign • Toiletries • Toys & games • Trading stamps • Video/computer games • Watches

COLLECTION SERVICE Yes

■ Age Concern (South Tyneside)

ADDRESS 23–25 New Green Street, South Shields, Tyne & Wear NE33 5DL

TELEPHONE 0191-456 6903

CATEGORY Baby equipment • Bed linen and mattresses *mattresses must bear fire safety label* • Bicycles • Books hardback • Books paperback • Bric-a-brac • Clocks • Clothing adults' • Clothing children's • Fur coats • Furniture • Household items *ironing boards etc* • Jewellery • Knitting wool • Records & tapes • Sports equipment • Toys & games • Watches

COLLECTION SERVICE Yes

■ Age Concern (Suffolk)

ADDRESS Station Square, Lowestoft, Suffolk NR32 1SU

TELEPHONE 01502 538315

CATEGORY Air miles • Antique post cards • Arts & crafts equipment • Bed linen and mattresses *not mattresses* • Books hardback • Books paperback • Bric-a-brac • Clocks *not electrical* • Clothing adults' *in clean condition only* • Clothing children's *in clean condition only* • Coins foreign • Coins old • Fabric remnants • Jewellery *all jewellery welcomed* • Knitting, crochet and sewing equipment • Knitting wool • Magazines & comics • Medals • Money-off coupons • Musical instruments • Petrol vouchers • Photographic equipment • Records & tapes • Sports equipment • Stamps British • Stamps foreign • Toiletries • Toys & games • Trading stamps • Video/ computer games • Watches • Wedding clothes for hire

COLLECTION SERVICE No

■ Age Concern (Suffolk)

ADDRESS 19 The Precinct, Mildenhall, Suffolk IP28 7EF

TELEPHONE 01638 711632

CATEGORY Air miles • Antique post cards • Arts & crafts equipment • Bed linen and mattresses *not mattresses* • Books hardback • Books paperback • Bric-a-brac • Clocks *not electrical* • Clothing adults' *in clean condition only* • Clothing children's *in clean condition only* • Coins foreign • Coins old • Fabric remnants • Jewellery *all jewellery welcomed* • Knitting, crochet and sewing equipment • Knitting wool • Magazines & comics • Medals • Money-off coupons • Musical instruments • Petrol vouchers • Photographic equipment • Records & tapes • Sports equipment • Stamps British • Stamps foreign • Toiletries • Toys & games • Trading stamps • Video/ computer games • Watches • Wedding clothes for hire

COLLECTION SERVICE No

■ Age Concern (Suffolk)

ADDRESS 17 Gaol Lane, Sudbury, Suffolk CO10 6JL

TELEPHONE 01787 378663

CATEGORY Air miles • Antique post cards • Arts & crafts equipment • Bed linen and mattresses *not mattresses* • Books hardback • Books paperback • Bric-a-brac • Clocks *not electrical* • Clothing adults' *in clean condition only* • Clothing children's *in clean condition only* • Coins foreign • Coins old • Fabric remnants • Jewellery *all jewellery welcomed* • Knitting, crochet and sewing equipment • Knitting wool • Magazines & comics • Medals • Money-off coupons • Musical instruments • Petrol vouchers • Photographic equipment • Records & tapes • Sports equipment • Stamps British • Stamps foreign • Toiletries • Toys & games • Trading stamps • Video/ computer games • Watches • Wedding clothes for hire

COLLECTION SERVICE No

■ Age Concern (Suffolk)

ADDRESS 8 Northgate Street, Ipswich, Suffolk IP1 3BZ

TELEPHONE 01473 257039

CATEGORY Air miles • Antique post cards • Arts & crafts equipment • Bed linen and mattresses *not mattresses* • Books hardback • Books paperback • Bric-a-brac • Clocks *not electrical* • Clothing adults' *in clean condition only* • Clothing children's • Coins foreign • Coins old • Fabric remnants • Jewellery *all jewellery welcomed* • Knitting, crochet and sewing equipment • Knitting wool • Magazines & comics • Medals • Money-off coupons • Musical instruments • Petrol vouchers • Photographic equipment • Records & tapes • Sports equipment • Stamps British • Stamps foreign • Toiletries • Toys & games • Trading stamps • Video/computer games • Watches • Wedding clothes for hire

COLLECTION SERVICE No

■ Age Concern (Sutton Borough (Shop))

ADDRESS 281 High Street, Sutton, Surrey SM1 1LD

TELEPHONE 0181-770 0206

FAX 0181-770 4093 (office)

CATEGORY Antique post cards • Arts & crafts equipment • Baby equipment *small saleable items* • Bed linen and mattresses *not mattresses* • Books hardback • Books paperback • Bric-a-brac • Clocks • Clothing adults' *must be clean and saleable* • Clothing children's *must be clean and saleable* • Coins foreign • Coins old • Diy equipment *small items/hand tools/no electrical items* • Fabric remnants • Furniture *small items only* • Gardening equipment *hand tools, small items only* • Household items *ironing boards etc small saleable items, no electrical items* • Jewellery *not pierced earrings* • Knitting, crochet and sewing equipment • Knitting wool • Medals • Musical instruments • Photographic equipment • Records & tapes • Sports equipment

- Stamps British • Toiletries *new and unopened only* • Toys & games *ec approved* • Watches

COLLECTION SERVICE Yes

■ Age Concern (Thamesdown)

ADDRESS 14 Milton Road, Swindon, Wilts SN1 5JE

TELEPHONE 01793 692166

CATEGORY Antique post cards • Bric-a-brac • Clothing adults' • Clothing children's • Coins foreign • Coins old • Jewellery • Knitting wool • Medals • Photographic equipment • Records & tapes • Stamps British • Stamps foreign • Toys & games • Watches

COLLECTION SERVICE Yes

■ Age Concern (Torquay)

ADDRESS 12 Union Square, Torquay, Devon TQ1 3UT

TELEPHONE 01803 213212

CATEGORY Antique post cards • Arts & crafts equipment • Bed linen and mattresses *no mattresses* • Books hardback • Books paperback • Bric-a-brac • Clocks • Clothing adults' • Clothing children's • Coins foreign • Coins old • Fabric remnants • Household items *ironing boards etc* • Jewellery • Knitting, crochet and sewing equipment • Knitting wool • Medals • Musical instruments • Records & tapes • Sports equipment • Stamps British • Stamps foreign • Toiletries • Toys & games • Video/computer games • Wedding clothes for hire

COLLECTION SERVICE Yes

■ Age Concern (Ulverston & District)

ADDRESS 4 Theatre Street, Ulverston, Cumbria LA12 7AQ

TELEPHONE 01229 586351

CATEGORY Baby equipment • Books hardback • Books paperback • Bric-a-brac • Clocks • Clothing adults' • Clothing children's • Furniture • Gardening equipment • Household items *ironing boards etc* • Jewellery • Knitting wool • Magazines & comics • Spectacles • Toiletries • Toys & games • Watches

COLLECTION SERVICE Yes

■ Age Concern (Wakefield District)

ADDRESS 29 Cornmarket, Pontefract, W Yorks WF8 1BJ

TELEPHONE 01977 706751

FAX 01977 600541

CATEGORY Air miles • Antique post cards • Arts & crafts equipment • Baby equipment • Bed linen and mattresses *bed linen only* • Books hardback • Books paperback • Bric-a-brac • Clocks • Clothing adults' • Clothing children's • Coins old • Fabric remnants • Household items *ironing boards etc* • Jewellery • Knitting, crochet and sewing equipment • Knitting wool • Magazines & comics • Medals • Money-off coupons • Musical instruments • Petrol vouchers •

Photographic equipment • Records & tapes • Sports equipment • Stamps British • Stamps foreign • Toys & games • Trading stamps • Video/computer games

COLLECTION SERVICE No

■ Age Concern (Wandsworth)

ADDRESS 1c Yukon Road, Balham, London SW12 9PZ

TELEPHONE 0181-675 7000

FAX 0181-675 2872

CATEGORY Books hardback • Books paperback • Bric-a-brac • Clocks • Coins foreign • Coins old • Records & tapes • Toiletries

COLLECTION SERVICE No

■ Age Concern (Westminster)

ADDRESS 4 Frampton Street, London NW8 4LF

TELEPHONE 0171-798 1563

FAX 0171-723 0405

CATEGORY Antique post cards • Arts & crafts equipment • Baby equipment • Bed linen and mattresses *only bed linen* • Bicycles *only children's* • Books hardback • Books paperback • Bric-a-brac • Clocks • Clothing adults' • Clothing children's • Fabric remnants • Household items *ironing boards etc* • Jewellery *not pierced earrings* • Knitting, crochet and sewing equipment • Knitting wool • Magazines & comics • Musical instruments • Photographic equipment • Records & tapes • Sports equipment • Toiletries • Toys & games • Video/computer games • Watches • Wedding clothes for hire

COLLECTION SERVICE No

■ Age Concern (Weston-super-Mare)

ADDRESS 5 Dolphin Square, Oxford Street, Weston-super-Mare, Avon BS23 1TT

TELEPHONE 01934 626479

CATEGORY Antique post cards • Arts & crafts equipment • Bed linen and mattresses *no mattresses* • Books hardback • Books paperback • Bric-a-brac • Clocks • Clothing adults' • Clothing children's • Coins foreign • Coins old • Fabric remnants • Household items *ironing boards etc* • Jewellery • Knitting, crochet and sewing equipment • Knitting wool • Medals • Musical instruments • Records & tapes • Sports equipment • Stamps British • Stamps foreign • Toiletries • Toys & games • Video/computer games • Wedding clothes for hire

COLLECTION SERVICE Yes

■ Age Concern (Wirral)

ADDRESS 42–44 Market Street, Birkenhead, Wirral, Merseyside L41 5BT

TELEPHONE 0151-666 2220

FAX 0151-650 0212

CATEGORY Antique post cards • Arts & crafts equipment • Bed linen and mattresses *no*

mattresses *unless base included* ● Bicycles ● Books hardback *must be in good condition* ● Books paperback *must be in good condition* ● Bric-a-brac ● Clocks ● Clothing adults' ● Clothing children's ● Computer hardware and software ● Diy equipment ● Fur coats ● Furniture *must meet current fire safety regulations* ● Gardening equipment ● Household items *ironing boards etc* ● Jewellery ● Knitting wool *complete balls only* ● Medals ● Musical instruments ● Office equipment and stationery ● Photographic equipment ● Records & tapes *must be in good condition* ● Sports equipment ● Toys & games *must be complete* ● Video/computer games ● Watches

COLLECTION SERVICE Yes

■ Age Concern (York)

ADDRESS Norman Collison House, 70 Walmgate, York, N Yorks YO1 2TL

TELEPHONE 01904 627995

CATEGORY Books hardback ● Books paperback ● Bric-a-brac ● Clothing adults' *good quality* ● Clothing children's *good quality* ● Jewellery ● Knitting wool ● Toys & games

COLLECTION SERVICE Yes

■ Alloa Community Enterprises Limited

ADDRESS 15a Mar Street, Alloa, Central FK10 1HR

TELEPHONE 01259 215090

FAX 01259 215090

CATEGORY Aluminium ● Antique post cards ● Arts & crafts equipment ● Baby equipment ● Bed linen and mattresses ● Bicycles ● Books hardback ● Books paperback ● Bric-a-brac ● Clocks ● Clothing adults' ● Clothing children's ● Computer hardware and software ● Diy equipment ● Fabric remnants ● Fur coats ● Furniture ● Gardening equipment ● Glass ● Household items *ironing boards etc* ● Jewellery ● Knitting, crochet and sewing equipment ● Knitting wool ● Magazines & comics ● Medals ● Musical instruments ● Office equipment and stationery ● Other metals ● Pets equipment ● Photographic equipment ● Rags ● Records & tapes ● Sports equipment ● Toiletries ● Toys & games ● Used toner cartridges ● Video/computer games ● Watches ● Wedding clothes for hire

COLLECTION SERVICE Yes

■ Alsager Animals in Need

ADDRESS 26 Poplar Drive, Alsager, Stoke on Trent, Staffs ST7 2RW

TELEPHONE 01270 872784

CATEGORY Arts & crafts equipment ● Bed linen and mattresses *blankets for kennels* ● Books hardback ● Books paperback ● Bric-a-brac ● Clocks *working* ● Clothing adults' *good quality* ● Clothing children's *good quality* ● Coins foreign ● Coins old ● Diy equipment ● Jewellery ● Knitting, crochet and sewing equipment ● Medals ● Pets equipment ● Photographic equipment ● Records

& tapes ● Stamps British ● Stamps foreign ● Toiletries ● Toys & games ● Watches *working*

COLLECTION SERVICE No

■ Arthritis & Rheumatism Council

ADDRESS Copeman House, St Mary's Court, St Mary's Gate, Chesterfield, Derbys S41 7TD

TELEPHONE 01246 558033

FAX 01246 558007

CATEGORY Air miles ● Aluminium ● Arts & crafts equipment ● Baby equipment ● Bed linen and mattresses ● Books hardback ● Books paperback ● Bric-a-brac ● Clothing adults' ● Clothing children's ● Coins foreign ● Coins old ● Jewellery ● Knitting, crochet and sewing equipment ● Knitting wool ● Magazines & comics, money-off coupons ● Musical instruments ● Petrol vouchers ● Records & tapes ● Sports equipment ● Stamps British ● Stamps foreign ● Toiletries ● Toys & games ● Trading stamps ● Watches ● Wedding clothes for hire

COLLECTION SERVICE Yes

■ Arthritis & Rheumatism Council for Research

ADDRESS 16 Rozel Court, Aspal Lane, Beck Row, Mildenhall, Suffolk IP28 8AX

TELEPHONE 01638 714370

CATEGORY Air miles ● Antique post cards ● Arts & crafts equipment ● Baby equipment ● Bed linen and mattresses *clean/unused* ● Bicycles ● Books hardback ● Books paperback ● Bric-a-brac ● Clocks *non-electrical* ● Clothing adults' ● Clothing children's ● Coins foreign ● Coins old ● Diy equipment *non-electrical* ● Fabric remnants ● Gardening equipment ● Hearing aids ● Household items *ironing boards etc* ● Jewellery ● Knitting, crochet and sewing equipment ● Knitting wool ● Magazines & comics ● Medals ● Money-off coupons ● Musical instruments ● Office equipment and stationery ● Petrol vouchers ● Pets equipment ● Photographic equipment ● Records & tapes ● Spectacles ● Sports equipment ● Stamps British ● Stamps foreign ● Toiletries ● Toys & games *non-electrical* ● Trading stamps ● Video/computer games ● Watches

COLLECTION SERVICE No

■ Arthritis & Rheumatism Council for Research

ADDRESS 10 Whimple Street, Plymouth, Devon PL1 2DH

TELEPHONE 01752 668573

CATEGORY Bed linen and mattresses ● Books hardback ● Books paperback ● Bric-a-brac ● Clocks ● Clothing adults' ● Clothing children's ● Jewellery ● Knitting wool ● Medals ● Photographic equipment ● Records & tapes ● Spectacles ● Toiletries ● Watches

COLLECTION SERVICE No

■ Arthritis & Rheumatism Council for Research

ADDRESS Merravay, Station Road, Angmering, W Sussex BN16 4HY

TELEPHONE 01903 850184

CATEGORY Air miles ● Antique post cards ● Baby equipment ● Books hardback ● Books paperback ● Bric-a-brac ● Clocks ● Clothing adults' ● Clothing children's ● Coins foreign ● Coins old ● Fur coats ● Furniture *small items* ● Gardening equipment ● Jewellery ● Knitting, crochet and sewing equipment ● Knitting wool ● Magazines & comics ● Medals ● Money-off coupons ● Musical instruments ● Office equipment and stationery *especially filing cabinets* ● Petrol vouchers ● Records & tapes ● Stamps British ● Stamps foreign ● Toiletries ● Toys & games ● Trading stamps ● Watches ● Wedding clothes for hire

COLLECTION SERVICE No

■ Arthritis & Rheumatism Council (NI)

ADDRESS 17 Cleland Park South, Bangor, Co Down, N Ireland BT20 3EW

TELEPHONE 01247 463109

FAX 01247 461561

CATEGORY Air miles ● Baby equipment ● Bed linen and mattresses ● Books hardback ● Books paperback ● Bric-a-brac ● Clocks ● Clothing adults' ● Clothing children's ● Coins foreign ● Coins old ● Fabric remnants ● Furniture ● Household items *ironing boards etc* ● Jewellery ● Knitting, crochet and sewing equipment ● Knitting wool ● Magazines & comics ● Money-off coupons ● Musical instruments ● Petrol vouchers ● Records & tapes ● Sports equipment ● Stamps British ● Stamps foreign ● Toiletries ● Toys & games ● Trading stamps ● Wedding clothes for hire

COLLECTION SERVICE Yes

■ Arthritis Care

ADDRESS 96 High Street, Scotter, Gainsborough, Lincs DN21 3SF

TELEPHONE 01724 762075

CATEGORY Air miles ● Coins foreign *notes only* ● Money-off coupons ● Petrol vouchers ● Trading stamps

COLLECTION SERVICE No

■ Arthritis Research

ADDRESS Arthritis & Rheumatism Council, NEC Office, 31 Crimicar Avenue, Sheffield, S Yorks S10 4EQ

TELEPHONE 0114-230 8492

CATEGORY Baby equipment ● Bicycles ● Books hardback ● Books paperback ● Bric-a-brac ● Clocks ● Clothing adults' ● Clothing children's ● Coins foreign ● Coins old ● Diy equipment ● Fabric remnants ● Fur coats ● Furniture *small items* ● Gardening equipment ● Household items *ironing boards etc* ● Jewellery ● Knitting, crochet and sewing equipment ● Knitting wool ● Money-off coupons ● Musical instruments ● Petrol vouchers ● Photographic equipment ● Records & tapes ● Sports equipment ● Stamps British ● Stamps foreign ● Toiletries ● Toys & games ● Trading stamps ● Video/computer games ● Watches ● Wedding clothes for hire

COLLECTION SERVICE Yes

■ Arthritis Research (Arthritis & Rheumatism Council)

ADDRESS Regional Office, 17 Lyme Grove, Marple, Cheshire SK6 7NW

TELEPHONE 0161-427 4632

CATEGORY Air miles ● Antique post cards ● Arts & crafts equipment ● Baby equipment ● Bed linen and mattresses *not mattresses* ● Books hardback ● Books paperback ● Bric-a-brac ● Clocks ● Clothing adults' ● Clothing children's ● Coins foreign ● Coins old ● Diy equipment *not electrical* ● Fabric remnants ● Fur coats ● Furniture *not large items* ● Gardening equipment *not electrical* ● Household items *ironing boards etc* ● Jewellery ● Knitting, crochet and sewing equipment ● Knitting wool ● Medals ● Money-off coupons ● Musical instruments ● Non perishable foods ● Office equipment and stationery ● Petrol vouchers ● Pets equipment ● Photographic equipment ● Records & tapes ● Sports equipment ● Stamps British ● Stamps foreign ● Toiletries ● Toys & games ● Trading stamps ● Video/computer games *not X-rated videos* ● Watches ● Wedding clothes for hire

COLLECTION SERVICE No

■ Arthritis Research Charity Shop

ADDRESS 6 Oat Street, Evesham, Hereford & Worcs WR11 4PJ

TELEPHONE 01386 47710

CATEGORY Air miles ● Antique post cards ● Arts & crafts equipment ● Baby equipment *in good order* ● Bed linen and mattresses *not mattresses* ● Bicycles *in good condition* ● Books hardback *cookery, gardening, educational, non-fiction* ● Books paperback *Mills & Boon* ● Bric-a-brac ● Clocks *in working order* ● Clothing adults' *in good condition* ● Clothing children's *in good condition* ● Coins foreign ● Coins old ● Diy equipment *limited* ● Fabric remnants ● Furniture *small to medium items* ● Gardening equipment ● Hearing aids ● Household items *ironing boards etc* ● Jewellery ● Knitting, crochet and sewing equipment ● Knitting wool ● Medals ● Musical instruments *in working order* ● Office equipment and stationery ● Petrol vouchers ● Photographic equipment ● Rags *cotton only* ● Records & tapes ● Spectacles ● Sports equipment ● Stamps British ● Stamps foreign ● Toys & games ● Trading stamps ● Watches ● Wedding clothes for hire

COLLECTION SERVICE Yes

■ Artlandish Limited

ADDRESS The Nunsthorpe and Bradley Park Resource Centre, Second Avenue, Grimsby, Lincs DN33 1NU

TELEPHONE 01472 311979

FAX 01472 311979

CATEGORY Antique post cards ● Arts & crafts equipment *not broken* ● Books hardback *general information & art books, good clean condition* ● Childrens play/craft scrap *no egg cartons or toilet rolls* ● Diy equipment ● Furniture *shelving, tables, chairs – must be safe* ● Jewellery *also accept broken jewellery* ● Knitting wool ● Magazines & comics *children's in good clean condition* ● Photographic equipment *cameras, tripods etc* ● Postcards used ● Silver paper & aluminium foil

COLLECTION SERVICE No

■ Aspire

ADDRESS RNOHT, Brockley Hill, Stanmore, Middx HA7 4LP

TELEPHONE 0181-954 0701

FAX 0181-420 6352

CATEGORY Air miles ● Aluminium ● Christmas cards ● Magazines & comics ● Money-off coupons ● Petrol vouchers ● Trading stamps ● Waste paper

COLLECTION SERVICE No

■ Baby Gear

ADDRESS Units 3 & 8, Matrix House, Constitution Hill, Leicester, Leics LE1 1PL

CATEGORY Baby equipment ● Bed linen and mattresses *cot bedding only* ● Clothing children's *children under one year* ● Fabric remnants ● Knitting wool ● Toiletries *for child use only*

COLLECTION SERVICE Yes

■ Banbury & District CVS (Furniture Store)

ADDRESS North Bar Place, Banbury, Oxon OX16 0TD

TELEPHONE 01295 267741

CATEGORY Baby equipment ● Diy equipment ● Furniture ● Gardening equipment ● Household items *ironing boards etc* ● Office equipment and stationery

COLLECTION SERVICE Yes

■ Barnardos (Belfast)

ADDRESS 542–544 Upper Newtownards Road, Belfast, N Ireland BT4 3HE

TELEPHONE 01232 672366

FAX 01232 672399

CATEGORY Antique post cards ● Arts & crafts equipment ● Bicycles ● Books hardback ● Books paperback ● Bric-a-brac ● Clocks ● Clothing adults' ● Clothing children's ● Coins foreign ● Fabric remnants ● Fur coats ● Gardening equipment ● Household items *ironing boards etc* ● Jewellery ● Knitting, crochet and sewing equipment ● Knitting wool ● Magazines & comics *of a family nature only* ● Medals ● Musical instruments ● Photographic equipment ● Records & tapes ● Sports equipment ● Toiletries ● Toys & games ● Video/computer games ● Watches ● Wedding clothes for hire

COLLECTION SERVICE Yes

■ Barnardos (East Retail Region)

ADDRESS Cottage 8, Tanners Lane, Barkingside, Ilford, Essex IG6 1QG

TELEPHONE 0181-550 8822

FAX 0181-551 7840

CATEGORY Antique post cards ● Arts & crafts equipment ● Bicycles ● Books hardback ● Books paperback ● Bric-a-brac ● Clocks ● Clothing adults' ● Clothing children's ● Coins foreign ● Fabric remnants ● Fur coats ● Gardening equipment ● Household items *ironing boards etc* ● Jewellery ● Knitting, crochet and sewing equipment ● Knitting wool ● Magazines & comics *of a family nature only* ● Medals ● Musical instruments ● Photographic equipment ● Records & tapes ● Sports equipment ● Toiletries ● Toys & games ● Video/computer games ● Watches ● Wedding clothes for hire

COLLECTION SERVICE Yes

■ Barnardos (North Retail Region)

ADDRESS 9 Town Square, Sale, Gtr Manchester M33 1XZ

TELEPHONE 0161-905 2390

FAX 0161-905 2730

CATEGORY Antique post cards ● Arts & crafts equipment ● Bicycles ● Books hardback ● Books paperback ● Bric-a-brac ● Clocks ● Clothing adults' ● Clothing children's ● Coins foreign ● Fabric remnants ● Fur coats ● Gardening equipment ● Household items *ironing boards etc* ● Jewellery ● Knitting, crochet and sewing equipment ● Knitting wool ● Magazines & comics *of a family nature only* ● Medals ● Musical instruments ● Photographic equipment ● Records & tapes ● Sports equipment ● Toiletries ● Toys & games ● Video/computer games ● Watches ● Wedding clothes for hire

COLLECTION SERVICE Yes

■ Barnardos (West Retail Region)

ADDRESS 724–726 Stratford Road, Sparkhill, Birmingham, W Midlands B11 4BP

TELEPHONE 0121-777 2804

FAX 0121-702 2959

CATEGORY Antique post cards ● Arts & crafts equipment ● Bicycles ● Books hardback ● Books paperback ● Bric-a-brac ● Clocks ● Clothing adults' ● Clothing children's ● Coins foreign ● Fabric remnants ● Fur coats ● Gardening equipment ● Household items *ironing boards etc* ● Jewellery ●

Knitting, crochet and sewing equipment
• Knitting wool • Magazines & comics *of a family nature only* • Medals • Musical instruments
• Photographic equipment • Records & tapes
• Sports equipment • Toiletries • Toys & games
• Video/computer games • Watches • Wedding clothes for hire

COLLECTION SERVICE Yes

■ Base, Dacorum and St Albans Homeless Development Team

ADDRESS 22a High Street, Hemel Hempstead, Herts HP1 3AE

TELEPHONE 01442 219121

CATEGORY Arts & crafts equipment *occasionally*
• Baby equipment *small items only* • Bed linen and mattresses *bed linen only* • Computer hardware and software • Household items *ironing boards etc small items only* • Magazines & comics *for young people* • Money-off coupons
• Musical instruments • Non perishable foods
• Office equipment and stationery • Petrol vouchers • Photographic equipment • Records & tapes • Stamps British • Stamps foreign
• Telephone cards • Toiletries • Trading stamps
• Video/computer games • Waste paper *only A4/A3 sheets which we can use for letters and posters, etc*

COLLECTION SERVICE No

■ Batley Family & Community Centre, Community Furniture Service

ADDRESS 56 Wellington Street, Batley, W Yorks WF17 5HU

TELEPHONE 01924 477183

FAX 01924 477146

CATEGORY Baby equipment • Bed linen and mattresses • Bric-a-brac • Clothing adults'
• Clothing children's • Furniture • Household items *ironing boards etc* • Toys & games

COLLECTION SERVICE Yes

■ Bedford Refuge (part of Christian Family Care)

ADDRESS PO Box 515, Bedford, Beds MK40 1YD

TELEPHONE 01234 353592

FAX 01234 270155

CATEGORY Arts & crafts equipment • Baby equipment • Bed linen and mattresses *no mattresses – duvet covers, sheets, pillowcases only*
• Bicycles *children's – in good order* • Clothing adults' *women only, good condition* • Clothing children's *good condition* • Furniture *no transport is provided and storage is limited* • Gardening equipment • Household items *ironing boards etc*
• Non perishable foods • Stamps British • Stamps foreign • Toiletries • Toys & games *in complete condition*

COLLECTION SERVICE No

■ The Bedfordshire Region of the National Deaf Children's Society

ADDRESS 43 Stotfold Road, Arlesey, Beds SG15 6XL

TELEPHONE 01462 732927

CATEGORY Computer hardware and software

COLLECTION SERVICE No

■ Beeston Volunteer Bureau

ADDRESS 46a High Road, Beeston, Nottingham, Notts NG9 2JP

TELEPHONE 0115-922 5238

CATEGORY Baby equipment • Bed linen and mattresses *bed linen only* • Books hardback
• Books paperback • Bric-a-brac • Clothing children's • Fabric remnants • Household items *ironing boards etc* • Jewellery • Knitting wool
• Office equipment and stationery • Stamps British • Toiletries • Toys & games

COLLECTION SERVICE Yes

■ Bentley Association for Supportive Help

ADDRESS c/o The Vicarage, 3a High Street, Bentley, Doncaster, S Yorks DN5 0AA

TELEPHONE 01302 876011

FAX 01302 876272

CATEGORY Antique post cards • Arts & crafts equipment • Baby equipment • Bed linen and mattresses *sheets and pillowcases only* • Bicycles • Bric-a-brac • Clocks • Clothing adults'
• Clothing children's • Coins foreign • Coins old
• Computer hardware and software • Diy equipment • Furniture • Gardening equipment
• Household items *ironing boards etc* • Jewellery
• Knitting, crochet and sewing equipment
• Magazines & comics • Medals • Office equipment and stationery • Silver paper & aluminium foil • Toiletries • Toys & games
• Video/computer games • Watches

COLLECTION SERVICE Yes

■ Berkshire Multiple Sclerosis Therapy Centre

ADDRESS 26 Patrick Road, Caversham, Berks RG4 8DD

TELEPHONE 01734 482072

FAX 01734 463675

CATEGORY Aluminium • Coins foreign • Petrol vouchers • Stamps British • Stamps foreign
• Waste paper

COLLECTION SERVICE No

■ **Bethany Christian Trust**

ADDRESS 22–24 Ferry Road Drive, West Pilton, Edinburgh, Lothian EH4 4BR

TELEPHONE 0131-343 3993

FAX 0131-343 1005

CATEGORY Antique post cards ● Arts & crafts equipment ● Bed linen and mattresses ● Bicycles ● Books hardback ● Books paperback ● Bric-a-brac ● Clocks ● Clothing adults' ● Clothing children's ● Coins foreign ● Coins old ● Computer hardware and software *suitable for our own use only* ● Fabric remnants ● Furniture *no parts missing/ broken, must meet fire regulations* ● Gardening equipment ● Household items *ironing boards etc no parts missing/broken* ● Jewellery ● Knitting, crochet and sewing equipment ● Knitting wool ● Magazines & comics ● Medals ● Musical instruments ● Non perishable foods ● Office equipment and stationery *suitable for our own use only* ● Photographic equipment ● Records & tapes ● Sports equipment ● Stamps British ● Stamps foreign ● Toiletries *must be unused* ● Toys & games ● Watches

COLLECTION SERVICE Yes

■ **Bethany House**

ADDRESS 36 Muslim Street, Bridgeton, Glasgow, Strathclyde G40 4AP

TELEPHONE 0141-554 2497

FAX 0141-554 2497

CATEGORY Arts & crafts equipment ● Bed linen and mattresses ● Bric-a-brac ● Clothing adults' ● Clothing children's ● Furniture ● Household items *ironing boards etc* ● Non perishable foods ● Sports equipment ● Toiletries ● Video/ computer games

COLLECTION SERVICE Yes

■ **Betts Memorial Heart Foundation**

ADDRESS 114 Seaside Road, Eastbourne, E Sussex BN22

TELEPHONE 01323 731914 (evenings)

CATEGORY Air miles ● Antique post cards ● Books hardback ● Books paperback ● Bric-a-brac ● Clocks ● Clothing adults' ● Clothing children's ● Fabric remnants ● Jewellery ● Knitting, crochet and sewing equipment ● Knitting wool ● Money-off coupons ● Petrol vouchers ● Photographic equipment ● Records & tapes ● Toiletries ● Trading stamps ● Video/computer games ● Watches

COLLECTION SERVICE No

■ **Bexhill & District Diabetic Group**

ADDRESS 25 Warnham Gardens, Bexhill-on-Sea, E Sussex TN39 3SP

TELEPHONE 01424 844798

CATEGORY Antique post cards ● Bric-a-brac ● Clocks ● Coins foreign ● Coins old ● Jewellery ● Medals ● Office equipment and stationery ● Postcards

used ● Stamps British ● Stamps foreign ● Telephone cards ● Watches

COLLECTION SERVICE No

■ **Bexley Downs Syndrome Group**

ADDRESS 32 Iris Crescent, Bexleyheath, Kent DA7 5QD

TELEPHONE 0181-310 5018

CATEGORY Air miles ● Antique post cards ● Arts & crafts equipment ● Baby equipment ● Bicycles ● Books hardback ● Books paperback ● Bric-a-brac ● Clocks ● Clothing children's ● Coins foreign ● Coins old ● Diy equipment ● Gardening equipment ● Glass ● Household items *ironing boards etc* ● Jewellery ● Knitting, crochet and sewing equipment ● Magazines & comics ● Medals ● Money-off coupons ● Musical instruments ● Non perishable foods ● Office equipment and stationery ● Petrol vouchers ● Photographic equipment ● Records & tapes ● Spectacles ● Sports equipment ● Stamps British ● Stamps foreign ● Toiletries ● Toys & games ● Trading stamps ● Video/computer games ● Watches

COLLECTION SERVICE No

■ **Birmingham Play Resource Centre**

ADDRESS Ward End Park, Washwood Heath Road, Ward End, Birmingham, W Midlands B3 2HB

TELEPHONE 0121-327 6981

FAX 0121-327 1505

CATEGORY Arts & crafts equipment ● Bicycles ● Books hardback ● Books paperback ● Bric-a-brac ● Childrens play/craft scrap ● Christmas cards ● Clocks ● Computer hardware and software ● Diy equipment ● Fabric remnants ● Furniture ● Gardening equipment ● Jewellery ● Knitting, crochet and sewing equipment ● Knitting wool ● Magazines & comics ● Musical instruments ● Office equipment and stationery ● Photographic equipment ● Plastics ● Postcards used ● Rags ● Records & tapes ● Silver paper & aluminium foil ● Sports equipment ● Telephone cards ● Toys & games ● Used toner cartridges ● Video/computer games ● Waste paper ● Watches

COLLECTION SERVICE Yes

■ **Blaby & Whetstone Boys Club**

ADDRESS Warwick Road, Whetstone, Leics LE8 6LW

TELEPHONE 0116-286 4852

CATEGORY Air miles ● Aluminium ● Arts & crafts equipment ● Coins foreign ● Sports equipment ● Toys & games *suitable for 11–16 years* ● Video/ computer games

COLLECTION SERVICE Yes

■ Blacon Project

ADDRESS Blacon Library, Western Avenue, Blacon, Chester, Cheshire CH1 5QY

TELEPHONE 01244 390344

FAX 01244 382095

CATEGORY Baby equipment ● Bed linen and mattresses ● Bric-a-brac ● Clocks ● Clothing adults' ● Clothing children's ● Furniture ● Gardening equipment ● Household items *ironing boards etc*

COLLECTION SERVICE Yes

■ The Blue Cross

ADDRESS Shilton Road, Burford, Oxon OX18 4PF

TELEPHONE 01993 822651

FAX 01993 823083

CATEGORY Antique post cards ● Books hardback ● Books paperback ● Bric-a-brac ● Gardening equipment ● Jewellery ● Pets equipment *inlcuding equine equipment* ● Toiletries ● Toys & games

COLLECTION SERVICE No

■ Bognor Regis and District Council for Voluntary Service

ADDRESS Town Hall, Clarance Road, Bognor Regis, W Sussex PO21 1LD

TELEPHONE 01243 840305/830885

CATEGORY Baby equipment ● Bed linen and mattresses ● Computer hardware and software ● Furniture ● Household items *ironing boards etc* ● Office equipment and stationery

COLLECTION SERVICE Yes

■ Bolton Community Transport

ADDRESS BCT, c/o Clare Court, Exeter Avenue, Farnworth, Bolton, Gtr Manchester BL4 0NE

TELEPHONE 01204 364777

CATEGORY Baby equipment ● Bed linen and mattresses ● Books hardback ● Books paperback ● Computer hardware and software ● Furniture ● Household items *ironing boards etc* ● Musical instruments ● Office equipment and stationery ● Toys & games

COLLECTION SERVICE Yes

■ Book Aid

ADDRESS 271 Church Road, London SE19 2QQ

TELEPHONE 0181-857 7794

FAX 0181-653 0851

CATEGORY Books hardback *only bibles and Christian – no dated materials* ● Books paperback *only bibles and Christian – no dated materials*

COLLECTION SERVICE No

■ Book Aid International

ADDRESS 39–41 Coldharbour Lane, Camberwell, London SE5 9NR

TELEPHONE 0171-733 3577

FAX 0171-978 8006

E-MAIL r/s@gn.apc.org

CATEGORY Books hardback *under 15 years old, good condition, relevant to our subject areas – please contact for more details* ● Books paperback *under 15 years old, good condition, relevant to our subject areas – please contact for more details*

COLLECTION SERVICE No

■ Boscombe Salvation Army Charity Concern

ADDRESS Palmerston Road, Boscombe, Bournemouth, Dorset BH1 4HP

TELEPHONE 01202 304295

FAX 01202 396088

CATEGORY Air miles ● Antique post cards ● Arts & crafts equipment ● Baby equipment ● Bed linen and mattresses ● Bicycles ● Books hardback ● Books paperback ● Bric-a-brac ● Clocks ● Clothing adults' ● Clothing children's ● Coins foreign ● Coins old ● Diy equipment ● Fabric remnants ● Fur coats ● Furniture *items of soft furnishings must have fire label* ● Gardening equipment ● Hearing aids ● Household items *ironing boards etc* ● Jewellery ● Knitting wool ● Magazines & comics ● Medals ● Money-off coupons ● Motorbike engines, car engines, spare parts ● Non perishable foods ● Petrol vouchers ● Photographic equipment ● Records & tapes ● Spectacles ● Sports equipment ● Stamps British ● Stamps foreign ● Toiletries ● Toys & games ● Trading stamps ● Video/computer games ● Watches

COLLECTION SERVICE Yes

■ Bradford Gingerbread Centre

ADDRESS 45 Darley Street, Bradford, W Yorks BD1 3HN

TELEPHONE 01274 720564

CATEGORY Baby equipment ● Bed linen and mattresses ● Bric-a-brac ● Clothing adults' ● Clothing children's ● Computer hardware and software ● Household items *ironing boards etc* ● Non perishable foods ● Rags ● Toiletries

COLLECTION SERVICE Yes

■ Bransby Home of Rest for Horses

ADDRESS Bransby, Saxilby, Lincs LN1 2PH

TELEPHONE 01427 788464

FAX 01427 787657

CATEGORY Books hardback ● Books paperback ● Magazines & comics ● Money-off coupons ● Petrol vouchers ● Stamps British ● Stamps foreign

- Telephone cards • Toiletries • Toys & games
- Trading stamps

COLLECTION SERVICE No

■ Brent Gingerbread

ADDRESS 108 Mortimer Road, London NW10 5SN

TELEPHONE 0181-969 1985

CATEGORY Arts & crafts equipment • Baby equipment • Bed linen and mattresses • Bicycles • Books hardback • Books paperback • Bric-a-brac • Childrens play/craft scrap • Clocks • Clothing adults' • Clothing children's • Computer hardware and software • Diy equipment • Fur coats • Furniture • Gardening equipment • Household items *ironing boards etc* • Jewellery • Money-off coupons • Non perishable foods • Office equipment and stationery • Photographic equipment • Records & tapes • Spectacles • Sports equipment • Toiletries • Toys & games • Video/computer games • Watches

COLLECTION SERVICE Yes

■ The Bridge Trust

ADDRESS East Street, Tonbridge, Kent TN9 1HP

TELEPHONE 01732 368363

FAX 01732 368363

CATEGORY Baby equipment *must be clean and in good condition* • Bed linen and mattresses *not blankets* • Clocks *working order* • Furniture *must be clean and in good condition* • Gardening equipment • Household items *ironing boards etc* • Toiletries

COLLECTION SERVICE Yes

■ British Kidney Patient Association

ADDRESS Bordon, Hants GU35 9JZ

TELEPHONE 01420 472021

FAX 01420 475831

CATEGORY Air miles • Antique post cards • Coins foreign • Coins old • Medals • Money-off coupons • Petrol vouchers • Stamps British • Stamps foreign • Telephone cards • Trading stamps

COLLECTION SERVICE No

■ British Lung Foundation (Breathe North)

ADDRESS Sir G B Hunter Memorial Hospital, The Green, Wallsend, Tyne & Wear NE28 7PB

TELEPHONE 0191-263 0276

FAX 0191-262 2660

CATEGORY Antique post cards • Bric-a-brac *good quality small items* • Coins foreign • Coins old • Medals • Office equipment and stationery • Petrol vouchers • Postcards used *pre-1950* • Stamps British *commemorative only* • Stamps foreign • Toiletries • Used toner cartridges

COLLECTION SERVICE Yes

■ British Red Cross

ADDRESS 47 Coombe Road, Croydon, Surrey CR0 1BQ

TELEPHONE 0181-688 6895

FAX 0181-688 6895

CATEGORY Bed linen and mattresses *not mattresses* • Books hardback • Books paperback • Bric-a-brac • Clocks • Clothing adults' • Clothing children's • Coins foreign • Computer hardware and software *we are desperate for PCs* • Jewellery • Office equipment and stationery • Records & tapes • Toiletries • Toys & games • Watches

COLLECTION SERVICE No

■ British Red Cross

ADDRESS 244 London Road, Leicester, Leics LE3 3LT

TELEPHONE 0116-270 5087

FAX 0116-244 8252

CATEGORY Antique post cards • Arts & crafts equipment • Baby equipment *small items only* • Bed linen and mattresses *linen only* • Books hardback • Books paperback • Bric-a-brac • Clocks • Clothing adults' • Clothing children's *no cords through anorak hoods* • Coins foreign • Coins old • Diy equipment • Fabric remnants • Gardening equipment *small items only* • Household items *ironing boards etc* • Jewellery • Knitting, crochet and sewing equipment • Knitting wool • Medals • Musical instruments • Non perishable foods • Office equipment and stationery • Photographic equipment • Toiletries • Toys & games • Watches

COLLECTION SERVICE No

■ British Red Cross

ADDRESS 84 Noel Rise, Burgess Hill, W Sussex RH15 8BT

TELEPHONE 01444 241781

CATEGORY Aluminium • Books paperback • Bric-a-brac • Childrens play/craft scrap • Coins foreign • Coins old • Knitting wool • Milk bottle tops • Petrol vouchers • Silver paper & aluminium foil *including cans* • Spectacles • Stamps British • Stamps foreign

COLLECTION SERVICE No

■ British Red Cross Margate Centre

ADDRESS The Limes, Addington Road, Margate, Kent CT9 1NH

TELEPHONE 01843 223739

CATEGORY Arts & crafts equipment • Bicycles • Books hardback • Books paperback • Bric-a-brac • Christmas cards • Clocks • Coins foreign • Coins old • Computer hardware and software • Diy equipment • Fabric remnants • Gardening equipment • Jewellery • Knitting, crochet and sewing equipment • Knitting wool • Magazines & comics • Medals • Musical instruments • Non perishable foods • Office equipment and stationery • Photographic equipment • Records & tapes • Sports equipment • Stamps British •

Stamps foreign • Toiletries • Toys & games • Video/computer games • Watches

COLLECTION SERVICE No

■ British Red Cross Society

ADDRESS 75–77 Victoria Road, Ruislip Manor, Middx HA4 9BH

TELEPHONE 01895 633458

CATEGORY Air miles • Antique post cards • Arts & crafts equipment • Books hardback • Books paperback • Bric-a-brac • Clocks • Clothing adults' • Clothing children's • Coins foreign • Coins old • Computer hardware and software • Diy equipment • Fabric remnants • Gardening equipment • Jewellery • Knitting, crochet and sewing equipment • Knitting wool • Medals • Musical instruments • Office equipment and stationery • Petrol vouchers • Photographic equipment • Records & tapes • Sports equipment • Stamps British • Stamps foreign • Toiletries • Toys & games • Trading stamps • Video/ computer games • Watches

COLLECTION SERVICE No

■ British Red Cross Somerset Branch

ADDRESS Livingstone Way, Taunton, Somerset TA2 6BD

TELEPHONE 01823 284039

FAX 01823 323204

CATEGORY Antique post cards • Arts & crafts equipment • Baby equipment • Bed linen and mattresses *mattresses must meet certain standard – manager would advise donor if we could accept the item* • Bicycles • Books hardback • Books paperback • Bric-a-brac • Clocks • Clothing adults' • Clothing children's • Coins foreign • Coins old • Diy equipment *not knives* • Fabric remnants • Furniture *we are not allowed to sell certain items – manager would advise donor if we could accept the item* • Household items *ironing boards etc* • Jewellery *not pierced earrings* • Knitting, crochet and sewing equipment • Knitting wool • Medals • Musical instruments • Office equipment and stationery • Photographic equipment • Records & tapes • Sports equipment *not horse riding helmets/crash helmets* • Stamps British • Stamps foreign • Toys & games • Watches

COLLECTION SERVICE Yes

■ Brittle Bone Society

ADDRESS 30 Guthrie Street, Dundee, Tayside DD1 5BS

TELEPHONE 01382 204446/7

FAX 01382 206771

CATEGORY Books hardback • Books paperback • Clothing adults' • Clothing children's • Fur coats *fun fur only* • Jewellery • Knitting wool • Stamps British • Stamps foreign • Toys & games • Watches

COLLECTION SERVICE No

■ Bryson House

ADDRESS 28 Bedford Street, Belfast, County Antrim, N Ireland BT2 7FE

TELEPHONE 01232 325835

FAX 01232 439156

CATEGORY Aluminium *used drink cans* • Baby equipment *for re-use by families in need* • Clothing adults' *for resale, no 'nearly new'* • Clothing children's *for resale, no 'nearly new'* • Diy equipment • Furniture *for re-use by families in need* • Gardening equipment • Household items *ironing boards etc for re-use by families in need*

COLLECTION SERVICE Yes

■ Burnbake Trust

ADDRESS 29 North Street, Wilton, Salisbury, Wilts SP2 0HE

TELEPHONE 01722 743727

FAX 01722 744787

CATEGORY Baby equipment • Bed linen & mattresses • Bric-a-brac • Furniture • Gardening equipment • Household items *ironing boards, etc* • Books hardback • Books paperback

COLLECTION SERVICE Yes

■ Burnley Community Business & Resource Centre

ADDRESS c/o Burnley Borough Council, 20 Nicholas Street, Burnley, Lancs BB11 2AP

TELEPHONE 01282 425011 ext 2392

FAX 01282 455464

CATEGORY Aluminium • Arts & crafts equipment • Childrens play/craft scrap • Computer hardware and software • Fabric remnants • Milk bottle tops • Office equipment and stationery • Photographic equipment • Silver paper & aluminium foil • Sports equipment • Toys & games

COLLECTION SERVICE Yes

■ Burton YMCA

ADDRESS 5 Borough Road, Burton on Trent, Staffs DE14 2DA

TELEPHONE 01283 538802

FAX 01283 538802

CATEGORY Baby equipment *no car seats* • Bed linen and mattresses • Books hardback • Books paperback • Furniture • Household items *ironing boards etc* • Office equipment and stationery • Waste paper

COLLECTION SERVICE Yes

■ Cambridge SOFA

ADDRESS Units 6 & 7, 25 Owydir Street, Cambridge, Cambs CB1 2LG

TELEPHONE 01223 576535

FAX 01223 576535

CATEGORY Arts & crafts equipment • Baby equipment *not cot mattresses* • Bed linen and mattresses • Bicycles • Books hardback • Books paperback • Bric-a-brac • Clocks • Computer hardware and software • Diy equipment • Furniture • Gardening equipment • Household items *ironing boards etc* • Jewellery • Knitting, crochet and sewing equipment • Knitting wool • Musical instruments • Office equipment and stationery • Pets equipment • Photographic equipment • Records & tapes • Sports equipment • Toys & games • Video/computer games • Watches

COLLECTION SERVICE Yes

■ Cancer Prevention Research Trust

ADDRESS 36 Roehampton Vale, London SW15 3RY

TELEPHONE 0181-785 6470

FAX 0181-780 0167

CATEGORY Coins foreign • Computer hardware and software • Office equipment and stationery • Stamps British • Stamps foreign

COLLECTION SERVICE Yes

■ Cancer Relief Macmillan Fund

ADDRESS Laser Office, 3rd Floor, 3 Angel Walk, London W6 9HX

TELEPHONE 0181-563 9699

FAX 0181-563 9640

CATEGORY Air miles • Coins foreign • Coins old • Petrol vouchers • Stamps British *must include postmark* • Stamps foreign *must include postmark* • Trading stamps

COLLECTION SERVICE No

■ Cancer Research Campaign Scotland

ADDRESS 226 Queensferry Road, Edinburgh, Lothian EH4 2BP

TELEPHONE 0131-343 1344

CATEGORY Air miles • Antique post cards • Arts & crafts equipment • Bed linen and mattresses *no mattresses* • Books hardback • Books paperback • Bric-a-brac • Clocks • Clothing adults' • Clothing children's • Coins foreign • Coins old • Fabric remnants • Household items *ironing boards etc* • Jewellery • Knitting, crochet and sewing equipment • Knitting wool • Magazines & comics • Medals • Musical instruments • Petrol vouchers • Photographic equipment • Records & tapes • Sports equipment • Stamps British • Stamps foreign • Toys & games • Used toner cartridges • Watches

COLLECTION SERVICE No

■ Canterbury Women's Refuge

ADDRESS PO Box 123, Canterbury, Kent CT1 1DS

TELEPHONE 01227 769677

FAX 01227 769677

CATEGORY Arts & crafts equipment • Baby equipment • Bed linen and mattresses • Bicycles children's • Books hardback • Books paperback • Bric-a-brac • Clothing adults' *women's clothes wanted* • Clothing children's • Furniture • Gardening equipment • Household items *ironing boards etc* • Jewellery • Non perishable foods • Office equipment and stationery • Sports equipment • Toiletries • Toys & games • Video/computer games

COLLECTION SERVICE Yes

■ Cardinal Hume Centre for Young Homeless People

ADDRESS 3–7 Arneway Street, Horseferry Road, London SW1P 2BG

TELEPHONE 0171-222 1602

FAX 0171-233 2513

CATEGORY Air miles • Arts & crafts equipment • Baby equipment • Bric-a-brac • Clocks • Clothing adults' • Clothing children's • Computer hardware and software • Furniture • Household items *ironing boards etc* • Jewellery • Money-off coupons • Non perishable foods • Office equipment and stationery • Toys & games

COLLECTION SERVICE Yes

■ Care Shop

ADDRESS 46–47 Alexandra Road, Cleethorpes, Lincs DN35 8LE

TELEPHONE 01472 291629

CATEGORY Antique post cards • Arts & crafts equipment • Baby equipment • Bed linen and mattresses *must comply with 1988 fire regulations* • Bicycles • Books hardback • Books paperback • Bric-a-brac • Clocks • Clothing adults' • Clothing children's • Coins foreign • Coins old • Diy equipment • Furniture *upholstered items must comply with 1988 fire regulations* • Gardening equipment • Household items *ironing boards etc* • Jewellery • Magazines & comics • Medals • Musical instruments • Records & tapes • Sports equipment • Stamps British • Stamps foreign • Toys & games • Video/computer games • Watches

COLLECTION SERVICE Yes

■ Caring & Sharing Trust

ADDRESS Cotton's Farm House, Whiston Road, Cogenhoe, Northants NN7 1NL

TELEPHONE 01604 891487

FAX 01604 890405

CATEGORY Arts & crafts equipment • Computer hardware and software *working* • Diy equipment *working* • Gardening equipment *unbroken* • Jewellery • Money-off coupons • Musical

instruments • Office equipment and stationery
• Petrol vouchers • Photographic equipment
• Sports equipment • Trading stamps • Watches
working

COLLECTION SERVICE No

■ Cash from Trash in Aid of Charities

ADDRESS 17 Forest Close, Pinders Heath, Wakefield,
W Yorks WF1 4TL

TELEPHONE 01924 210382

FAX 01924 210382

CATEGORY Air miles • Aluminium *drink cans, pots &
pans* • Diy equipment • Milk bottle tops *foil must
be clean* • Office equipment and stationery
• Silver paper & aluminium foil *must be clean*
• Used toner cartridges • Waste paper *office
waste only* • Watches

COLLECTION SERVICE Yes

■ Cat Action Trust

ADDRESS 227 Sketchley Road, Burbage, Hinckley,
Leics LE10 2DY

TELEPHONE 01455 631213

CATEGORY Aluminium • Arts & crafts equipment
• Books hardback • Books paperback • Bric-a-brac
• Clocks • Diy equipment *only small items*
• Gardening equipment *only small items*
• Jewellery • Knitting, crochet and sewing
equipment • Magazines & comics • Milk bottle
tops • Money-off coupons • Office equipment
and stationery • Petrol vouchers • Pets
equipment • Photographic equipment • Records
& tapes • Silver paper & aluminium foil • Sports
equipment • Toiletries • Toys & games • Trading
stamps • Video/computer games

COLLECTION SERVICE No

■ Catholic Children's Society (Westminster)

ADDRESS 73 St Charles Square, London W10 6EJ

TELEPHONE 0181-969 5305

FAX 0181-960 1464

CATEGORY Arts & crafts equipment • Baby
equipment • Bed linen and mattresses • Bicycles
children's only • Bric-a-brac • Clothing children's
• Coins foreign • Coins old • Fur coats • Furniture
• Household items *ironing boards etc* • Jewellery
• Non perishable foods • Office equipment and
stationery • Toiletries • Toys & games

COLLECTION SERVICE Yes

■ Catholic Fund for Overseas Development (Cafod) Southwark

ADDRESS Coldart Business Centre, Unit 16, 3 King
Edward Avenue, Dartford, Kent DA1 2HZ

TELEPHONE 01322 294924

FAX 01322 294924

CATEGORY Waste paper *newspapers & magazines
only*

COLLECTION SERVICE No

■ Cats in Care

ADDRESS 11 Lower Barn Road, Purley, Surrey
CR8 1HY

TELEPHONE 0181-660 6011

FAX 0181-660 6011

CATEGORY Air miles • Bric-a-brac • Jewellery
• Postcards used *with franked stamps* • Stamps
foreign • Toiletries • Toys & games • Trading
stamps

COLLECTION SERVICE No

■ The Cats Protection League

ADDRESS 17 Kings Road, Horsham, W Sussex
RH13 5PN

TELEPHONE 01403 221900

FAX 01403 218414

CATEGORY Air miles • Antique post cards • Money-
off coupons • Petrol vouchers • Stamps British
• Stamps foreign • Telephone cards • Trading
stamps

COLLECTION SERVICE Yes

■ Cats Protection League (Bexley Branch)

ADDRESS 95 Bedonwell Road, Bexleyheath, Kent
DA7 5PS

TELEPHONE 01322 445097

CATEGORY Books hardback • Books paperback • Bric-
a-brac • Clothing adults' • Clothing children's
• Jewellery • Knitting, crochet and sewing
equipment • Knitting wool • Stamps British
• Stamps foreign • Toiletries • Toys & games

COLLECTION SERVICE No

■ Centre '70 Community Shop

ADDRESS 198 Tulse Hill, London SW2 3BU

TELEPHONE 0181-671 4044

CATEGORY Baby equipment • Bicycles • Books
hardback • Books paperback • Bric-a-brac • Clocks
• Clothing adults' • Clothing children's • Computer
hardware and software • Diy equipment
• Furniture • Household items *ironing boards etc*
• Jewellery • Knitting wool • Medals • Musical
instruments • Office equipment and stationery •

Pets equipment • Records & tapes • Spectacles • Toys & games • Watches

COLLECTION SERVICE Yes

■ **Centre 81**

ADDRESS Tarworks Road, Great Yarmouth, Norfolk NR30 1QR

TELEPHONE 01493 852573

FAX 01493 331541

CATEGORY Air miles • Aluminium • Antique post cards • Arts & crafts equipment • Baby equipment • Bed linen and mattresses • Books hardback • Books paperback • Bric-a-brac • Clocks • Clothing adults' • Clothing children's • Coins foreign • Coins old • Computer hardware and software • Diy equipment • Fur coats • Household items *ironing boards etc* • Knitting, crochet and sewing equipment • Knitting wool • Magazines & comics • Medals • Musical instruments • Office equipment and stationery • Photographic equipment • Records & tapes • Sports equipment • Stamps British • Stamps foreign • Toys & games • Video/computer games • Watches • Wedding clothes for hire

COLLECTION SERVICE Yes

■ **Charis Mother & Baby Care (part of Christian Family Care)**

ADDRESS 2 Ashburnham Road, Bedford, Beds MK40 1DS

TELEPHONE 01234 273677

FAX 01234 273678

CATEGORY Baby equipment • Clothing children's *babies up to two years* • Toiletries

COLLECTION SERVICE No

■ **Cheshire Wildlife Trust**

ADDRESS Grebe House, Reaseheath, Nantwich, Cheshire CW5 6DA

TELEPHONE 01270 610180

FAX 01270 610430

CATEGORY Aluminium • Milk bottle tops • Silver paper & aluminium foil

COLLECTION SERVICE No

■ **The Children's Society**

ADDRESS Edward Rudolf House, Margery Street, London WC1X 0JL

TELEPHONE 0171-837 4299

FAX 0171-837 0211

CATEGORY Air miles • Antique post cards • Arts & crafts equipment • Books hardback • Books paperback • Bric-a-brac • Clocks • Clothing adults' • Clothing children's • Coins foreign • Coins old • Diy equipment • Fabric remnants • Household items *ironing boards etc* • Jewellery • Knitting, crochet and sewing equipment • Medals • Money-off coupons • Musical instruments • Petrol vouchers • Pets equipment •

Photographic equipment • Postcards used • Records & tapes *plus CDs* • Sports equipment • Stamps British • Stamps foreign • Telephone cards • Toys & games • Trading stamps • Used toner cartridges • Watches

COLLECTION SERVICE No

■ **Chiltern Voluntary Services**

ADDRESS 150 High Street, Chesham, Bucks HP5 1EF

TELEPHONE 01494 793470

CATEGORY Bed linen and mattresses *from within Chiltern District Council area* • Furniture *from within Chiltern District Council area* • Gardening equipment *from within Chiltern District Council area* • Household items *ironing boards etc from within Chiltern Distric Council area* • Office equipment and stationery *from within Bucks & neighbouring counties*

COLLECTION SERVICE Yes

■ **Chorley & South Ribble Crossroads Care Scheme**

ADDRESS Apex Business Centre, Stump Lane, Chorley, Lancs PR6 0DE

TELEPHONE 01257 230698

CATEGORY Computer hardware and software • Office equipment and stationery

COLLECTION SERVICE No

■ **Christchurch Hospital League of Friends**

ADDRESS Fairmile Road, Christchurch, Dorset BH23 2JX

TELEPHONE 01202 705283/485926

CATEGORY Antique post cards • Books paperback • Bric-a-brac • Clocks • Jewellery • Knitting, crochet and sewing equipment • Knitting wool • Stamps British • Stamps foreign • Toiletries • Toys & games • Watches

COLLECTION SERVICE No

■ **Christian Community Action**

ADDRESS 19 Stanshawe Road, Reading, Berks RG1 1PB

TELEPHONE 01734 512323

FAX 01734 573808

CATEGORY Air miles • Aluminium • Antique post cards • Arts & crafts equipment • Baby equipment • Bed linen and mattresses • Bicycles • Books hardback • Books paperback • Bric-a-brac • Clocks • Clothing adults' • Clothing children's • Coins foreign • Coins old • Computer hardware and software • Diy equipment • Fabric remnants • Fur coats • Furniture • Gardening equipment • Hearing aids • Household items *ironing boards etc* • Jewellery • Knitting, crochet and sewing equipment • Knitting wool • Medals • Milk bottle tops • Money-off coupons • Musical instruments • Non perishable foods • Office equipment and stationery • Other metals • Petrol vouchers • Pets equipment • Photographic equipment • Postcards used • Rags • Records & tapes • Silver paper & aluminium foil • Spectacles • Sports equipment • Stamps British • Stamps foreign • Telephone cards • Toiletries • Toys & games • Trading stamps • Watches • Wedding clothes for hire

COLLECTION SERVICE Yes

■ Christian Family Concern

ADDRESS Wallis House, 42 South Park Hill Road, South Croydon, Surrey CR2 7YB

TELEPHONE 0181-688 0251

FAX 0181-686 7114

CATEGORY Arts & crafts equipment • Baby equipment • Bed linen and mattresses *clean* • Clothing children's • Furniture • Household items *ironing boards etc* • Toiletries • Toys & games

COLLECTION SERVICE Yes

■ Colchester Furniture Project/Shake

ADDRESS 2 Whitewell Road, Colchester, Essex CO2 7DE

TELEPHONE 01206 43438

CATEGORY Furniture *colchester area only*

COLLECTION SERVICE Yes

■ Comic Relief

ADDRESS 74 New Oxford Street, London WC1A 1EF

TELEPHONE 0171 436 1122

FAX 0171 436 1541

CATEGORY Computer hardware and software office equipment and stationery

COLLECTION SERVICE No

■ Community Chest

ADDRESS 49a–49b West Street, Leominster, Hereford HR6 8EP

TELEPHONE 01568 613534

CATEGORY Baby equipment • Bed linen and mattresses *mattresses must meet fire regulations* • Books hardback • Books paperback • Bric-a-brac • Clocks • Clothing adults' • Clothing children's • Fabric remnants • Furniture *small items only, eg coffee tables, bedside units* • Household items *ironing boards etc* • Jewellery • Knitting, crochet and sewing equipment • Knitting wool • Magazines & comics • Musical instruments • Pets equipment • Records & tapes • Toys & games

COLLECTION SERVICE No

■ Community Chest Furniture Recycling Project

ADDRESS c/o 53 Abbey Road, Grimsby, Lincs DN32 0HQ

TELEPHONE 01472 343773

CATEGORY Bed linen and mattresses • Furniture • Household items *ironing boards etc*

COLLECTION SERVICE Yes

■ Community Furniture Project

ADDRESS c/o Victim Support, 9 Oldgate, Morpeth, Northumberland NE61 1PY

TELEPHONE 01670 510259

CATEGORY Baby equipment *in good repair and ready for passing on to cllients* • Bed linen and mattresses *in good repair and ready for passing on to clients* • Furniture *in good repair and ready for passing on to clients* • Household items *ironing boards etc in good repair and ready for passing on to clients*

COLLECTION SERVICE Yes

■ The Community Furniture Project

ADDRESS Unit 11, Crawford Street, Newport, Gwent NP9 7AY

TELEPHONE 01633 216855/216856

FAX 01633 216856

CATEGORY Baby equipment • Bric-a-brac • Childrens play/craft scrap • Furniture • Household items • Office equipment and stationery

COLLECTION SERVICE Yes

■ Community Furniture Service

ADDRESS 6 Heaton Terrace, Byker, Newcastle-upon-Tyne, Tyne & Wear NE6 1JR

TELEPHONE 0191-224 0555

FAX 0191-276 5042

CATEGORY Baby equipment • Bed linen and mattresses • Bicycles • Books hardback • Books paperback • Bric-a-brac • Clocks • Clothing adults' • Computer hardware and software • Diy equipment • Fabric remnants • Furniture • Gardening equipment • Household items *ironing boards etc* • Knitting, crochet and sewing equipment • Knitting wool • Magazines & comics • Musical instruments • Office equipment and stationery • Records & tapes • Sports equipment • Toys & games • Video/computer games

COLLECTION SERVICE Yes

■ Community Scrap Scheme

ADDRESS Canterbury Centre, Canterbury Road, Morden, Surrey SM4 6PT

TELEPHONE 0181-640 9510

CATEGORY Baby equipment • Bric-a-brac • Clocks • Computer hardware and software *depending on space* • Diy equipment • Fabric remnants *large*

pieces only ● Jewellery ● Knitting, crochet and sewing equipment ● Knitting wool ● Milk bottle tops *clean only* ● Musical instruments ● Plastics ● Records & tapes ● Silver paper & aluminium foil *safe ones only* ● Spectacles ● Toys & games ● Video/computer games ● Watches

COLLECTION SERVICE Yes

■ Community Transport

ADDRESS Heaton Terrace, Byker, Newcastle-upon-Tyne, Tyne & Wear NE6 1JR

TELEPHONE 0191 2240555

CATEGORY Baby equipment ● Bed linen and mattresses ● Bicycles ● Books hardback ● Books paperback ● Bric-a-brac ● Clothing adults' ● Clothing children's ● Computer hardware and software ● Diy equipment ● Fabric remnants ● Furniture ● Gardening equipment ● Household items *ironing boards etc* ● Magazines & comics ● Musical instruments ● Office equipment and stationery ● Records & tapes ● Sports equipment ● Toys & games, Video/computer games

COLLECTION SERVICE Yes

■ Community Transport

ADDRESS 43 Broad Street, Bilston, W Midlands WV14 0BU

TELEPHONE 01902 496010

CATEGORY Bed linen and mattresses ● Bicycles ● Bric-a-brac ● Clothing adults' ● Clothing children's ● Computer hardware and software ● Furniture ● Household items *ironing boards etc* ● Musical instruments ● Office equipment and stationery ● Photographic equipment ● Records & tapes ● Sports equipment ● Toys & games

COLLECTION SERVICE No

■ Community Transport

ADDRESS 269 Sovereign Road, Earlsdon, Coventry, W Midlands CV5 6LT

TELEPHONE 01203 691433

CATEGORY Bric-a-brac ● Furniture *no gas appliances, steel framed beds or furniture past using* ● Household items

COLLECTION SERVICE No

■ Community Transport – Birmingham Project

ADDRESS The Old School Building, Dixon Road, Small Heath, Birmingham, W Midlands B10 0BS

TELEPHONE 0121-773 2858

CATEGORY Baby equipment ● Bed linen and mattresses ● Books hardback ● Books paperback ● Bric-a-brac ● Clocks ● Clothing adults' ● Clothing children's ● Fabric remnants ● Furniture ● Gardening equipment ● Household items *ironing boards etc* ● Office equipment and stationery ● Records & tapes ● Sports equipment ● Toys & games

COLLECTION SERVICE Yes

■ Community Transport Sandwell

ADDRESS 34 Oldbury Road, Greets Green, West Bromwich, W Midlands B70 9ED

TELEPHONE 0121-520 8168

CATEGORY Bed linen and mattresses *mattresses only* ● Bric-a-brac ● Furniture ● Household items *ironing boards etc*

COLLECTION SERVICE Yes

■ Conservation Volunteers Northern Ireland

ADDRESS Beech House, 159 Ravenhill Road, Belfast, N Ireland BT6 0BD

TELEPHONE 01232 645169

FAX 01232 644409

E-MAIL cvni@btcv.org.uk

CATEGORY Air miles ● Bicycles ● Books hardback ● Books paperback ● Computer hardware and software *for computers only 386s & 8MB RAM or better* ● Diy equipment ● Furniture *in good condition* ● Gardening equipment ● Office equipment and stationery ● Petrol vouchers

COLLECTION SERVICE No

■ Cot-Age – Child Safety & Nursery Equipment

ADDRESS 23 Filey Street, Sheffield, S Yorks S10 2FH

TELEPHONE 0114-279 7971

CATEGORY Baby equipment ● Clothing children's *only up to age three* ● Petrol vouchers ● Toys & games *small, in good condition, suitable for under-fives*

COLLECTION SERVICE Yes

■ Council for Voluntary Service

ADDRESS Beach House, Beach Street, Herne Bay, Kent CT6 5PT

TELEPHONE 01227 373293

FAX 01227 742575

CATEGORY Computer hardware and software ● Furniture *office furniture only* ● Office equipment and stationery

COLLECTION SERVICE No

■ Craven Voluntary Action

ADDRESS 33 Coach Street, Skipton, N Yorks BD23 1LQ

TELEPHONE 01756 701056

CATEGORY Baby equipment ● Bed linen and mattresses ● Furniture ● Gardening equipment ● Household items *ironing boards etc* ● Office equipment and stationery

COLLECTION SERVICE Yes

■ Crawley Furni-Aid

ADDRESS 40 Linchmere Place, Ifield, Crawley, W Sussex RH11 0EX

TELEPHONE 01293 618844

CATEGORY Baby equipment *Crawley area only* ● Bed linen and mattresses *Crawley area only* ● Furniture *Crawley area only* ● Household items *ironing boards etc Crawley area only*

COLLECTION SERVICE Yes

■ Crisis

ADDRESS 7 Whitechapel Road, London E1 1DU

TELEPHONE 0171-377 0489

FAX 0171-247 1525

E-MAIL crisis.uk@easynet.co.uk

CATEGORY Arts & crafts equipment ● Bed linen and mattresses ● Books hardback ● Books paperback ● Clothing adults' *all men's and women's sizes 20 plus* ● Diy equipment ● Fabric remnants ● Knitting, crochet and sewing equipment ● Knitting wool ● Magazines & comics ● Non perishable foods *only in December* ● Petrol vouchers ● Pets equipment *dogs only* ● Toiletries *individual sizes only* ● Toys & games *board games for adults*

COLLECTION SERVICE No

■ Croctal (Crochet & Other Handcrafts)

ADDRESS c/o 66 Hendon Rise, Nottingham, Notts NG3 3AN

TELEPHONE 0115-941 1340

FAX 0115-941 9514

CATEGORY Antique post cards *only if craft pictures* ● Arts & crafts equipment *only to do with thread crafts* ● Books hardback *craft – especially crochet, knitting and embroidery* ● Books paperback *craft – especially crotchet, knitting and embroidery* ● Knitting, crochet and sewing equipment *all, modern and old* ● Knitting wool ● Magazines & comics *craft – especially old ones*

COLLECTION SERVICE Yes

■ Croydon Voluntary Action

ADDRESS 9 High Street, Purley, Croydon, Surrey CR8 2AF

TELEPHONE 0181-668 0246

CATEGORY Books hardback ● Books paperback ● Bric-a-brac ● Clothing adults' *must be clean and in good condition* ● Clothing children's *must be clean and in good condition* ● Household items *ironing boards etc* ● Jewellery ● Records & tapes ● Toys & games

COLLECTION SERVICE No

■ CSV Vocal Project

ADDRESS Social Service Offices, Howdale Road, Downham Market, Norfolk PE38 9EN

CATEGORY Air miles ● Arts & crafts equipment ● Fabric remnants ● Household items *ironing boards etc* ● Knitting, crochet and sewing equipment ● Knitting wool ● Money-off coupons ● Musical instruments ● Petrol vouchers ● Photographic equipment ● Records & tapes ● Sports equipment ● Trading stamps ● Video/computer games

COLLECTION SERVICE Yes

■ Dacorum Council for Voluntary Service

ADDRESS 48 High Street, Hemel Hempstead, Herts HP1 3AF

TELEPHONE 01442 253935

FAX 01442 239775

CATEGORY Jewellery ● Money-off coupons ● Office equipment and stationery ● Petrol vouchers ● Records & tapes ● Video/computer games

COLLECTION SERVICE Yes

■ Dartford District Volunteer Bureau

ADDRESS 33 Essex Road, Dartford, Kent DA1 2AU

TELEPHONE 01322 272476

CATEGORY Books paperback ● Bric-a-brac ● Clocks ● Jewellery ● Records & tapes ● Toiletries ● Toys & games ● Waste paper *cardboard, telephone directories, catalogues* ● Watches

COLLECTION SERVICE Yes

■ Daventry Contact

ADDRESS Units 1 & 2, High March, Long March Industrial Estate, Daventry, Northants NN11 4PH

TELEPHONE 01327 310711

CATEGORY Baby equipment ● Bed linen and mattresses ● Bicycles ● Books hardback ● Books paperback ● Bric-a-brac ● Clocks ● Clothing adults' ● Clothing children's ● Diy equipment ● Fabric remnants ● Fur coats ● Furniture ● Gardening equipment ● Hearing aids ● Household items *ironing boards etc* ● Jewellery ● Knitting, crochet and sewing equipment ● Knitting wool ● Magazines & comics ● Non perishable foods ● Spectacles ● Toys & games ● Watches

COLLECTION SERVICE Yes

■ David Livingstone International

ADDRESS 9a Woodside Terrace, Glasgow, Strathclyde G3 7UY

TELEPHONE 0141-332 9423

FAX 0141-331 1321

CATEGORY Computer hardware and software ● Gardening equipment ● Musical instruments ● Non perishable foods ● Office equipment and stationery • Photographic equipment • Spectacles • Video/computer games • Watches

COLLECTION SERVICE No

■ Derby Furniture Project

ADDRESS 52 St Helen's Street, Derby, Derbys DE1 3GY

TELEPHONE 01332 291121

FAX 01332 291121

CATEGORY Baby equipment • Bed linen and mattresses • Bicycles • Books hardback • Books paperback • Bric-a-brac • Clocks • Furniture • Gardening equipment • Household items *ironing boards etc* • Office equipment and stationery • Other metals • Records & tapes

COLLECTION SERVICE Yes

■ Dereham Gingerbread Club

ADDRESS 7 William Way, Toftwood, Dereham, Norfolk NR19 1TQ

TELEPHONE 01362 697123

CATEGORY Arts & crafts equipment • Books hardback *children's books* • Books paperback *children's books* • Childrens play/craft scrap • Clothing adults' *clothes suitable for children's dressing up* • Clothing children's • Money-off coupons • Musical instruments • Office equipment and stationery • Petrol vouchers • Sports equipment *children's bats and balls, etc* • Toys & games

COLLECTION SERVICE No

■ Devres & District PHAB

ADDRESS The Firs, 70 Martins Road, Keevil, Trowbridge, Wilts BA14 6NA

TELEPHONE 01380 870274

CATEGORY Bric-a-brac • Money-off coupons • Petrol vouchers *diesel only* • Records & tapes • Stamps British • Stamps foreign • Toiletries • Toys & games • Trading stamps

COLLECTION SERVICE No

■ Directorate of Health Promotion

ADDRESS 79 London Road, Stoke, Staffs ST4 7PZ

TELEPHONE 01782 744444

FAX 01782 745107

CATEGORY Office equipment and stationery • Used toner cartridges

COLLECTION SERVICE No

■ Disability Action Sutton

ADDRESS Sutton West Centre, Robin Hood Lane, Sutton, Surrey SM1 2SD

TELEPHONE 0181-643 6059

FAX 0181-643 4144

CATEGORY Air miles • Antique post cards • Bicycles • Books hardback • Books paperback • Bric-a-brac • Christmas cards • Clocks • Clothing adults' • Clothing children's • Coins foreign • Coins old • Computer hardware and software • Diy equipment • Fabric remnants • Furniture • Gardening equipment • Household items *ironing boards etc* • Jewellery • Knitting, crochet and sewing equipment • Knitting wool • Magazines & comics • Medals • Money-off coupons • Musical instruments • Office equipment and stationery • Petrol vouchers • Photographic equipment • Postcards used • Records & tapes • Stamps British • Stamps foreign • Toiletries • Toys & games • Trading stamps • Video/computer games • Watches

COLLECTION SERVICE No

■ Disability Network

ADDRESS Templeton Business Centre, 62 Templeton Street, Glasgow, Strathclyde G40 1DA

TELEPHONE 0141-556 5299

CATEGORY Baby equipment • Bric-a-brac • Clocks • Clothing adults' • Clothing children's • Diy equipment • Hearing aids • Jewellery • Spectacles • Watches

COLLECTION SERVICE No

■ Disabled Photographers' Society

ADDRESS PO Box 130, Richmond, Surrey TW10 6XQ

CATEGORY Computer hardware and software *small PCs laptops and printers only* • Photographic equipment *no cine equipment*

COLLECTION SERVICE Yes

■ Dorcas Project/Basics Bank

ADDRESS Southampton City Mission, c/o St John's Centre, St James Road, Shirley, Southampton, Hants SO15 5FB

TELEPHONE 01703 773132

CATEGORY Baby equipment • Bed linen and mattresses • Bicycles *children's* • Clothing children's • Furniture • Gardening equipment • Household items *ironing boards etc* • Non perishable foods • Toys & games

COLLECTION SERVICE Yes (please note – items must not be delivered to office address)

■ Dover District Volunteer Bureau

ADDRESS Biggin Hall, High Street, Dover, Kent
CT16 1DL

TELEPHONE 01304 211696

CATEGORY Fabric remnants *must be new* ● Knitting
wool *must be new*

COLLECTION SERVICE No

■ Drumchapel Furnishaid Project

ADDRESS Drumchapel Community Business, Unit 18,
42 Dalsetter Avenue, Glasgow, Strathclyde
G15 8SL

TELEPHONE 0141-944 1537

CATEGORY Baby equipment ● Bed linen and
mattresses ● Bric-a-brac ● Clocks ● Diy equipment
● Furniture ● Gardening equipment ● Household
items *ironing boards etc* ● Toys & games

COLLECTION SERVICE Yes

■ Dumfries Furniture Project Limited

ADDRESS 24 Friars Vennel, Dumfries, Dumfries &
Galloway DG1 2RL

TELEPHONE 01387 256736

CATEGORY Bed linen and mattresses ● Bric-a-brac
● Clocks ● Furniture ● Household items *ironing
boards etc* ● Office equipment and stationery

COLLECTION SERVICE Yes

■ Dundee Voluntary Action

ADDRESS Kandahar House, 71 Meadowside,
Dundee, Angus DD1 1EN

TELEPHONE 01382 221545

FAX 01382 223238

CATEGORY Books hardback ● Books paperback ● Bric-
a-brac ● Clothing adults' ● Clothing children's
● Jewellery ● Records & tapes ● Toys & games

COLLECTION SERVICE No

■ Eastbourne Playbus

ADDRESS 8 Saffron's Road, Eastbourne, E Sussex
BN21 3YD

TELEPHONE 01323 646655

CATEGORY Arts & crafts equipment ● Baby
equipment ● Childrens play/craft scrap ● Fabric
remnants ● Milk bottle tops ● Musical
instruments ● Office equipment and stationery
● Silver paper & aluminium foil ● Sports
equipment ● Toys & games ● Waste paper

COLLECTION SERVICE No

■ Eastwood Volunteer Bureau

ADDRESS 89a Nottingham Road, Eastwood, Notts
NE16 3AJ

TELEPHONE 01773 710238

FAX 01773 531838

CATEGORY Baby equipment ● Bed linen and
mattresses ● Clocks ● Furniture ● Gardening
equipment ● Household items *ironing boards etc*
● Knitting wool ● Spectacles

COLLECTION SERVICE Yes

■ Edinburgh Furniture Initiative

ADDRESS 157 Slateford Road, Edinburgh, Lothian
EN14 1PB

TELEPHONE 0131-455 8521

FAX 0131-455 7399

CATEGORY Bed linen and mattresses *useable
condition only* ● Furniture *useable condition only*
● Household items *ironing boards etc*

COLLECTION SERVICE Yes

■ Elimination of Leukaemia Fund

ADDRESS 17 Venetian Road, London SE5 9RR

TELEPHONE 0171-737 4141

FAX 0171-737 4141

CATEGORY Air miles ● Books hardback *good quality
ones* ● Books paperback *good quality only*
● Clothing adults' *good quality only* ● Clothing
children's *good quality only* ● Coins foreign ● Fur
coats *good quality only* ● Jewellery *good quality
only* ● Petrol vouchers ● Records & tapes *good
quality only* ● Trading stamps

COLLECTION SERVICE No

■ Emmanuel House Day Centre

ADDRESS 53–61 Goosegate, Nottingham, Notts
NG1 1FE

TELEPHONE 0115-950 7140

FAX 0115-941 0663

CATEGORY Arts & crafts equipment ● Books hardback
● Books paperback ● Clothing adults' ● Clothing
children's ● Computer hardware and software
● Gardening equipment ● Household items
ironing boards etc ● Jewellery ● Knitting wool
● Musical instruments ● Non perishable foods
● Office equipment and stationery ● Toiletries
● Toys & games *games only*

COLLECTION SERVICE No

■ Emmaus (Cambridge)

ADDRESS Green End, Landbeach, Cambridge, Cambs CB4 4ED

TELEPHONE 01223 863657

FAX 01223 860387

CATEGORY Aluminium • Antique post cards • Arts & crafts equipment • Bed linen and mattresses • Bicycles • Books hardback • Books paperback • Bric-a-brac • Clocks • Clothing adults' • Clothing children's • Coins foreign • Coins old • Computer hardware and software • Diy equipment • Fabric remnants • Furniture • Gardening equipment • Household items *ironing boards etc* • Jewellery • Knitting, crochet and sewing equipment • Medals • Money-off coupons • Musical instruments • Office equipment and stationery • Other metals • Photographic equipment • Records & tapes • Silver paper & aluminium foil • Spectacles • Sports equipment • Stamps British • Stamps foreign • Toys & games • Video/computer games

COLLECTION SERVICE Yes

■ Emmaus (Coventry & Warwickshire)

ADDRESS The Old Vicarage, Brinklow Road, Coventry, Warks CV3 2DT

TELEPHONE 01203 651094

FAX 01203 651094

CATEGORY Aluminium • Antique post cards • Arts & crafts equipment • Baby equipment • Bed linen and mattresses • Bicycles • Books hardback • Books paperback • Bric-a-brac • Childrens play/craft scrap • Christmas cards • Clocks • Clothing adults' • Clothing children's • Coins foreign • Coins old • Computer hardware and software • Diy equipment • Fabric remnants • Furniture • Gardening equipment • Glass • Hearing aids • Household items *ironing boards etc* • Jewellery • Knitting, crochet and sewing equipment • Knitting wool • Magazines & comics • Medals • Milk bottle tops • Motorbike engines, car engines, spare parts • Musical instruments • Non perishable foods • Office equipment and stationery • Other metals • Pets equipment • Photographic equipment • Plastics • Postcards used • Rags • Records & tapes • Silver paper & aluminium foil • Spectacles • Sports equipment • Stamps British • Stamps foreign • Telephone cards • Toiletries • Toys & games • Video/computer games • Waste paper • Watches • Wedding clothes for hire

COLLECTION SERVICE Yes

■ Emmaus (Greater Manchester)

ADDRESS Emmaus (Mossley), Longlands Mill, Mossley, Ashton-under-Lyme, Lancs OL5 9AH

TELEPHONE 01457 838608

CATEGORY Air miles • Aluminium • Antique post cards • Arts & crafts equipment • Baby equipment • Bed linen and mattresses • Bicycles • Books hardback • Books paperback • Bric-a-brac • Childrens play/craft scrap • Christmas cards • Clocks • Clothing adults' • Clothing children's • Coins foreign • Coins old • Computer hardware andsoftware • Diyequipment • Fabricremnants •

Furniture • Gardening equipment • Household items *ironing boards etc* • Jewellery • Knitting, crochet and sewing equipment • Knitting wool • Magazines & comics • Medals • Milk bottle tops • Money-off coupons • Musical instruments • Non perishable foods • Office equipment and stationery • Other metals • Petrol vouchers • Pets equipment • Photographic equipment • Plastics • Postcards used • Rags • Records & tapes • Silver paper & aluminium foil • Sports equipment • Stamps British • Stamps foreign • Telephone cards • Toiletries • Toys & games • Trading stamps • Used toner cartridges • Video/computer games • Waste paper *a4 sheets only* • Watches

COLLECTION SERVICE Yes

■ Emmaus Liberty Belfast

ADDRESS 32 Clifton Street, Belfast, N Ireland BT13 1AA

TELEPHONE 01232 323631

CATEGORY Aluminium • Arts & crafts equipment • Baby equipment • Bed linen and mattresses • Bicycles • Books hardback • Books paperback • Bric-a-brac • Clocks • Clothing adults' • Clothing children's • Computer hardware and software • Diy equipment • Furniture • Gardening equipment • Household items *ironing boards etc* • Jewellery • Knitting, crochet and sewing equipment • Knitting wool • Musical instruments • Non perishable foods • Office equipment and stationery • Records & tapes • Sports equipment • Toiletries • Toys & games • Video/computer games

COLLECTION SERVICE Yes

■ Emmaus (Scarborough)

ADDRESS 15 Hanover Road, Scarborough, N Yorks YO11 1LS

TELEPHONE 01723 355591

CATEGORY Antique post cards • Arts & crafts equipment • Baby equipment • Bed linen and mattresses • Bicycles • Books hardback • Books paperback • Bric-a-brac • Clocks • Clothing adults' • Clothing children's • Coins foreign • Coins old • Diy equipment • Fabric remnants • Furniture • Gardening equipment • Glass • Household items *ironing boards etc* • Jewellery • Knitting, crochet and sewing equipment • Knitting wool • Magazines & comics • Medals • Musical instruments • Pets equipment • Photographic equipment • Postcards used • Records & tapes • Spectacles • Sports equipment • Stamps British • Stamps foreign • Toiletries • Toys & games • Video/computer games • Watches

COLLECTION SERVICE Yes

■ Enable (Scottish Society for the Mentally Handicapped)

ADDRESS Curran House, 9 Lynedoch Street, Glasgow, Strathclyde G3 6EF

TELEPHONE 0141-332 7420

CATEGORY Arts & crafts equipment • Baby equipment • Books hardback • Books paperback • Bric-a-brac • Clothing adults' *in good condition*

suitable for resale ● Clothing children's *in good condition suitable for resale* ● Fabric remnants ● Furniture ● Household items *ironing boards etc* ● Jewellery ● Knitting, crochet and sewing equipment ● Knitting wool ● Petrol vouchers ● Postcards used ● Sports equipment ● Stamps British ● Stamps foreign ● Toiletries ● Toys & games ● Trading stamps ● Video/computer games

COLLECTION SERVICE Yes

■ Enfield Preservation Society

ADDRESS 107 Parsonage Lane, Enfield, Middx EN2 0AB

TELEPHONE 0181-366 3016

CATEGORY Antique post cards *LB Enfield only* ● Bric-a-brac ● Office equipment and stationery ● Postcards used *LB Enfield only*

COLLECTION SERVICE Yes

■ Epilepsy Network Gravesend

ADDRESS 13 St George's Crescent, Gravesend, Kent DA12 4AR

TELEPHONE 01474 351673

CATEGORY Air miles ● Money-off coupons ● Office equipment and stationery ● Petrol vouchers ● Stamps British ● Stamps foreign ● Trading stamps

COLLECTION SERVICE No

■ Epping Forest Field Centre

ADDRESS High Beech, Nr Loughton, Essex IG10 4AF

TELEPHONE 0181-508 7714

FAX 0181-508 8429

CATEGORY Clothing adults' *wellingtons & waterproofs only* ● Clothing children's *wellingtons & waterproofs only* ● Office equipment and stationery ● Petrol vouchers

COLLECTION SERVICE No

■ Epsom & Ewell Phab Club

ADDRESS 119 East Street, Epsom, Surrey KT17 1EJ

TELEPHONE 01372 720123

CATEGORY Arts & crafts equipment ● Books paperback ● Bric-a-brac ● Computer hardware and software ● Diy equipment ● Fabric remnants ● Jewellery ● Knitting, crochet and sewing equipment ● Knitting wool ● Musical instruments ● Office equipment and stationery ● Photographic equipment ● Records & tapes ● Sports equipment ● Stamps British ● Stamps foreign ● Toiletries ● Toys & games ● Trading stamps ● Video/computer games

COLLECTION SERVICE No

■ Exeter CVS Charity Shop

ADDRESS 102 Sidwell Street, Exeter, Devon

TELEPHONE 01392 427963

CATEGORY Books hardback ● Books paperback ● Bric-a-brac ● Clothing adults' ● Clothing children's ● Jewellery ● Records & tapes ● Toys & games

COLLECTION SERVICE No

■ Family Advice Centre

ADDRESS Woodhouse Clinic, Fell View Avenue, Woodhouse, Whitehaven, Cumbria CA28 9LH

TELEPHONE 01946 67645

CATEGORY Arts & crafts equipment ● Baby equipment ● Bed linen and mattresses ● Books hardback ● Books paperback ● Bric-a-brac ● Clocks ● Clothing adults' ● Clothing children's ● Furniture ● Household items *ironing boards etc* ● Toys & games

COLLECTION SERVICE Yes

■ Family First Limited

ADDRESS 375 Alfred Street North, Nottingham, Notts NG3 1AA

TELEPHONE 0115-950 7295

CATEGORY Baby equipment ● Bed linen and mattresses ● Bicycles ● Books hardback ● Books paperback ● Bric-a-brac ● Clocks ● Clothing adults' ● Clothing children's ● Computer hardware and software ● Diy equipment ● Fabric remnants ● Furniture ● Household items *ironing boards etc* ● Musical instruments ● Office equipment and stationery ● Photographic equipment ● Records & tapes ● Sports equipment ● Toys & games ● Video/computer games

COLLECTION SERVICE Yes

■ Family Holiday Association

ADDRESS 16 Mortimer Street, London W1N 7RD

TELEPHONE 0171-436 3302

CATEGORY Air miles ● Money-off coupons ● Petrol vouchers ● Trading stamps

COLLECTION SERVICE No

■ Family Support Scheme Stotford & Arlesey (part of Christian Family Care)

ADDRESS 97 Church Road, Stotford, Nr Hitchin, Herts SG5 4NE

TELEPHONE 01462 733769

FAX 01462 733769

CATEGORY Arts & crafts equipment ● Baby equipment *storage restricted* ● Furniture *storage restricted* ● Gardening equipment ● Non perishable foods ● Toys & games *in good order and condition*

COLLECTION SERVICE No

■ Farleigh (Mid-Essex Hospice)

ADDRESS 212 New London Road, Chelmsford, Essex CM1 1HL

TELEPHONE 01245 358130

FAX 01245 344412

CATEGORY Air miles ● Antique post cards ● Arts & crafts equipment ● Baby equipment ● Bed linen and mattresses ● Bicycles ● Books hardback ● Books paperback ● Bric-a-brac ● Christmas cards ● Clocks ● Clothing adults' ● Clothing children's ● Coins foreign ● Coins old ● Computer hardware and software ● Diy equipment ● Fabric remnants ● Fur coats *for recycling to rag only* ● Furniture ● Gardening equipment ● Household items *ironing boards etc* ● Jewellery ● Knitting, crochet and sewing equipment ● Knitting wool ● Magazines & comics ● Medals ● Money-off coupons ● Musical instruments ● Petrol vouchers ● Photographic equipment ● Postcards used ● Rags ● Records & tapes ● Sports equipment ● Stamps British ● Stamps foreign ● Toys & games ● Video/computer games ● Waste paper ● Watches ● Wedding clothes for hire

COLLECTION SERVICE Yes

■ Feed the Minds

ADDRESS Robertson House, Leas Road, Guildford, Surrey GU1 4QW

TELEPHONE 01483 577877

FAX 01483 301387

E-MAIL feedtheminds@ gn.apc.org

CATEGORY Air miles ● Books hardback ● Books paperback ● Computer hardware and software ● Magazines & comics ● Office equipment and stationery ● Petrol vouchers ● Photographic equipment ● Records & tapes ● Stamps foreign ● Waste paper

COLLECTION SERVICE No

■ Feline Foster

ADDRESS 31 Battle Road, St Leonards-on-Sea, E Sussex TN37 7AA

TELEPHONE 01424 432687

CATEGORY Antique post cards ● Bric-a-brac ● Clocks ● Coins foreign ● Jewellery ● Musical instruments ● Pets equipment *cat items only* ● Records & tapes ● Stamps British ● Stamps foreign ● Toiletries ● Watches

COLLECTION SERVICE No

■ Ferne Animal Sanctuary

ADDRESS Wambrook, Nr Chard, Somerset TA20 3DH

TELEPHONE 01460 62514

FAX 01460 62514

CATEGORY Bric-a-brac ● Office equipment and stationery ● Stamps British ● Stamps foreign

COLLECTION SERVICE No

■ FRADE

ADDRESS Green Lane, Stockton on Tees, Cleveland, Durham TS19 0DP

TELEPHONE 01642 608791

CATEGORY Baby equipment ● Bed linen and mattresses ● Bric-a-brac ● Furniture ● Household items *ironing boards etc* ● Office equipment and stationery ● Toys & games

COLLECTION SERVICE Yes

■ Friends of Animals League

ADDRESS FOAL Farm, Jail Lane, Biggin Hill, Kent TN16 3AX

TELEPHONE 01959 572386

CATEGORY Air miles ● Antique post cards ● Arts & crafts equipment ● Bed linen and mattresses *blankets only* ● Bicycles ● Books hardback ● Books paperback ● Bric-a-brac ● Clocks ● Clothing adults' ● Clothing children's ● Coins foreign ● Coins old ● Computer hardware and software ● Diy equipment ● Fur coats ● Gardening equipment ● Household items *ironing boards etc not electrical* ● Jewellery ● Knitting wool ● Medals ● Money-off coupons ● Office equipment and stationery ● Petrol vouchers ● Pets equipment ● Records & tapes ● Stamps British ● Stamps foreign ● Toiletries ● Toys & games ● Trading stamps ● Waste paper *newspapers only* ● Watches

COLLECTION SERVICE Yes

■ Friends of Biggleswade Hospital

ADDRESS 15 Chaucer Drive, Biggleswade, Beds SG18 8QG

TELEPHONE 01767 312381

CATEGORY Antique post cards ● Books hardback ● Books paperback ● Bric-a-brac ● Knitting wool ● Records & tapes ● Spectacles ● Used toner cartridges

COLLECTION SERVICE Yes

■ The Friends of Blandford Community Hospital

ADDRESS Blandford Community Hospital, Milldown Road, Blandford, Dorset DT11 7DD

TELEPHONE 01258 450095

FAX 01258 450095

CATEGORY Bed linen and mattresses *no mattresses* ● Books hardback ● Books paperback ● Bric-a-brac ● Clocks ● Clothing adults' ● Clothing children's ● Coins foreign ● Coins old ● Diy equipment ● Fabric remnants ● Furniture *only small occasional type* ● Household items *ironing boards etc* ● Jewellery ● Knitting, crochet and sewing equipment ● Knitting wool ● Musical instruments ● Photographic equipment ● Records & tapes ● Sports equipment ● Toiletries ● Toys & games ● Video/computer games ● Watches

COLLECTION SERVICE No

■ Friends of Danesbury

ADDRESS Danesbury Home, School Lane, Welwyn, Herts AL6 9SB

TELEPHONE 01438 840514

E-MAIL (a.toms)101642.1040@compuserve.com

CATEGORY Aluminium *cans only* ● Antique post cards ● Arts & crafts equipment ● Baby equipment ● Bed linen and mattresses *not mattresses* ● Bicycles ● Books hardback ● Books paperback ● Bric-a-brac ● Clocks ● Clothing adults' ● Clothing children's ● Coins foreign ● Coins old ● Diy equipment ● Fabric remnants ● Furniture ● Gardening equipment ● Household items *ironing boards etc* ● Jewellery ● Knitting wool ● Magazines & comics ● Medals ● Musical instruments ● Photographic equipment ● Records & tapes ● Sports equipment ● Toiletries ● Toys & games ● Watches

COLLECTION SERVICE No

■ Friends of the Eastbourne Hospitals

ADDRESS Eastbourne District General Hospital, Kings Drive, Eastbourne, E Sussex BN21 2UD

TELEPHONE 01323 417400 ext 4696

CATEGORY Antique post cards ● Books hardback ● Books paperback ● Bric-a-brac ● Clothing adults' *nearly new only* ● Diy equipment ● Fabric remnants ● Household items *ironing boards etc* ● Jewellery ● Knitting wool ● Postcards *used* ● Records & tapes ● Stamps British ● Stamps foreign ● Toiletries ● Toys & games ● Used toner cartridges *hewlett packard 51625a only*

COLLECTION SERVICE No

■ Friends of King's College Hospital

ADDRESS King's College Hospital, Denmark Hill, London SE5 9RS

TELEPHONE 0171-346 3370

FAX 0171-346 3445

CATEGORY Books hardback ● Books paperback ● Bric-a-brac ● Jewellery ● Knitting, crochet and sewing equipment ● Knitting wool ● Toiletries ● Toys & games

COLLECTION SERVICE No

■ Friends of Moorfields Eye Hospital

ADDRESS 162 City Road, London EC1V 2PD

TELEPHONE 0171-251 1240

FAX 0171-253 4696

CATEGORY Books hardback *good condition only* ● Books paperback *good condition only* ● Bric-a-brac *good condition only* ● Coins foreign ● Records & tapes *good condition* ● Spectacles ● Toiletries *new items only* ● Toys & games *new or good condition*

COLLECTION SERVICE No

■ The Friends of St Francis Hospice (Shops) Ltd

ADDRESS The Hall, Havering-atte-Bower, Romford, Essex RM4 1QH

TELEPHONE 01708 640838

CATEGORY Antique post cards ● Arts & crafts equipment ● Baby equipment ● Bed linen and mattresses ● Bicycles ● Bric-a-brac ● Clocks ● Clothing adults' ● Clothing children's ● Coins foreign ● Coins old ● Diy equipment ● Furniture *foam filled must comply with trading standards* ● Gardening equipment ● Household items *ironing boards etc* ● Jewellery ● Knitting, crochet, sewing equipment ● Knitting wool ● Medals ● Musical instruments ● Photographic equipment ● Records & tapes ● Sports equipment ● Toiletries ● Toys & games ● Video/computer games ● Watches ● Wedding clothes for hire

COLLECTION SERVICE Yes

■ Friends of Wallace Kennels

ADDRESS The Haven, Lower Dunton Road, Upminster, Essex RM14 3TD

TELEPHONE 01268 413522

CATEGORY Books paperback ● Bric-a-brac ● Pets equipment ● Toiletries ● Toys & games

COLLECTION SERVICE No

■ Full House Furniture and Recycling Service

ADDRESS Unit 5, Longhope Industrial Estate, Church Road, Longhope, Gloucs GL17 0LB

TELEPHONE 01452 830820

FAX 01452 830822

CATEGORY Antique post cards ● Arts & crafts equipment ● Baby equipment ● Bed linen and mattresses ● Bicycles ● Books hardback ● Books paperback ● Bric-a-brac ● Clocks ● Clothing adults' ● Clothing children's ● Coins foreign ● Coins old ● Computer hardware and software ● Diy equipment ● Fabric remnants ● Furniture ● Gardening equipment ● Household items *ironing boards etc* ● Jewellery ● Knitting, crochet and sewing equipment ● Knitting wool ● Medals ● Musical instruments ● Office equipment and stationery ● Photographic equipment ● Records & tapes ● Sports equipment ● Toiletries ● Toys & games ● Video/computer games ● Watches

COLLECTION SERVICE Yes

■ Full House Furniture & Recycling Service

ADDRESS Unit 2, Holme Lacy Industrial Estate, Holme Lacy Road, Hereford & Worcs HR2 6DR

TELEPHONE 01432 342042

FAX 01432 342014

CATEGORY Arts & crafts equipment ● Baby equipment ● Bed linen and mattresses ● Bicycles ● Books hardback ● Books paperback ● Bric-a-brac ● Clocks ● Clothing adults' ● Clothing children's ● Computer hardware and software ● Diy equipment • Furniture • Gardening equipment • Household items *ironing boards etc* • Jewellery • Knitting, crochet and sewing equipment • Musical instruments • Office equipment and stationery • Photographic equipment • Records & tapes • Sports equipment • Toys & games • Video/computer games • Watches

COLLECTION SERVICE Yes

■ Furnicare

ADDRESS Unit 6, Houndstone Small Business Park, Yeovil, Somerset BA22 8WA

TELEPHONE 01935 33416

CATEGORY Baby equipment • Bed linen and mattresses • Bric-a-brac • Clocks • Furniture • Gardening equipment • Household items *ironing boards etc* • Video/computer games

COLLECTION SERVICE Yes

■ Furnish

ADDRESS 1 Swanscombe Garages, Queensdale Crescent, London W11 4TT

TELEPHONE 0171-602 3443

FAX 0171-610 4441

CATEGORY Diy equipment *only hand tools which are electric* • Furniture • Household items *ironing boards etc*

COLLECTION SERVICE Yes

■ Furniture Action

ADDRESS Malvern Hills Council of Community Service, Library Buildings, 44 Graham Road, Malvern, Hereford & Worcs WR14 2HU

TELEPHONE 01684 563872

CATEGORY Baby equipment • Bed linen and mattresses *mattresses and bedbases only – no bed linen* • Furniture *and carpets* • Household items *ironing boards etc*

COLLECTION SERVICE Yes

■ Furniture Aid South Thames

ADDRESS Block F, Offley Works, Prima Road, London SW9 0LR

TELEPHONE 0171-793 7787

FAX 0171-793 7787

CATEGORY Baby equipment • Bed linen and mattresses *must be in good condition* • Furniture *must be in good condition* • Household items *ironing boards etc*

COLLECTION SERVICE Yes

■ The Furniture Project

ADDRESS Unit 190, Road E, Boughton Industrial Estate, Northside, Boughton Newark, Notts NG22 9LD

TELEPHONE 01623 836410

CATEGORY Baby equipment • Bed linen and mattresses • Bicycles • Bric-a-brac • Furniture • Household items *ironing boards etc* • Toys & games

COLLECTION SERVICE Yes

■ The Furniture Recycling Project

ADDRESS Warehouse No 5, West Quay, The Docks, Gloucester, Gloucs GL1 2EH

TELEPHONE 01452 331333

FAX 01452 331333

CATEGORY Baby equipment • Bed linen and mattresses *mattresses must be clean* • Bicycles • Books hardback • Books paperback • Bric-a-brac • Clocks • Computer hardware and software • Diy equipment • Furniture • Gardening equipment • Household items *ironing boards etc* • Office equipment and stationery

COLLECTION SERVICE Yes

■ 'Garden Call'

ADDRESS 14 Town Hall Street, Grimsby, Lincs DN31 1HN

TELEPHONE 01472 353446

FAX 01472 359935

CATEGORY Diy equipment • Gardening equipment

COLLECTION SERVICE Yes

■ The Gideons International

ADDRESS Western House, George Street, Lutterworth, Leics LE17 4EE

TELEPHONE 01455 554241

FAX 01455 558267

CATEGORY Air miles • Computer hardware and software • Money-off coupons • Office equipment and stationery • Petrol vouchers • Stamps British *commemoratives only* • Stamps foreign • Toys & games • Trading stamps

COLLECTION SERVICE No

■ Gingerbread

ADDRESS c/o 69 Bedford Road South, Alderney, Poole, Dorset BH12 4PR

TELEPHONE 01202 241281

CATEGORY Antique post cards • Arts & crafts equipment • Baby equipment • Bed linen and mattresses • Bicycles • Bric-a-brac • Clocks • Clothing adults' • Clothing children's • Coins foreign • Coins old • Diy equipment • Fabric remnants • Furniture • Gardening equipment • Household items *ironing boards etc* • Jewellery •

Knitting, crochet and sewing equipment
• Knitting wool • Medals • Money-off coupons
• Motorbike engines, car engines, spare parts
• Non perishable foods • Petrol vouchers
• Records & tapes • Sports equipment • Stamps
British • Stamps foreign • Toiletries • Toys &
games • Video/computer games

COLLECTION SERVICE No

■ Gloucestershire Resource Centre

ADDRESS City Works, Alfred Street, Gloucester,
Gloucs GL1 4DF

TELEPHONE 01452 504442

CATEGORY Arts & crafts equipment • Childrens play/
craft scrap • Fabric remnants • Photographic
equipment • Plastics *clean* • Used toner
cartridges • Waste paper *clean*

COLLECTION SERVICE Yes

■ The Guide Dogs for the Blind Association

ADDRESS Hillfields, Burghfield, Berks RG7 3YG

TELEPHONE 0118-983 5555

FAX 0118-983 5211

CATEGORY Air miles • Aluminium • Antique post
cards • Coins foreign • Coins old • Milk bottle tops
• Money-off coupons • Petrol vouchers
• Postcards used • Silver paper & aluminium foil
• Stamps British • Stamps foreign • Telephone
cards • Trading stamps • Used toner cartridges
• Waste paper *in some parts of the country only*

COLLECTION SERVICE No

■ Guide Dogs for the Blind Association

ADDRESS 2 Park Lane, Bretton, Nr Wakefield,
W Yorks WF4 4JT

TELEPHONE 01924 830228

CATEGORY Aluminim • Coins foreign • Coins old
• Milk bottle tops • Silver paper & aluminium foil
• Stamps British • Stamps foreign

COLLECTION SERVICE No

■ Guide Dogs for the Blind – Poole & District Branch

ADDRESS 42 Wedgwood Drive, Poole, Dorset
BH14 8EX

TELEPHONE 01202 731116

CATEGORY Aluminium *foil* • Antique post cards *any
postcards* • Coins foreign • Coins old • Milk bottle
tops • Postcards used • Silver paper & aluminium
foil • Stamps British • Stamps foreign • Telephone
cards

COLLECTION SERVICE Yes

■ Guild Care

ADDRESS 1 Aldsworth Parade, Gorling Way, Gorling
by Sea, W Sussex BN12 4TX

TELEPHONE 01903 700960

FAX 01903 700296

CATEGORY Arts & crafts equipment • Bed linen and
mattresses • Books hardback • Books paperback
• Computer hardware and software • Furniture
• Gardening equipment • Hearing aids
• Knitting, crochet and sewing equipment
• Knitting wool • Magazines & comics • Office
equipment and stationery • Spectacles • Toys &
games

COLLECTION SERVICE Yes

■ Hackney Pensioners' Association

ADDRESS 34 Dalston Lane, Dalston, London E8 3AZ

TELEPHONE 0171-254 5330

CATEGORY Bed linen and mattresses *no mattresses*
• Books hardback • Books paperback • Bric-a-brac
• Clocks • Clothing adults' • Clothing children's
• Fabric remnants • Fur coats • Jewellery
• Knitting, crochet and sewing equipment
• Knitting wool • Magazines & comics • Non
perishable foods • Pets equipment • Records &
tapes • Spectacles • Stamps British • Stamps
foreign • Toiletries • Toys & games • Watches

COLLECTION SERVICE No

■ Halcyon Neighbourhood Centre (Furniture & Thrift Store)

ADDRESS Dingle Road, North Prospect, Plymouth,
Devon PL6 6PS

TELEPHONE 01752 558572

FAX 01752 606162

CATEGORY Arts & crafts equipment • Baby
equipment • Bed linen and mattresses • Bric-a-
brac • Clothing adults' • Clothing children's
• Fabric remnants • Furniture *no foam filled, no
three piece suites, etc without fire label*
• Gardening equipment • Household items
ironing boards etc • Knitting, crochet and sewing
equipment • Knitting wool

COLLECTION SERVICE Yes

■ Hamelin Trust

ADDRESS 20 Norsey Trust, Billericay, Essex
CM11 2AA

TELEPHONE 01277 653889

FAX 01277 634307

CATEGORY Arts & crafts equipment • Baby
equipment • Bicycles • Books hardback • Books
paperback • Bric-a-brac • Clocks • Clothing adults'
• Clothing children's • Coins foreign • Coins old
• Computer hardware and software • Diy
equipment • Furniture • Gardening equipment
• Household items *ironing boards etc* • Jewellery
• Knitting, crochet and sewing equipment
• Medals • Musical instruments • Office
equipment and stationery • Photographic

equipment • Records & tapes • Sports equipment • Toiletries • Toys & games • Video/computer games • Watches

COLLECTION SERVICE Yes

■ **Harlow Council for Voluntary Service**

ADDRESS Bentham House, Hamstel Road, Harlow, Essex CM20 1EP

TELEPHONE 01279 446659

FAX 01279 452211

CATEGORY Baby equipment • Bed linen and mattresses • Bicycles • Bric-a-brac • Clothing adults' • Clothing children's • Computer hardware and software • Diy equipment • Furniture *including white goods, no gas appliances* • Gardening equipment • Household items *ironing boards etc* • Office equipment and stationery

COLLECTION SERVICE Yes

■ **Hastings Furniture Service**

ADDRESS Robert Tressell Workshops, Devonshire Road, Hastings, E Sussex TN34 1NF

TELEPHONE 01424 441112

CATEGORY Baby equipment • Bed linen and mattresses • Bric-a-brac • Furniture • Household items *ironing boards etc*

COLLECTION SERVICE Yes

■ **Hearing Dogs for the Deaf**

ADDRESS The Training Centre, London Road, Lewknor, Oxon OX9 5KY

TELEPHONE 01844 353898

FAX 01844 353099

CATEGORY Air miles • Bric-a-brac • Clothing adults' • Clothing children's • Coins foreign • Coins old • Jewellery • Stamps British *post direct to: Hearing Dogs for the Deaf, PO Box No 1, Chesham, Bucks HP5 2YJ* • Stamps foreign *post direct to: Hearing Dogs for the Deaf, PO Box No1, Chesham, Bucks, HP5 2YJ* • Telephone cards • Toys & games • Video/computer games

COLLECTION SERVICE No

■ **Help the Aged**

ADDRESS St James' Walk, London EC1R 0BE

TELEPHONE 0171-253 0253

FAX 0171-250 4467

CATEGORY Arts & crafts equipment • Bed linen and mattresses *no mattresses* • Books hardback • Books paperback • Bric-a-brac • Clocks • Clothing adults' • Clothing children's • Fabric remnants • Jewellery • Knitting, crochet and sewing equipment • Knitting wool • Musical instruments • Photographic equipment • Records & tapes • Sports equipment • Toys & games • Video/computer games • Watches • Wedding clothes for hire

COLLECTION SERVICE No

■ **High Wycombe General Aid Society**

ADDRESS 1/3 Cornmarket, High Wycombe, Bucks HP11 2BW

TELEPHONE 01494 535890

FAX 01494 538256

CATEGORY Baby equipment • Bed linen and mattresses • Bric-a-brac • Clocks • Clothing adults' • Clothing children's • Furniture *including working gas & electrical cookers, fridges, washing machines, fires, etc* • Gardening equipment • Household items *ironing boards etc* • Jewellery • Knitting wool • Non perishable foods • Toiletries • Watches

COLLECTION SERVICE Yes

■ **Highway Tools & Crafts Centre**

ADDRESS 37 Church Street, Conisbrough, Doncaster, S Yorks DN12 3HP

TELEPHONE 01709 861269

CATEGORY Arts & crafts equipment • Christmas cards • Diy equipment • Fabric remnants • Furniture *furniture redistribution is the main project of our organisation* • Household items *ironing boards etc* • Knitting wool • Office equipment and stationery

COLLECTION SERVICE Yes

■ **Hillingdon Community Furniture**

ADDRESS Room 37, Barnhill Community Centre, Barnhill Lane, Hayes, Middx UB4 9HD

TELEPHONE 0181-842 4696

CATEGORY Baby equipment • Books hardback • Books paperback • Bric-a-brac • Furniture • Household items *ironing boards etc*

COLLECTION SERVICE Yes

■ **Hillingdon Community Furniture Recycling Project**

ADDRESS Room 37, Barnhill Community Centre, Barnhill Lane, Hayes, Middx UB4 9HD

TELEPHONE 0181-842 4696

CATEGORY Baby equipment • Bed linen and mattresses *clean and good condition only* • Books hardback • Books paperback • Bric-a-brac • Clocks • Clothing adults' • Clothing children's • Diy equipment • Fur coats • Furniture *clean and good condition – may collect* • Gardening equipment • Hearing aids • Household items *ironing boards etc* • Jewellery • Knitting, crochet and sewing equipment • Knitting wool • Magazines & comics • Musical instruments • Records & tapes • Spectacles • Sports equipment • Toys & games • Watches • Wedding clothes for hire

COLLECTION SERVICE No

■ Home Farm Trust

ADDRESS 9 St John's Street, Bury St Edmunds, Suffolk IP33 1SQ

TELEPHONE 01284 723604

CATEGORY Arts & crafts equipment ● Books hardback ● Books paperback ● Bric-a-brac ● Clocks ● Clothing adults' ● Clothing children's ● Fabric remnants ● Household items *ironing boards etc* ● Jewellery ● Knitting, crochet and sewing equipment ● Knitting wool ● Magazines & comics ● Musical instruments ● Photographic equipment ● Rags ● Records & tapes ● Sports equipment ● Toiletries ● Toys & games ● Watches ● Wedding clothes for hire

COLLECTION SERVICE No

■ The Home Farm Trust

ADDRESS The Trust Shop, 24 Chandos Road, Bristol, Avon BS6 6PG

CATEGORY Bed linen and mattresses *bed linen only* ● Books paperback ● Bric-a-brac ● Clothing adults' *in good condition only* ● Clothing children's *in good condition only* ● Jewellery ● Photographic equipment ● Records & tapes ● Toiletries ● Toys & games

COLLECTION SERVICE No

■ The Home Farm Trust

ADDRESS 76 Bridge Street, Worksop, Notts S80 1JA

TELEPHONE 01909 501253

CATEGORY Baby equipment ● Books hardback ● Books paperback ● Bric-a-brac ● Clocks ● Clothing adults' ● Clothing children's ● Fabric remnants ● Household items *ironing boards etc* ● Jewellery ● Knitting, crochet and sewing equipment ● Knitting wool ● Photographic equipment ● Records & tapes ● Sports equipment ● Toiletries ● Toys & games ● Video/computer games ● Watches

COLLECTION SERVICE Yes

■ The Homeless Furniture Project

ADDRESS Unit 6, Ellerslie Square, Lyham Road, London SW2 5DZ

TELEPHONE 0171-738 7080

FAX 0171-501 9381

CATEGORY Aluminium ● Antique post cards ● Arts & crafts equipment ● Bed linen and mattresses ● Bicycles ● Books hardback ● Books paperback ● Clocks ● Coins foreign ● Coins old ● Computer hardware and software ● Diy equipment ● Fabric remnants ● Furniture ● Gardening equipment ● Household items *ironing boards etc* ● Medals ● Musical instruments ● Office equipment and stationery ● Photographic equipment ● Records & tapes ● Sports equipment ● Stamps British ● Stamps foreign ● Toys & games ● Video/computer games ● Watches

COLLECTION SERVICE Yes

■ Homeless in Blackpool

ADDRESS 'Seekers' (Homeless in Blackpool's Charity Shop), 54 Tithebarn Street, Poulton-le-Fylde, Lancs FY6 7BY

TELEPHONE 01253 894069

CATEGORY Antique post cards ● Arts & crafts equipment ● Baby equipment ● Bed linen and mattresses *not mattresses* ● Bicycles ● Books hardback ● Books paperback ● Bric-a-brac ● Clocks ● Clothing adults' ● Clothing children's ● Coins foreign ● Coins old ● Diy equipment ● Fabric remnants ● Furniture *only small items* ● Gardening equipment ● Household items *ironing boards etc* ● Jewellery ● Knitting, crochet and sewing equipment ● Knitting wool ● Magazines & comics ● Medals ● Musical instruments ● Non perishable foods ● Office equipment and stationery ● Pets equipment ● Photographic equipment ● Rags *if bagged and labelled 'rags'* ● Records & tapes ● Sports equipment ● Toiletries ● Toys & games ● Video/computer games ● Watches

COLLECTION SERVICE No

■ Hope Romania

ADDRESS Birch Lodge, 52 Cossington Road, Canterbury, Kent CT1 3HU

TELEPHONE 01227 462200

FAX 01227 462200

CATEGORY Air miles ● Bicycles *only children's* ● Books hardback *to raise funds in this country* ● Books paperback *to raise funds in this country* ● Bric-a-brac ● Clothing children's *in very good condition only* ● Fur coats ● Hearing aids ● Non perishable foods ● Records & tapes *classical music tapes only* ● Stamps British *to raise funds in this country* ● Stamps foreign *to raise funds in this country* ● Toiletries ● Toys & games *as new please*

COLLECTION SERVICE No

■ Horses & Ponies Protection Association

ADDRESS The Stables, Burnley Wharf, Manchester Road, Burnley, Lancs BB11 1JZ

TELEPHONE 01282 455992

FAX 01282 451992

CATEGORY Air miles ● Antique post cards ● Bric-a-brac ● Clocks ● Coins foreign ● Coins old ● Diy equipment ● Jewellery ● Medals ● Petrol vouchers Pets' equipment *saddlery, bridles, etc for horses* ● Stamps British ● Stamps foreign ● Trading stamps ● Watches

COLLECTION SERVICE No

■ Hospital Radio Bedford

ADDRESS c/o Bedford South Wing Hospital, Kempston Road, Bedford, Beds MK42 9DJ

TELEPHONE 01234 792020

FAX 01234 792222

E-MAIL mattcjones@msn.com

CATEGORY Computer hardware and software • Records & tapes

COLLECTION SERVICE No

■ Hounslow Community Transport Furniture Project

ADDRESS Carnegie Hall, Northcote Avenue, Isleworth, Middlesex TW7 7JQ

TELEPHONE 0181-744 0615

FAX 0181-744 0623

CATEGORY Baby equipment • Bed linen and mattresses • Bric-a-brac • Clocks • Furniture • Household items *ironing boards, etc* • Computer hardware and software • Office equipment and stationery • Books hardback • Books paperback • Toys and games • Video/ computer games

COLLECTION SERVICE Yes

■ The House Project Charity Shop

ADDRESS 168 South Coast Road, Peacehaven, E Sussex BN10

TELEPHONE 01273 582467

CATEGORY Antique post cards • Bric-a-brac • Clothing adults' • Clothing children's • Jewellery • Records & tapes • Toys & games

COLLECTION SERVICE No

■ Hove YMCA

ADDRESS 17 Marmion Road, Hove, E Sussex BN3 5FS

TELEPHONE 01273 731724

FAX 01273 885565

CATEGORY Aluminium • Clothing adults' • Clothing children's • Jewellery • Bed linen and mattresses • Bric-a-brac • Clocks • DIY equipment • Furniture • Gardening equipment • Household items *ironing boards, etc* • Toiletries • Office equipment and stationery • Bicyles • Books hardback • Books paperback • Fabric remnants • Knitting, crochet, sewing equipment • Knitting wool • Magazines and comics • Musical intruments • Photographic equipment • Rags • Records and tapes • Sports equipment • Toys and games • Video/computer games

COLLECTION SERVICE Yes

■ Hull Resettlement Furniture Service

ADDRESS Unit 8, Factory Industrial Estate, English Street, Kingston-upon-Hull, E Yorks HU3 2BE

TELEPHONE 01482 212950

CATEGORY Baby equipment • Bed linen and mattresses • Fabric remnants *curtains* • Furniture • Household items *ironing boards etc* • Knitting, crochet and sewing equipment • Musical instruments

COLLECTION SERVICE Yes

■ Hydestile Wildlife Hospital

ADDRESS New Road, Hydestile, Godalming, Surrey GU8 4DJ

TELEPHONE 01483 860313

CATEGORY Air miles • Antique post cards • Arts & crafts equipment • Bed linen and mattresses *blankets, sheets, towels, sleeping bags* • Books hardback • Books paperback • Bric-a-brac *small items* • Coins foreign • Coins old • Computer . hardware and software • Fabric remnants • Knitting wool • Money-off coupons • Non perishable foods *suitable for animals* • Office equipment and stationery • Petrol vouchers • Pets equipment *beds, cages* • Records & tapes • Toys & games • Trading stamps • Video/ computer games • Waste paper

COLLECTION SERVICE No

■ Hydon Hill Cheshire Home

ADDRESS Clock Barn Lane, Godalming, Surrey GU8 4BA

TELEPHONE 01483 860516

FAX 01483 860316

CATEGORY Air miles • Aluminium *cans* • Antique post cards • Arts & crafts equipment • Baby equipment • Bed linen and mattresses • Books hardback • Books paperback • Bric-a-brac • Christmas cards *any greetings cards* • Clocks • Clothing adults' • Clothing children's • Coins foreign • Coins old • Diy equipment • Fabric remnants • Fur coats • Furniture • Gardening equipment • Household items *ironing boards etc* • Jewellery • Knitting, crochet and sewing equipment • Knitting wool • Magazines & comics • Medals • Money-off coupons • Musical instruments • Office equipment and stationery • Petrol vouchers • Photographic equipment • Postcards used • Records & tapes • Spectacles • Sports equipment • Stamps British • Stamps foreign • Telephone cards • Toys & games • Trading stamps • Video/computer games • Waste paper • Watches

COLLECTION SERVICE No

■ Immigration Welfare & Legal Advisory Services

ADDRESS Hackney Centre, 277 Mare Street, London E8 1HB

TELEPHONE 0181-985 4284

CATEGORY Baby equipment • Books hardback • Books paperback • Clocks • Clothing adults' • Clothing children's • Computer hardware and software • Furniture • Jewellery • Musical instruments • Non perishable foods • Office equipment and stationery • Toiletries • Toys & games • Video/computer games • Watches

COLLECTION SERVICE No

■ Imperial Cancer Research Fund

ADDRESS Northern Appeals, Unit 16, Pavilion Business Park, Royds Hall Road, Leeds, W Yorks LS12 6AJ

TELEPHONE 0113-231 9828

FAX 0113-231 1394

CATEGORY Air miles • Petrol vouchers • Trading stamps • Used toner cartridges *collections arranged by us* • Waste paper *Gtr Manchester & Birmingham only, companies with at least 30 paper – generating, admin, staff. all equipment and collections arranged by us*

COLLECTION SERVICE No

■ Imperial Cancer Research Fund

ADDRESS Units B1 & B2, Building 7400, The Quorum, Oxford Business Park, Garsington Road, Cowley, Oxon OX4 2JZ

TELEPHONE 0181-399 0805

CATEGORY Air miles • Aluminium • Coins foreign • Coins old • Money-off coupons • Petrol vouchers • Trading stamps • Used toner cartridges • Waste paper *office waste paper only*

COLLECTION SERVICE Yes

■ Imperial Cancer Research Fund

ADDRESS 6 White Hart Lane, Wellington, Somerset TA21 8HN

TELEPHONE 01823 660251

FAX 01823 660256

CATEGORY Air miles • Aluminium • Antique post cards • Arts & crafts equipment • Bicycles • Books hardback • Books paperback • Bric-a-brac • Clocks • Clothing adults' • Clothing children's • Coins foreign • Coins old • Diy equipment • Fabric remnants • Gardening equipment • Jewellery • Knitting, crochet and sewing equipment • Knitting wool • Magazines & comics • Medals • Musical instruments • Office equipment and stationery • Photographic equipment • Records & tapes • Sports equipment • Stamps British • Stamps foreign • Toiletries • Toys & games • Trading stamps • Used toner cartridges • Wedding clothes for hire

COLLECTION SERVICE No

■ Imperial Cancer Research Fund

ADDRESS PO Box 123, 61 Lincoln's Inn Fields, London WC2A 3PX

TELEPHONE 0171-269 3412

FAX 0171-269 3183

CATEGORY Air miles • Antique post cards • Arts & crafts equipment • Books hardback • Books paperback • Bric-a-brac • Clocks • Clothing adults' • Clothing children's • Coins foreign • Coins old • Jewellery • Knitting, crochet and sewing equipment • Knitting wool • Medals • Musical instruments • Petrol vouchers • Photographic equipment • Records & tapes • Sports equipment • Toiletries • Toys & games • Video/computer games • Watches

COLLECTION SERVICE No

■ Inland Waterways Association

ADDRESS 114 Regent's Park Road, London NW1 8UQ

TELEPHONE 0171-586 2510

FAX 0171-722 7213

E-MAIL iwa@waterway.demon.co.uk.

CATEGORY Air miles • Aluminium • Antique post cards • Books hardback • Coins foreign • Coins old • Diy equipment • Gardening equipment • Medals • Milk bottle tops • Other metals • Petrol vouchers *including out of date* • Postcards used • Silver paper & aluminium foil • Stamps British • Stamps foreign • Trading stamps *including out of date*

COLLECTION SERVICE No

■ Inner Wheel Club of Ewell

ADDRESS 119 East Street, Epsom, Surrey KT17 1EJ

TELEPHONE 01372 720123

CATEGORY Air miles • Arts & crafts equipment • Books hardback • Books paperback • Fabric remnants • Jewellery • Knitting, crochet and sewing equipment • Knitting wool • Office equipment and stationery • Spectacles • Stamps British • Stamps foreign • Toiletries • Used toner cartridges

COLLECTION SERVICE No

■ Iris Fund for Prevention of Blindness

ADDRESS York House, 199 Westminster Bridge Road, London SE1 7UT

TELEPHONE 0171-928 7743

FAX 0171-928 7919

CATEGORY Air miles • Coins foreign • Coins old • Medals • Stamps British • Stamps foreign • Telephone cards • Trading stamps

COLLECTION SERVICE No

■ Islington Age Concern

ADDRESS 424 St John Street, London EC1V 4NJ

TELEPHONE 0171-278 6994

FAX 0171-278 6995

CATEGORY Aluminium *drink cans only*

COLLECTION SERVICE No

■ IW RCC (Wight Play Project)

ADDRESS Read's Posting House, 24 Holyrood Street, Newport, Isle of Wight PO30 5AZ

TELEPHONE 01983 524058

FAX 01983 526095

CATEGORY Arts & crafts equipment • Childrens play/craft scrap • Computer hardware and software • Fabric remnants • Knitting, crochet and sewing equipment • Knitting wool • Magazines & comics • Plastics • Rags • Silver paper & aluminium foil • Sports equipment • Toys & games • Video/computer games • Waste paper

COLLECTION SERVICE Yes

■ Jennifer Trust for SMA

ADDRESS 11 Ash Tree Close, Wellesbourne, Warwick, Cumbria CV35 9SA

TELEPHONE 01789 842377

FAX 01789 842377

E-MAIL anita@jtsma.demon.co.uk

CATEGORY Computer hardware and software • Office equipment and stationery • Petrol vouchers • Toys & games • Trading stamps • Video/computer games

COLLECTION SERVICE No

■ Katharine House Hospice

ADDRESS East End, Adderbury, Banbury, Oxon OX17 3NL

TELEPHONE 01295 811866

FAX 01295 810953

CATEGORY Coins foreign • Coins old • Jewellery • Knitting wool • Musical instruments • Petrol vouchers • Photographic equipment • Sports equipment • Stamps British • Stamps foreign • Toiletries • Watches

COLLECTION SERVICE Yes

■ Keighley Council for Voluntary Service

ADDRESS Voluntary Services Centre, Spring Gardens Lane, Keighley, W Yorks BD20 6LB

TELEPHONE 01535 665258

FAX 01535 691436

CATEGORY Arts & crafts equipment • Bed linen and mattresses *clean to pass straight onto clients* • Books hardback • Books paperback • Clothing adults' *clean & tidy* • Clothing children's *clean & tidy* • Fabric remnants • Furniture *clean and not too worn* • Gardening equipment • Household items *ironing boards etc* • Jewellery *not broken* • Knitting, crochet and sewing equipment • Knitting wool • Magazines & comics • Office equipment and stationery *fit to pass straight on* • Sports equipment • Toys & games • Watches *not broken*

COLLECTION SERVICE Yes

■ Kent Information Federation

ADDRESS Ground Floor, Cygnet House, Windmill Street, Gravesend, Kent DA12 1BQ

TELEPHONE 01474 534777

FAX 01474 566128

E-MAIL admin@kif.compulink.co.uk

CATEGORY Computer hardware and software *IBM compatible only* • Office equipment and stationery

COLLECTION SERVICE Yes

■ Kent Red Cross Charity Shops

ADDRESS 25 College Road, Maidstone, Kent ME15 6SX

TELEPHONE 01622 690011

FAX 01622 690012

CATEGORY Antique post cards • Arts & crafts equipment • Books hardback • Books paperback • Bric-a-brac • Clocks • Clothing adults' *not underwear* • Clothing children's *not underwear* • Coins foreign • Coins old • Computer hardware and software • Fabric remnants • Glass • Jewellery • Knitting, crochet and sewing equipment • Knitting wool • Medals • Musical instruments • Office equipment and stationery • Photographic equipment • Postcards used • Records & tapes • Sports equipment • Stamps British • Stamps foreign • Toiletries • Toys & games • Video/computer games • Watches

COLLECTION SERVICE Yes

■ Kirby Volunteer Centre

ADDRESS 6 Pond Street, Kirby in Ashfield, Notts NG17 7AH

TELEPHONE 01623 753192

CATEGORY Arts & crafts equipment • Baby equipment • Bed linen and mattresses • Bicycles • Books hardback • Books paperback • Bric-a-brac • Childrens play/craft scrap • Clocks • Clothing adults' • Clothing children's • Computer hardware and software • Diy equipment • Fabric remnants • Furniture • Gardening equipment • Household items *ironing boards etc* • Jewellery • Knitting, crochet and sewing equipment • Knitting wool • Musical instruments • Office equipment and stationery • Photographic equipment • Records & tapes • Sports equipment • Toiletries • Toys & games • Video/computer games • Watches

COLLECTION SERVICE Yes

■ Kirkwood Hospice

ADDRESS 21 Albany Road, Dalton, Huddersfield, W Yorks HD5 9UY

TELEPHONE 01484 421503

FAX 01484 421503

CATEGORY Air miles ● Antique post cards ● Arts & crafts equipment ● Baby equipment ● Bed linen and mattresses ● Books hardback ● Books paperback ● Bric-a-brac ● Clocks ● Clothing adults' ● Clothing children's ● Coins foreign ● Coins old ● Diy equipment ● Fabric remnants ● Furniture *small items only* ● Gardening equipment ● Household items *ironing boards etc* ● Jewellery ● Knitting, crochet and sewing equipment ● Knitting wool ● Magazines & comics ● Medals ● Money-off coupons ● Musical instruments *small only* ● Non perishable foods ● Petrol vouchers ● Photographic equipment ● Rags ● Records & tapes ● Spectacles ● Sports equipment ● Stamps British ● Stamps foreign ● Toiletries ● Toys & games ● Trading stamps ● Video/computer games ● Watches ● Wedding clothes for hire

COLLECTION SERVICE No

■ Knowle Sports Association

ADDRESS The Knowle, Tenbury Road, Clee Hill, Nr Ludlow, Salop SY8 3NJ

TELEPHONE 01584 890644

CATEGORY Aluminium *for Clee Hill youth club* ● Antique post cards ● Arts & crafts equipment ● Baby equipment ● Bed linen and mattresses ● Bicycles ● Books hardback ● Books paperback ● Bric-a-brac ● Christmas cards ● Clocks ● Clothing adults' ● Clothing children's ● Coins foreign ● Coins old ● Computer hardware and software ● Diy equipment ● Fabric remnants ● Fur coats *sold to make soft toys* ● Furniture ● Gardening equipment ● Glass ● Household items *ironing boards etc* ● Jewellery ● Knitting, crochet and sewing equipment ● Knitting wool ● Magazines & comics ● Medals ● Motorbike engines, car engines, spare parts ● Musical instruments ● Office equipment and stationery ● Other metals *scrap iron* ● Pets equipment ● Photographic equipment ● Postcards used ● Rags ● Records & tapes ● Spectacles ● Sports equipment ● Stamps British ● Stamps foreign ● Telephone cards ● Toiletries ● Toys & games ● Trading stamps *sent to Kidderminster Hospital* ● Used toner cartridges ● Video/computer games ● Waste paper ● Watches ● Wedding clothes for hire *for sale, not hire*

COLLECTION SERVICE Yes

■ Lancaster District CVS

ADDRESS Trinity Community Centre, Middle Street, Lancaster, Lancs LA1 1SZ

TELEPHONE 01524 63760

FAX 01524 68988

CATEGORY Computer hardware and software *must be in good working order* ● Office equipment and stationery *must be in good working order*

COLLECTION SERVICE No

■ League of Friends – James Paget Hospital

ADDRESS 2 Bridge Road, Gorleston, Norfolk NR31 6HQ

TELEPHONE 01493 664047

CATEGORY Books hardback ● Books paperback ● Bric-a-brac *good quality* ● Clocks ● Jewellery ● Knitting wool ● Records & tapes ● Toys & games ● Watches

COLLECTION SERVICE Yes

■ League of Friends of Lewisham Hospital

ADDRESS League of Friends Shop, Lewisham Hospital, Lewisham High Street, London SE13 6LH

TELEPHONE 0181-697 0786

CATEGORY Arts & crafts equipment ● Bed linen and mattresses *not mattresses* ● Books paperback *in good condition* ● Bric-a-brac ● Clothing adults' *nearly new – not jumble* ● Clothing children's *nearly new – not jumble* ● Fabric remnants ● Gardening equipment *not electrical* ● Household items *ironing boards etc not electrical* ● Jewellery ● Knitting, crochet and sewing equipment ● Knitting wool ● Records & tapes ● Toiletries *unwanted gifts* ● Toys & games ● Video/computer games

COLLECTION SERVICE No

■ League of Friends of Teddington Memorial Hospital

ADDRESS Hampton Road, Teddington, Middx TW11 0JL

TELEPHONE 0181-977 2212

FAX 0181-977 1914

CATEGORY Antique post cards ● Bric-a-brac ● Coins foreign ● Coins old ● Jewellery ● Medals ● Stamps British ● Stamps foreign

COLLECTION SERVICE No

■ League of Friends of the Shrewsbury Hospitals

ADDRESS League of Friends Office, Royal Shrewsbury Hospital North, Shrewsbury, Shropshire SY3 8XQ

TELEPHONE 01743 261007

CATEGORY Aluminium ● Waste paper

COLLECTION SERVICE No

■ League of Friends – Plymouth Psychiatric Service

ADDRESS Church of the Good Shepherd (Acorn Project), Octagan Street, Plymouth, Devon

CATEGORY Arts & crafts equipment ● Bed linen and mattresses *no mattresses* ● Books hardback ● Books paperback ● Bric-a-brac ● Clothing adults' ● Clothing children's ● Fabric remnants ● Gardening equipment ● Household items ironing boards etc • Jewellery • Knitting, crochet and sewing equipment • Knitting wool • Magazines & comics • Musical instruments • Records & tapes • Sports equipment • Toiletries

COLLECTION SERVICE Yes

■ League of Friends – Royal Hallamshire Hospital

ADDRESS Glossop Road, Sheffield, S Yorks S10 2JF

CATEGORY Books paperback • Bric-a-brac • Clothing adults' *only in good resaleable condition* • Clothing children's *only in good resaleable condition* • Jewellery • Toiletries

COLLECTION SERVICE No

■ Leicester Disabled Gardeners Club

ADDRESS Beez Kneez Charity Shop, 124 Granby Street, Leicester, Leics LE1 1DL

TELEPHONE 0116-223 7599

CATEGORY Antique postcards • Arts and crafts equipment • Baby equipment • Bed linen and mattresses • Bicycles • Books hardback • Books paperback • Bric-a-brac • Coins forein • Coins old • Clocks • Computer harware and software • DIY equipment • Fabric remnants • Furniture • Gardening equipment • Household items *ironing boards, etc* • Knitting, crochet, sewing equipment • Knitting wool • Magazines and comics • Medals • Motorbike engines, car engines, spare parts • Musical instruments • Non-perishable foods • Office equipment and stationery • Pets' equipment • Photographic equipment • Records and tapes • Sports equipment • Stamps British • Stamps foreign+Toiletries • Toys and games • Used toner cartridges • Video/computer games

COLLECTION SERVICE Yes

■ Leicestershire Disabled Adventure Club

ADDRESS 86 Queens Drive, Narborough, Leicester LE9 5LJ

TELEPHONE 0116-286 5035

CATEGORY Antique postcards • Arts and crafts equipment • Baby equipment • Bed linen and mattresses • Bicycles • Books hardback • Books paperback • Bric-a-brac • Coins forein • Coins old • Clocks • Computer harware and software • DIY equipment • Fabric remnants • Furniture • Gardening equipment • Household items *ironing boards, etc* • Knitting, crochet, sewing equipment • Knitting wool • Magazines and comics • Medals • Motorbike engines, car engines, spare parts • Musical instruments • Non-perishable foods • Office equipment and stationery • Pets' equipment • Photographic equipment • Records and tapes • Sports equipment • Stamps British • Stamps foreign+Toiletries • Toys and games • Used toner cartridges • Video/computer games

COLLECTION SERVICE No

■ The Leonard Cheshire Foundation

ADDRESS The Manor Cheshire Home, Church Road, Brampton, Huntingdon, Cambs PE18 8PW

TELEPHONE 01480 412412

FAX 01480 413737

CATEGORY Air miles • Arts & crafts equipment • Books hardback • Computer hardware and software • Diy equipment • Petrol vouchers • Photographic equipment • Stamps British • Stamps foreign • Trading stamps

COLLECTION SERVICE Yes

■ Leukaemia Research Fund

ADDRESS 43 Great Ormond Street, London WC1N 3JJ

TELEPHONE 0171-405 0101

FAX 0171-405 3139

E-MAIL lrf@leukre5.demon.co.uk

CATEGORY Air miles • Antique post cards • Bicycles • Books hardback • Books paperback • Bric-a-brac • Christmas cards • Clocks • Clothing adults' • Clothing children's • Coins foreign • Coins old • Computer hardware and software • Fur coats • Jewellery • Office equipment and stationery • Petrol vouchers • Postcards used • Records & tapes • Sports equipment • Stamps British • Stamps foreign • Telephone cards • Toiletries • Toys & games • Trading stamps • Used toner cartridges • Video/computer games • Watches

COLLECTION SERVICE No

■ Lewes Volunteer Bureau

ADDRESS 27–28 Station Street, Lewes, E Sussex BN7 2DB

TELEPHONE 01273 475845

CATEGORY Antique post cards • Arts & crafts equipment • Books hardback • Books paperback • Bric-a-brac • Clocks • Clothing adults' • Clothing children's • Coins foreign • Coins old • Computer hardware and software • Diy equipment • Fabric remnants • Gardening equipment • Jewellery • Knitting, crochet and sewing equipment • Knitting wool • Magazines & comics • Medals • Musical instruments • Office equipment and stationery • Photographic equipment • Records & tapes • Spectacles • Sports equipment • Stamps British • Stamps foreign • Toys & games • Video/computer games • Watches

COLLECTION SERVICE Yes

■ Living Room

ADDRESS Unit 3, Mill 2, Pleasley Vale Business Park, Pleasley Vale, Mansfield, Notts NG19 8RL

TELEPHONE 01623 810945

CATEGORY Antique post cards • Baby equipment • Bed linen and mattresses • Bric-a-brac • Coins foreign • Furniture • Household items *ironing boards etc* • Office equipment and stationery • Records & tapes

COLLECTION SERVICE Yes

■ **Lord Whisky Sanctuary Fund**

ADDRESS Park House, Stelling Minnis,
Nr Canterbury, Kent CT4 6AN

TELEPHONE 01303 862622

CATEGORY Arts & crafts equipment • Bicycles
• Books hardback • Books paperback • Bric-a-brac
needed urgently for all sales • Clocks • Coins
foreign • Coins old • Diy equipment • Fabric
remnants • Gardening equipment • Household
items *ironing boards etc* • Jewellery • Knitting,
crochet and sewing equipment • Knitting wool
• Medals • Musical instruments • Office
equipment and stationery • Pets equipment
• Records & tapes • Stamps British • Stamps
foreign • Toiletries *if not tested on animals* • Toys
& games • Watches

COLLECTION SERVICE Yes

■ **Loughborough Community Care**

ADDRESS Aurnberry Gap, Loughborough, Leics
LE11 1AA

TELEPHONE 01509 262557

CATEGORY Arts & crafts equipment *good condition*
• Baby equipment *good condition* • Bed linen
and mattresses *good condition* • Books hardback
good condition • Books paperback *good condition*
• Bric-a-brac *good condition* • Clocks *good
condition* • Clothing children's *good condition*
• Diy equipment *good condition* • Fabric
remnants *good condition* • Furniture *good
condition* • Gardening equipment *good condition*
• Household items *ironing boards etc good
condition* • Knitting, crochet and sewing
equipment *good condition* • Knitting wool *good
condition* • Magazines & comics *good condition*
• Musical instruments *good condition*
• Photographic equipment *good condition*
• Records & tapes *good condition* • Sports
equipment *good condition* • Toiletries *good
condition* • Toys & games *good condition*

COLLECTION SERVICE Yes

■ **Luton Day Centre for the Homeless**

ADDRESS 141 Park Street, Luton, Beds LU1 3HG

TELEPHONE 01582 28416

CATEGORY Arts & crafts equipment • Baby
equipment *good condition* • Bed linen and
mattresses • Bicycles • Books hardback • Books
paperback • Bric-a-brac *good condition* • Clocks
good condition • Clothing adults' • Clothing
children's • Computer hardware and software
good condition • Diy equipment *good condition*
• Fabric remnants • Furniture *can refurbish old
furniture* • Gardening equipment *good condition*
• Household items *ironing boards etc good
condition* • Jewellery • Knitting, crochet and
sewing equipment • Knitting wool • Magazines
& comics • Medals *religious medals for clients
who want them* • Milk bottle tops *must be clean*
• Non perishable foods *also accept offers of fresh
food* • Office equipment and stationery
equipment in good condition • Other metals
• Photographic equipment • Records & tapes •
Silver paper & aluminium foil *must be clean*

• Sports equipment • Stamps British • Stamps
foreign • Toiletries • Toys & games

COLLECTION SERVICE Yes

■ **The M25 Group**

ADDRESS Doncaster Open House, 4 Union Street,
Doncaster, S Yorks DN1 3AE

TELEPHONE 01302 769293

CATEGORY Non perishable foods • Toiletries

COLLECTION SERVICE No

■ **Magpie Recycling Co-op Limited**

ADDRESS Saunders Park Depot, Saunders Park,
Lewes Road, Brighton, E Sussex BN2 4AY

TELEPHONE 01273 677577

CATEGORY Aluminium • Bed linen and mattresses
• Clothing adults' • Clothing children's • Computer
hardware and software • Furniture • Milk bottle
tops • Office equipment and stationery *office
furniture* • Other metals • Rags • Silver paper &
aluminium foil • Used toner cartridges • Waste
paper *office grade white paper and computer
paper*

COLLECTION SERVICE Yes

■ **Malvern Churches Community
Network**

ADDRESS 12 Priory Road, Malvern, Worcs WR14 3DS

TELEPHONE 01684 891081

CATEGORY Antique postcards • Arts and crafts
equipment • Baby equipment • Bed linen and
mattresses *no stained mattresses* • Bicycles
• Books hardback • Books paperback • Bric-a-brac
• Children's play/craft scrap • Clocks • Clothing
adults' • Clothing children's • Computer harware
and software • DIY equipment • Fabric remnants
• Furniture • Gardening equipment • Household
items *ironing boards, etc* • Jewellery • Knitting,
crochet, sewing equipment • Knitting wool
• Musical instruments • Non-perishable foods
• Office equipment and stationery • Postcards
used • Records and tapes • Sports equipment
• Stamps British • Stamps foreign • Telephone
cards • Toiletries • Toys and games • Video/
computer games

COLLECTION SERVICE Yes

■ **Manchester & Salford Methodist
Mission**

ADDRESS Open Door, 35 Princess Road, Moss Side,
Gtr Manchester M14 4TE

TELEPHONE 0161-226 1751

FAX 0161-226 1751

CATEGORY Air miles • Antique post cards • Arts &
crafts equipment • Baby equipment • Bed linen
and mattresses *bed linen only* • Books hardback
• Books paperback • Bric-a-brac • Christmas cards
• Clocks • Clothing adults' • Clothing children's
• Coins foreign • Coins old • Computer hardware
and software • Diy equipment • Fabric remnants

• Fur coats • Gardening equipment • Household items *ironing boards etc* • Jewellery • Knitting, crochet and sewing equipment • Medals • Musical instruments • Non perishable foods • Office equipment and stationery • Sports equipment • Stamps British • Toiletries • Toys & games • Watches

COLLECTION SERVICE No

■ Manchester One Parent Family Advice Centre

ADDRESS Levenshulme Community Centre, 44 Chapel Street, Gtr Manchester M19 3GL

TELEPHONE 0161-248 6739

CATEGORY Arts & crafts equipment • Baby equipment • Clothing children's • Musical instruments • Sports equipment • Toys & games

COLLECTION SERVICE No

■ Marie Curie Cancer Care

ADDRESS Unit 1, Enterprise House, Cheney Manor, Swindon, Wilts SN2 2YZ

TELEPHONE 01793 512722

FAX 01793 430008

CATEGORY Antique post cards • Books paperback • Bric-a-brac • Clothing adults' • Clothing children's • Coins foreign • Coins old • Jewellery • Medals • Stamps British • Stamps foreign

COLLECTION SERVICE Yes

■ Marie Curie Cancer Care

ADDRESS The Marie Curie Collection, Freepost, 9 Belgrave Mews South, London SW1X 8YZ

TELEPHONE 0171-201 2342

FAX 0171-201 2344

CATEGORY Air miles • Antique post cards • Clocks • Coins foreign • Coins old • Jewellery • Medals • Petrol vouchers • Postcards used • Stamps British • Stamps foreign • Telephone cards • Trading stamps • Watches

COLLECTION SERVICE No

■ Marwell Zoological Society

ADDRESS c/o Marwell Zoological Park, Colden Common, Nr Winchester, Hants SO17 2GD

TELEPHONE 01703 557750

FAX 01703 557750

CATEGORY Antique post cards • Petrol vouchers • Trading stamps • Waste paper *newspapers and magazines only*

COLLECTION SERVICE No

■ ME Association Hereford & Worcester Group

ADDRESS Dovecote Barn, Cleeve Manor, Cleeve Prior, Evesham, Hereford & Worcs

TELEPHONE 01789 773664

CATEGORY Books hardback • Books paperback • Bric-a-brac • Clothing adults' • Clothing children's • Coins foreign • Coins old • Jewellery • Petrol vouchers • Records & tapes • Stamps British • Stamps foreign • Toiletries • Toys & games • Video/computer games

COLLECTION SERVICE No

■ Medway Homes Refuge

ADDRESS PO Box 141, Gillingham, Kent ME7 5DY

CATEGORY Baby equipment • Bed linen and mattresses *single beds only and cot linen* • Clothing adults' • Clothing children's • Computer hardware and software • Furniture • Gardening equipment • Household items *ironing boards etc* • Non perishable foods • Office equipment and stationery • Toiletries • Toys & games

COLLECTION SERVICE No

■ Mental Aid Projects

ADDRESS 'Fircroft', 96 Ditton Road, Surbiton, Surrey KT6 6RH

TELEPHONE 0181-399 1772

CATEGORY Antique post cards • Arts & crafts equipment • Baby equipment • Bed linen and mattresses • Bicycles • Books hardback • Books paperback • Bric-a-brac • Clocks • Clothing adults' • Clothing children's • Computer hardware and software • Diy equipment • Fabric remnants • Furniture • Gardening equipment • Household items *ironing boards etc* • Jewellery • Knitting, crochet and sewing equipment • Knitting wool • Magazines & comics • Medals • Musical instruments • Office equipment and stationery • Photographic equipment • Records & tapes • Sports equipment • Stamps British • Stamps foreign • Toiletries • Toys & games • Video/computer games • Watches

COLLECTION SERVICE Yes

■ Merseyside Council for Voluntary Service

ADDRESS Mount Vernon Green, Hall Lane, Liverpool, Merseyside L7 8TF

TELEPHONE 0151-709 0990

FAX 0151-709 9326

CATEGORY Computer hardware and software • Furniture *demand fluctuates for furniture* • Gardening equipment • Household items *ironing boards etc demand fluctuates for these items* • Non perishable foods • Office equipment and stationery • Toiletries

COLLECTION SERVICE Yes

■ Merton Furniture Project

ADDRESS Canterbury Centre, Canterbury Road, Mitcham, Surrey SM4 6PT

TELEPHONE 0181-640 9510

CATEGORY Furniture *merton area & sunday collection only*

COLLECTION SERVICE No

■ Merton Voluntary Service Council

ADDRESS Vestry Hall, London Road, Mitcham, Surrey CR4 3UD

TELEPHONE 0181-685 1771

FAX 0181-685 0249

CATEGORY Computer hardware and software • Office equipment and stationery

COLLECTION SERVICE Yes

■ Milton Keynes Council of Voluntary Organisations

ADDRESS Acorn House, 351 Midsummer Boulevard, Central Milton Keynes, Bucks MK9 3HP

TELEPHONE 01908 661623

FAX 01908 200979

CATEGORY Computer hardware and software • Office equipment and stationery

COLLECTION SERVICE Yes

■ Mind in Camden Charity Shop

ADDRESS 20 Camden Road, London NW1 9DP

TELEPHONE 0171-485 8936

FAX 0171-911 0825

CATEGORY Aluminium *foil only* • Arts & crafts equipment • Bed linen and mattresses *not mattresses* • Books hardback • Books paperback • Bric-a-brac • Clocks • Clothing adults' • Clothing children's • Fabric remnants • Household items *ironing boards etc* • Jewellery • Knitting wool • Magazines & comics • Milk bottle tops • Musical instruments • Records & tapes • Silver paper & aluminium foil • Spectacles • Toys & games • Video/computer games • Watches

COLLECTION SERVICE Yes

■ Mind in Croydon

ADDRESS 26 Pampisford Road, Purley, Surrey CR8 2NE

TELEPHONE 0181-668 2210

FAX 0181-763 2084

CATEGORY Antique post cards • Arts & crafts equipment • Baby equipment • Bed linen and mattresses *mattresses must be unstained* • Bicycles • Books hardback • Books paperback • Bric-a-brac • Clocks • Clothing adults' • Clothing children's • Coins foreign • Coins old • Computer hardware and software • Diy

equipment • Fabric remnants • Furniture • Gardening equipment • Household items *ironing boards etc* • Jewellery • Knitting, crochet and sewing equipment • Knitting wool • Magazines & comics • Medals • Money-off coupons • Musical instruments • Non perishable foods • Office equipment and stationery • Petrol vouchers • Photographic equipment • Postcards used • Rags • Records & tapes • Sports equipment • Stamps British • Stamps foreign • Toiletries • Toys & games • Trading stamps • Video/computer games • Waste paper *newspapers and magazines only* • Watches

COLLECTION SERVICE Yes

■ Mini-Scrapbox

ADDRESS Units 5 & 6, Colliers Way, Wood Dalling Road, Reepham, Norfolk NR10 4SW

TELEPHONE 01603 873128

CATEGORY Childrens play/craft scrap *safe and clean scrap only* • Office equipment and stationery *not electrical* • Waste paper *reusable waste card/art card only*

COLLECTION SERVICE Yes

■ The Missions to Seamen

ADDRESS Arundel Road, Littlehampton, W Sussex BN17 7BY

TELEPHONE 01903 726969

FAX 01903 734455

CATEGORY Books paperback • Clothing adults' *jerseys only* • Coins foreign • Coins old • Knitting wool • Stamps British *high value only* • Stamps foreign

COLLECTION SERVICE Yes

■ Monday Club

ADDRESS c/o Pop In, 6 Bank Buildings, Hastings, E Sussex

TELEPHONE 01424 435649

CATEGORY Books hardback • Books paperback • Bric-a-brac • Clocks • Clothing adults' • Coins foreign • Coins old • Household items *ironing boards etc* • Jewellery • Magazines & comics • Milk bottle tops • Musical instruments • Silver paper & aluminium foil • Stamps British • Stamps foreign

COLLECTION SERVICE No

■ Montrose Scrapstore

ADDRESS Community Education Office, 16 George Street, Montrose, Angus DD10 8EN

TELEPHONE 01674 673081

FAX 01674 673081

CATEGORY Arts & crafts equipment • Books hardback • Books paperback • Childrens play/craft scrap • Christmas cards • Fabric remnants • Knitting, crochet and sewing equipment • Knitting wool • Milk bottle tops • Musical instruments •

Records & tapes • Silver paper & aluminium foil • Sports equipment • Toys & games

COLLECTION SERVICE No

▣ Moorlands Community Association

ADDRESS c/o 32 Kesteven Way, Bitterne, Southampton, Hants SO18 5RJ

TELEPHONE 01703 323161

CATEGORY Air miles • Coins foreign • Coins old • Petrol vouchers • Postcards used • Stamps British • Stamps foreign • Trading stamps

COLLECTION SERVICE No

▣ National Animal Welfare Trust

ADDRESS Tyler's Way, Watford-by-Pass, Watford, Herts WD2 8HQ

TELEPHONE 0181-950 0177

FAX 0181-420 4454

CATEGORY Air miles • Antique post cards • Arts & crafts equipment • Baby equipment • Bed linen and mattresses • Bicycles • Books hardback • Books paperback • Bric-a-brac • Clocks • Clothing adults' • Clothing children's • Coins foreign • Coins old • Computer hardware and software • Diy equipment • Fabric remnants • Furniture *small pieces only* • Gardening equipment • Household items *ironing boards etc* • Jewellery • Knitting, crochet and sewing equipment • Knitting wool • Medals • Money-off coupons • Musical instruments • Non perishable foods • Office equipment and stationery • Petrol vouchers • Pets equipment • Photographic equipment • Records & tapes • Sports equipment • Stamps British • Stamps foreign • Toiletries • Toys & games • Trading stamps • Video/computer games • Watches

COLLECTION SERVICE Yes

▣ The National Bible Society of Scotland

ADDRESS 7 Hampton Terrace, Edinburgh, Lothian EH12 5XU

TELEPHONE 0131-337 9701

FAX 0131-337 0641

CATEGORY Air miles • Antique post cards • Clocks • Coins foreign • Coins old • Computer hardware and software • Jewellery • Medals • Musical instruments • Postcards used • Stamps British • Stamps foreign • Telephone cards • Watches

COLLECTION SERVICE Yes

▣ National Meningitis Trust

ADDRESS Fern House, Bath Road, Stroud, Gloucs GL5 3TS

TELEPHONE 01453 751738

FAX 01453 753588

CATEGORY Coins foreign

COLLECTION SERVICE Yes

▣ National Organisation for Counselling Adoptees and Parents (NORCAP)

ADDRESS 112 Church Road, Wheatley, Oxon OX33 1LU

TELEPHONE 01865 875000

FAX 01865 875686

CATEGORY Petrol vouchers • Stamps British • Stamps foreign • Trading stamps

COLLECTION SERVICE No

▣ National Schizophrenia Fellowship

ADDRESS 39 Whistler Close, Black Dam, Basingstoke, Hants RG21 3HN

TELEPHONE 01256 816215

CATEGORY Air miles • Arts & crafts equipment • Bric-a-brac • Coins foreign • Coins old • Computer hardware and software • Fabric remnants • Gardening equipment • Jewellery • Knitting, crochet and sewing equipment • Knitting wool • Medals • Money-off coupons • Non perishable foods • Office equipment and stationery • Petrol vouchers • Records & tapes • Stamps British • Stamps foreign • Toiletries • Toys & games • Trading stamps

COLLECTION SERVICE No

▣ The National Society for Epilepsy

ADDRESS Chalfont St Peter, Gerrards Cross, Bucks SL9 0RJ

TELEPHONE 01494 873991

FAX 01494 817927

CATEGORY Arts & crafts equipment • Fabric remnants • Knitting, crochet and sewing equipment • Knitting wool • Musical instruments • Records & tapes

COLLECTION SERVICE No

▣ The National Trust

ADDRESS PO Box 33, Hinckley, Leics LE10 1ZN

TELEPHONE 01455 611508

CATEGORY Aluminium *drinks can ring-pulls only* • Air miles • Aluminium • Coins foreign • Coins old • Milk bottle tops • Money-off coupons • Petrol vouchers • Postcards used • Silver paper & aluminium foil • Stamps British • Stamps foreign • Telephone cards • Trading stamps

COLLECTION SERVICE No

▣ NCH Action for Children

ADDRESS Halcon Family Centre, 110 Roman Road, Taunton, Somerset TA1 2BL

TELEPHONE 01823 256969

CATEGORY Arts & crafts equipment • Baby equipment • Books hardback *children's books* •

Gardening equipment • Money-off coupons • Non perishable foods • Toys & games *good condition*

COLLECTION SERVICE No

■ Network (Whitby Resource Centre)

ADDRESS Central Hall, 4a Well Close Square, Whitby, N Yorks YO21 3AP

TELEPHONE 01947 606173

FAX 01947 820611

CATEGORY Aluminium • Baby equipment • Bed linen and mattresses *must be covered by fire regulations* • Bicycles • Books hardback • Books paperback • Bric-a-brac • Christmas cards • Clothing adults' • Clothing children's • Fabric remnants • Furniture *must be covered by fire regulations* • Gardening equipment • Household items *ironing boards etc* • Knitting, crochet and sewing equipment • Knitting wool • Office equipment and stationery • Other metals • Records & tapes • Sports equipment • Toys & games

COLLECTION SERVICE Yes

■ Newark & Sherwood Play Support Group

ADDRESS Newark Play Centre, 17a Cartergate, Newark, Notts NG24 1UA

TELEPHONE 01636 72257

CATEGORY Childrens play/craft scrap *not polystyrene or containers that have previously contained hazardous substances* • Fabric remnants • Knitting wool • Milk bottle tops • Musical instruments • Plastics • Rags *clean* • Silver paper & aluminium foil • Toys & games • Waste paper *plain only please*

COLLECTION SERVICE No

■ Newark Play Association

ADDRESS Hill Close (Reeves Way), Peterborough, Cambs PE1 5LZ

TELEPHONE 01733 340605

CATEGORY Arts & crafts equipment • Diy equipment • Fabric remnants • Gardening equipment • Jewellery • Knitting, crochet and sewing equipment • Knitting wool • Magazines & comics *comics only* • Musical instruments • Office equipment and stationery • Sports equipment • Toiletries • Toys & games

COLLECTION SERVICE No

■ Newcastle Play Council

ADDRESS Pitfield House, Brampton, Newcastle, Staffs ST5 0QP

TELEPHONE 01782 615378

CATEGORY Arts & crafts equipment • Books hardback *only children's books* • Books paperback *only children's books* • Childrens play/craft scrap •

Fabric remnants • Knitting wool • Sports equipment • Toys & games

COLLECTION SERVICE No

■ Newham Baby Bank

ADDRESS Durning Hall, Earlham Grove, Forest Gate, London E13 8EW

TELEPHONE 0181-519 2244

FAX 0181-519 5472

CATEGORY Baby equipment

COLLECTION SERVICE Yes

■ Newhaven Volunteer Bureau

ADDRESS 10 High Street, Newhaven, E Sussex BN9 9PE

TELEPHONE 01273 514379

CATEGORY Arts & crafts equipment • Books hardback • Books paperback • Computer hardware and software • Diy equipment • Gardening equipment • Office equipment and stationery

COLLECTION SERVICE Yes

■ Newton Visual Impaired Group

ADDRESS 8 Planetree Grove, Haydock, St Helen's, Merseyside WA11 0QY

TELEPHONE 01942 722743

CATEGORY Antique post cards • Bric-a-brac • Coins foreign • Coins old • Jewellery • Knitting, crochet and sewing equipment • Knitting wool • Magazines & comics • Medals • Milk bottle tops • Money-off coupons • Non perishable foods • Petrol vouchers • Records & tapes • Silver paper & aluminium foil • Stamps British • Stamps foreign • Toiletries • Toys & games • Trading stamps • Video/computer games • Watches

COLLECTION SERVICE Yes

■ NiPlas Recycling

ADDRESS 2 Hallows Close, Kelsall, Nr Tarporley, Cheshire CW6 0QF

TELEPHONE 01829 752029

FAX 01829 752029

CATEGORY Plastics *polythene film & other plastic mouldings, clean*

COLLECTION SERVICE No

■ Non-Animal Medical Research

ADDRESS 81 Beresford Avenue, Skegness, Lincs PE25 3JQ

CATEGORY Fabric remnants *silks and cottons only* • Jewellery *including broken* • Kitting, crochet, sewing equipment *unfinished embroidery & tapestry, thimbles & needles only* • Watches *including broken*

COLLECTION SERVICE No

■ **Norfolk & Norwich Muscular Dystrophy Group**

ADDRESS c/o 5 Ampthill Street, Norwich, Norfolk NR2 2RG

TELEPHONE 01603 460461

CATEGORY Books hardback • Books paperback • Coins foreign • Knitting wool • Petrol vouchers • Stamps British • Stamps foreign • Telephone cards

COLLECTION SERVICE No

■ **Norfolk & Norwich Scope**

ADDRESS 200 Bowthorpe Road, Norwich, Norfolk NR2 3TZ

TELEPHONE 01603 630769

FAX 01603 630769

CATEGORY Air miles • Arts & crafts equipment • Baby equipment • Bed linen and mattresses • Bicycles • Books hardback • Books paperback • Bric-a-brac • Clocks • Clothing adults' • Clothing children's • Computer hardware and software • Fabric remnants • Gardening equipment • Household items *ironing boards etc* • Jewellery • Knitting, crochet and sewing equipment • Knitting wool • Musical instruments • Non perishable foods • Office equipment and stationery • Photographic equipment • Records & tapes • Sports equipment • Toiletries • Toys & games • Video/computer games

COLLECTION SERVICE No

■ **The Norfolk Society**

ADDRESS 7 The Old Church, St Matthew's Road, Norwich, Norfolk NR1 1SP

CATEGORY Antique post cards • Books hardback *good quailty only* • Books paperback *good quality only* • Bric-a-brac • Jewellery

COLLECTION SERVICE No

■ **North Ayr Training Group**

ADDRESS 22–26 Whitfield Drive, Heath Field Industrial Estate, Ayr, Ayrshire KA8 9RX

TELEPHONE 01292 285156

FAX 01292 285156

CATEGORY Bed linen and mattresses • Bric-a-brac • Furniture • Household items *ironing boards etc no gas appliances*

COLLECTION SERVICE Yes

■ **North Herts CVS/Lions Furniture Recycling Scheme**

ADDRESS c/o Free Church Hall, Gernon Road, Letchworth, Herts SG6 3HS

TELEPHONE 01462 683577

FAX 01462 683577

CATEGORY Baby equipment • Bed linen and mattresses • Clocks • Diy equipment • Furniture • Gardening equipment • Household items *ironing boards etc*

COLLECTION SERVICE Yes

■ **Norwich Community Workshop**

ADDRESS Music House Lane, Norwich, Norfolk NR1 1QL

TELEPHONE 01603 626316

CATEGORY Arts & crafts equipment • Bed linen and mattresses *plain white cotton sheets only* • Books hardback *on arts and crafts subjects only* • Books paperback *on arts and crafts subjects only* • Clothing adults' • Diy equipment • Fabric remnants • Glass *flat – coloured or clear for leaded glass, no bottles or jars* • Jewellery *only that which can be taken apart and reused* • Knitting, crochet and sewing equipment • Knitting wool • Non perishable foods • Office equipment and stationery • Rags *cotton only – ideally absorbant* • Waste paper *plain paper only – coloured paper or white, sheets or rolls*

COLLECTION SERVICE No

■ **Nottingham Mencap**

ADDRESS Centre House, 4 Chapel Bar, Nottingham, Notts NG1 6JR

TELEPHONE 0115-956 1130

FAX 0115-956 1131

CATEGORY Air miles • Antique post cards • Arts & crafts equipment • Bed linen and mattresses *not mattresses* • Books hardback • Books paperback • Bric-a-brac • Clocks • Clothing adults' • Clothing children's • Coins foreign • Coins old • Computer hardware and software • Fur coats • Jewellery • Medals • Musical instruments • Office equipment and stationery • Records & tapes • Sports equipment • Toys & games

COLLECTION SERVICE Yes

■ **Nuffield Orthopaedic Centre League of Friends**

ADDRESS Windmill Road, Headington, Oxon OX3 7LD

TELEPHONE 01865 227470/1

CATEGORY Books hardback • Books paperback • Bric-a-brac • Knitting, crochet and sewing equipment • Knitting wool • Records & tapes

COLLECTION SERVICE Yes

■ Oasis Aids Support Centre

ADDRESS 547 Battersea Park Road, London SW
SW11 3BL

TELEPHONE 0171-228 8331/924 7514

FAX 0171-228 6001

CATEGORY Air miles ● Antique post cards ● Arts &
crafts equipment ● Bed linen and mattresses
● Bicycles ● Books hardback ● Books paperback
● Bric-a-brac ● Clocks ● Clothing adults'
● Clothing children's ● Coins foreign ● Coins old
● Computer hardware and software ● Diy
equipment ● Furniture ● Gardening equipment
● Household items *ironing boards etc* ● Jewellery
● Medals ● Money-off coupons ● Musical
instruments ● Non perishable foods ● Office
equipment and stationery ● Petrol vouchers
● Pets equipment ● Photographic equipment
● Rags ● Records & tapes ● Sports equipment
● Telephone cards ● Toiletries ● Trading stamps
● Video/computer games ● Watches

COLLECTION SERVICE Yes

■ Octavia Hill Housing Trust

ADDRESS Quest Social Centre, 85 Clarendon Road,
London W11 4XQ

TELEPHONE 0171-243 0117

FAX 0171-727 8603

CATEGORY Bric-a-brac ● Fabric remnants
● Household items *ironing boards etc* ● Knitting,
crochet and sewing equipment ● Knitting wool

COLLECTION SERVICE Yes

■ Outset

ADDRESS Drake House, 18 Creekside, London
SE8 3DZ

TELEPHONE 0181-692 7141

FAX 0181-469 2532

CATEGORY Computer hardware and software

COLLECTION SERVICE No

■ Oxfam

ADDRESS 19 Regent Street, Rugby, Warks CV21 2PE

TELEPHONE 01788 578016

CATEGORY Air miles ● Aluminium ● Antique post
cards ● Arts & crafts equipment ● Bed linen and
mattresses *not mattresses, linen only* ● Books
hardback ● Books paperback ● Bric-a-brac ● Clocks
● Clothing adults' ● Clothing children's ● Coins
foreign ● Coins old ● Fabric remnants ● Jewellery
● Knitting wool ● Medals ● Milk bottle tops
● Money-off coupons ● Petrol vouchers
● Postcards used ● Records & tapes ● Silver paper
& aluminium foil ● Sports equipment ● Stamps
British ● Stamps foreign ● Telephone cards ● Toys
& games ● Trading stamps ● Watches ● Wedding
clothes for hire

COLLECTION SERVICE No

■ Oxfam

ADDRESS 274 Banbury Road, Oxford, Oxon OX2 7DZ

TELEPHONE 01865 311311

FAX 01865 313163

CATEGORY Air miles ● Aluminium ● Antique post
cards ● Bed linen and mattresses *only where we
have furniture shops* ● Bicycles ● Books hardback
● Books paperback ● Bric-a-brac ● Clocks
● Clothing adults' ● Clothing children's ● Coins
foreign ● Coins old ● Computer hardware and
software ● Diy equipment ● Furniture *only where
we have furniture shops* ● Gardening equipment
● Household items *ironing boards etc* ● Jewellery
● Knitting, crochet and sewing equipment
● Knitting wool ● Magazines & comics ● Medals
● Milk bottle tops ● Money-off coupons ● Musical
instruments ● Office equipment and stationery
only where we have furniture shops ● Petrol
vouchers ● Photographic equipment ● Postcards
used ● Rags ● Records & tapes ● Silver paper &
aluminium foil ● Sports equipment ● Stamps
British ● Stamps foreign ● Telephone cards
● Toiletries ● Toys & games ● Trading stamps
● Used toner cartridges ● Video/computer games
● Watches ● Wedding clothes for hire

COLLECTION SERVICE Yes

■ Oxford Mission

ADDRESS PO Box 86, Romsey, Hants SO51 8YD

TELEPHONE 01794 515004

FAX 01794 515004

CATEGORY Musical instruments *only string and brass*
● Stamps British *commemorative only* ● Stamps
foreign

COLLECTION SERVICE No

■ Peacehaven & Telscombe Volunteer Bureau

ADDRESS The House Project, 168 South Coast Road,
Peacehaven, E Sussex BN10 8JH

TELEPHONE 01273 587795

FAX 01273 587795

CATEGORY Bric-a-brac ● Diy equipment *tools, etc*
● Gardening equipment ● Household items
ironing boards etc small ● Jewellery ● Musical
instruments *small* ● Records & tapes ● Toys &
games

COLLECTION SERVICE Yes

■ Pet Animals Welfare Society (PAWS)

ADDRESS 3 Eskdale Close, Dewsbury, W Yorks
WF12 7PT

TELEPHONE 01924 462876

CATEGORY Air miles ● Antique post cards ● Books
hardback ● Books paperback ● Coins old
● Jewellery ● Medals ● Money-off coupons *not
stores' own coupons* ● Petrol vouchers ● Pets
equipment ● Toiletries ● Trading stamps

COLLECTION SERVICE No

■ Phoenix Sheltered Workshop

ADDRESS 14 Court Road, Sparkhill, Birmingham, W Midlands B11 4LY

TELEPHONE 0121-771 0380

FAX 0121-766 7430

CATEGORY Aluminium ● Baby equipment ● Bed linen and mattresses *bed linen only* ● Bicycles ● Books hardback ● Books paperback ● Bric-a-brac ● Clocks ● Clothing adults' ● Clothing children's ● Coins foreign ● Coins old ● Fabric remnants ● Gardening equipment ● Household items *ironing boards etc* ● Jewellery ● Knitting, crochet and sewing equipment ● Knitting wool ● Magazines & comics ● Money-off coupons ● Musical instruments *not organs or pianos* ● Petrol vouchers ● Pets equipment ● Photographic equipment ● Rags ● Records & tapes ● Spectacles ● Sports equipment *small items* ● Stamps British ● Stamps foreign ● Toiletries ● Toys & games ● Trading stamps ● Video/computer games ● Waste paper ● Watches

COLLECTION SERVICE No

■ Portsmouth Community Furniture Recycling

ADDRESS c/o Portsmouth Council of Community Service, 338 Commercial Road, Portsmouth, Hants PO1 4BT

TELEPHONE 01705 827110

FAX 01705 873785

E-MAIL :xccspohn@hantsnet.hants.gov.uk

CATEGORY Computer hardware and software ● Furniture ● Office equipment and stationery

COLLECTION SERVICE Yes

■ Prader-Willi Syndrome Association (UK)

ADDRESS 2 Wheatsheaf Close, Horsell, Woking, Surrey GU21 4BP

TELEPHONE 01483 724784

CATEGORY Air miles ● Knitting wool ● Money-off coupons ● Petrol vouchers ● Stamps British ● Stamps foreign ● Trading stamps

COLLECTION SERVICE No

■ Pramacare

ADDRESS 1 Grand Parade, Wimborne Road, Kinson, Bournemouth, Dorset BH10 7AZ

TELEPHONE 01202 599199

CATEGORY Air miles ● Antique post cards ● Arts & crafts equipment ● Books hardback ● Books paperback ● Bric-a-brac ● Clocks ● Clothing adults' *ladies* ● Clothing children's ● Coins foreign ● Coins old ● Computer hardware and software ● Diy equipment ● Fabric remnants ● Jewellery ● Knitting, crochet and sewing equipment ● Knitting wool ● Medals ● Money-off coupons ● Musical instruments ● Office equipment and stationery ● Petrol vouchers ● Photographic equipment ● Records & tapes ● Sports equipment

● Stamps British ● Stamps foreign ● Toiletries ● Toys & games ● Trading stamps ● Used toner cartridges ● Watches

COLLECTION SERVICE Yes

■ Preston Animal Welfare Society

ADDRESS 56 Manor Lane, Penwortham, Preston, Lancs PR1 0TA

TELEPHONE 01772 744428

CATEGORY Air miles ● Books hardback ● Books paperback ● Bric-a-brac ● Christmas cards ● Stamps British ● Stamps foreign

COLLECTION SERVICE No

■ Prosa Foundation

ADDRESS 15 Beaufort Close, Reigate, Surrey RW2 9DG

TELEPHONE 01737 217417

FAX 01737 217417

E-MAIL 70374.1165@compuserve

CATEGORY Air miles ● Baby equipment *not requiring repair* ● Bicycles ● Books hardback ● Books paperback ● Clothing adults' *only in excellent condition* ● Clothing children's *only in excellent condition* ● Computer hardware and software ● Fur coats *only in excellent condition* ● Furniture ● Household items *ironing boards etc* ● Knitting, crochet and sewing equipment ● Knitting wool ● Musical instruments ● Non perishable foods ● Office equipment and stationery ● Records & tapes ● Toiletries ● Trading stamps

COLLECTION SERVICE Yes

■ Prospect Hospice

ADDRESS Moormead Road, Wroughton, Swindon, Wilts SN4 9BY

TELEPHONE 01793 825583

FAX 01793 815432

CATEGORY Air miles ● Aluminium *drinks cans only* ● Antique post cards ● Bric-a-brac ● Clocks ● Clothing adults' ● Clothing children's ● Coins foreign ● Coins old ● Computer hardware and software ● Diy equipment ● Furniture *small items only* ● Gardening equipment ● Household items *ironing boards etc* ● Jewellery ● Medals ● Money-off coupons ● Office equipment and stationery ● Petrol vouchers ● Stamps British ● Stamps foreign ● Trading stamps ● Watches

COLLECTION SERVICE No

■ PSS – Toy Library & Resource Centre

ADDRESS 18 Seel Street, Liverpool, Merseyside L1 4BE

TELEPHONE 0151-707 0131

FAX 0151-707 0039

CATEGORY Arts & crafts equipmet ● Fabric remnants ● Knitting, sewing etc ● Knitting wool ● Musical instruments • Sports equipment • Toys & games • Video/computer games

COLLECTION SERVICE No

■ Queen Elizabeth's Foundation for Disabled People

ADDRESS Leatherhead Court, Woodlands Road, Leatherhead, Surrey KT22 0BN

TELEPHONE 01372 842204

FAX 01372 844072

CATEGORY Arts & crafts equipment • Clothing adults' *epsom and leatherhead, nearly new* • Computer hardware and software • Fabric remnants • Jewellery • Knitting, crochet and sewing equipment • Knitting wool • Musical instruments • Office equipment and stationery • Petrol vouchers • Stamps British • Stamps foreign • Used toner cartridges *leatherhead only, delivered* • Video/computer games

COLLECTION SERVICE Yes

■ Queens Hall Help Committee

ADDRESS 160 Gidlow Lane, Wigan, Lancs WN6 7EA

TELEPHONE 01942 324883

CATEGORY Antique post cards • Arts & crafts equipment • Baby equipment • Bed linen and mattresses *not mattresses, only complete beds* • Bicycles • Books hardback • Books paperback • Bric-a-brac • Clocks • Clothing adults' • Clothing children's • Computer hardware and software • Diy equipment • Fabric remnants • Furniture • Gardening equipment • Household items *ironing boards etc* • Jewellery • Knitting, crochet and sewing equipment • Knitting wool • Magazines & comics • Musical instruments • Non perishable foods • Office equipment and stationery • Photographic equipment • Records & tapes • Spectacles • Sports equipment • Toiletries • Toys & games • Video/computer games • Watches

COLLECTION SERVICE No

■ RACKS

ADDRESS c/o 43 Clifton Road, Warks CV21 3QE

TELEPHONE 01788 575183

CATEGORY Antique post cards • Bed linen and mattresses *no mattresses* • Bicycles • Books hardback • Books paperback • Bric-a-brac • Clocks *not electrical* • Clothing adults' • Clothing children's • Fabric remnants • Household items *ironing boards etc* • Jewellery • Knitting, crochet and sewing equipment *nothing electrical* • Knitting wool • Magazines & comics • Musical instruments • Pets equipment • Photographic equipment • Postcards used • Records & tapes • Sports equipment *items must not be too large, ie rowing machines, etc* • Toiletries • Toys & games • Video/computer games • Watches

COLLECTION SERVICE No

■ Raynaud's & Scleroderma Association

ADDRESS 112 Crewe Road, Alsager, Cheshire ST7 2JA

TELEPHONE 01270 872776

FAX 01270 883556

CATEGORY Books hardback • Books paperback • Bric-a-brac • Computer hardware and software • Fabric remnants • Office equipment and stationery • Petrol vouchers • Stamps British • Stamps foreign • Trading stamps • Used toner cartridges

COLLECTION SERVICE Yes

■ Rehab – Basingstoke & Alton Cardiac Appeal

ADDRESS 3 Rewlands Drive, Winchester, Hants SO22 6PA

TELEPHONE 01962 886399

CATEGORY Air miles • Antique post cards • Arts & crafts equipment • Baby equipment • Bicycles • Books hardback • Books paperback • Bric-a-brac • Clocks • Clothing adults' • Clothing children's • Coins foreign • Coins old • Computer hardware and software • Diy equipment • Fabric remnants • Fur coats • Furniture • Gardening equipment • Household items *ironing boards etc* • Jewellery • Knitting, crochet and sewing equipment • Knitting wool • Magazines & comics • Medals • Money-off coupons • Musical instruments • Office equipment and stationery • Petrol vouchers • Photographic equipment • Postcards used • Records & tapes • Sports equipment • Stamps British • Stamps foreign • Telephone cards • Toys & games • Trading stamps • Video/computer games • Watches

COLLECTION SERVICE Yes

■ Relate (Basingstoke & District)

ADDRESS Chute House, Church Street, Basingstoke, Hants RG21 7QT

TELEPHONE 01256 24364

FAX 01256 818209

CATEGORY Books hardback • Books paperback • Bric-a-brac • Clothing adults' *nearly new* • Jewellery • Stamps British • Stamps foreign • Toiletries • Toys & games • Watches

COLLECTION SERVICE No

■ Religious Society of Friends

ADDRESS 41 Park Road, Woking, Surrey GU22 7DB

CATEGORY Stamps British • Stamps foreign

COLLECTION SERVICE No

■ **Replay**

ADDRESS Kerry Road, Newtown, Powys SY16 1BJ

TELEPHONE 01686 622267

CATEGORY Aluminium • Arts & crafts equipment • Baby equipment • Books hardback • Books paperback • Bric-a-brac • Childrens play/craft scrap • Clocks • Clothing adults' • Clothing children's • Fabric remnants • Household items *ironing boards etc* • Jewellery • Knitting, crochet and sewing equipment • Knitting wool • Magazines & comics • Office equipment and stationery • Rags • Records & tapes • Silver paper & aluminium foil • Toys & games • Waste paper • Watches

COLLECTION SERVICE Yes

■ **Resettlement Project – South Hants**

ADDRESS 30 Oxford Street, Southampton, Hants SO14 3DJ

TELEPHONE 01703 223860

CATEGORY Baby equipment • Bed linen and mattresses *not mattresses on their own* • Clocks • Furniture • Gardening equipment • Household items *ironing boards etc* • Musical instruments *if working* • Toys & games *in good condition*

COLLECTION SERVICE Yes

■ **Rhyl & District Gingerbread Group**

ADDRESS Pierrot House, 10 Winnard Avenue, Rhyl, Denbighshire, Clwyd LL18 2ED

TELEPHONE 01745 344062

CATEGORY Bric-a-brac

COLLECTION SERVICE No

■ **Richmond Fellowship International**

ADDRESS Clyde House, 109 Strawberry Vale, Twickenham, Middx TW1 4SJ

TELEPHONE 0181-744 9585

FAX 0181-891 0500

CATEGORY Air miles • Arts & crafts equipment • Bed linen and mattresses *in good condition* • Bicycles • Books hardback • Computer hardware and software • Diy equipment • Fabric remnants • Gardening equipment *in good condition* • Knitting, crochet and sewing equipment • Knitting wool • Musical instruments • Non perishable foods • Office equipment and stationery *small desks only plus chairs* • Petrol vouchers • Photographic equipment • Records & tapes • Sports equipment • Toiletries • Toys & games • Video/computer games

COLLECTION SERVICE Yes

■ **Rokeby Infant School PTFA**

ADDRESS c/o 9 Long Furlong, Rugby, Warks CV22 5QS

TELEPHONE 01788 815452

CATEGORY Aluminium • Christmas cards *for recycling* • Clothing adults' *for recycling* • Clothing children's *for recycling* • Fabric remnants *for recycling* • Fur coats *for recycling* • Glass • Magazines & comics *for recycling* • Milk bottle tops • Other metals *steel cans* • Rags • Silver paper & aluminium foil • Waste paper

COLLECTION SERVICE Yes

■ **Rowan Cottage**

ADDRESS 4 Prince of Wales Road, Dorchester, Dorset DT4 7QZ

TELEPHONE 01305 263495

CATEGORY Knitting wool

COLLECTION SERVICE No

■ **Royal 945 AM**

ADDRESS PO Box 945, Liverpool, Merseyside L69 7QB

TELEPHONE 0151-706 2125

FAX 0151-706 2125

CATEGORY Records & tapes *must be in good condition*

COLLECTION SERVICE No

■ **Royal British Legion**

ADDRESS 'Home', Meeting Hill, Worstead, North Walsham, Norfolk NR28 9LT

TELEPHONE 01692 402316

CATEGORY Aluminium • Books paperback • Bric-a-brac • Christmas cards • Knitting wool • Medals • Milk bottle tops • Postcards *used* • Silver paper & aluminium foil • Stamps British • Stamps foreign • Waste paper

COLLECTION SERVICE No

■ **Royal National Lifeboat Institution**

ADDRESS 9 Drake Walk, Waterfront 2000, Atlantic Wharf, Cardiff, S Glamorgan CF1 5AN

TELEPHONE 01222 456999

FAX 01222 455999

CATEGORY Coins foreign • Coins old • Jewellery • Stamps British *used* • Stamps foreign *used* • Used toner cartridges

COLLECTION SERVICE No

Alphabetical list of organisations

■ Royal National Lifeboat Institution

ADDRESS 18 Half Edge Lane, Eccles, Gtr Manchester M30 9GJ

TELEPHONE 0161-787 8779

FAX 0161-787 8926

CATEGORY Antique post cards • Coins foreign • Coins old • Medals • Postcards used • Stamps British • Stamps foreign • Telephone cards • Used toner cartridges

COLLECTION SERVICE Yes

■ Royal National Lifeboat Institution

ADDRESS South East Region, Kennet House, River Way, Uckfield, E Sussex TN22 1SL

TELEPHONE 01825 761466

FAX 01825 768093

CATEGORY Antique post cards • Coins foreign • Coins old • Jewellery • Medals • Watches

COLLECTION SERVICE Yes

■ Royal National Lifeboat Institution

ADDRESS Bellevue House, Hopetown Street, Edinburgh, Lothian EH7 4ND

TELEPHONE 0131-557 9171

FAX 0131-557 6943

CATEGORY Antique post cards • Books hardback • Bric-a-brac • Clocks • Clothing adults' *good quality for resale* • Clothing children's *good quality for resale* • Coins foreign • Coins old • Furniture *small items* • Household items *ironing boards etc not electrical goods* • Jewellery • Medals • Photographic equipment *for resale* • Sports equipment *for resale* • Stamps British • Stamps foreign • Telephone cards • Toys & games *for resale* • Used toner cartridges • Video/ computer games *for resale* • Watches

COLLECTION SERVICE Yes

■ Royal National Mission To Deep Sea Fishermen

ADDRESS Culag Park, Lochimyer, Sutherland IV27 4LE

TELEPHONE 01571 844456

FAX 01571 844456

CATEGORY Books paperback • Jewellery • Magazines & comics • Stamps British • Stamps foreign

COLLECTION SERVICE No

■ Royal National Mission to Deep Sea Fishermen

ADDRESS 43 Nottingham Place, London W1M 4BX

TELEPHONE 0171-487 5101

FAX 0171-224 5240

CATEGORY Antique post cards • Bric-a-brac • Clocks • Coins foreign • Coins old • Jewellery • Medals •
Postcards used • Stamps British • Stamps foreign • Watches

COLLECTION SERVICE No

■ Royal National Mission to Deep Sea Fishermen

ADDRESS Harbour Road, Eyemouth, Berwickshire TD14 5HT

TELEPHONE 01890 751313

CATEGORY Antique post cards • Books hardback • Books paperback • Coins foreign • Coins old • Medals • Records & tapes • Stamps British • Stamps foreign

COLLECTION SERVICE No

■ The Royal Society for the Protection of Birds

ADDRESS The Lodge, Sandy, Beds SG19 2DL

TELEPHONE 01767 680551

FAX 01767 692365

CATEGORY Air miles • Jewellery • Petrol vouchers • Stamps British • Stamps foreign • Watches

COLLECTION SERVICE No

■ Royal Veterinary College Animal Care Trust

ADDRESS The Appeals Office, Royal Veterinary College, Hawkshead Lane, Hatfield, Herts AL9 7TA

TELEPHONE 01707 666237

FAX 01707 652090

CATEGORY Aluminium • Antique post cards • Coins foreign • Coins old • Milk bottle tops • Postcards used • Silver paper & aluminium foil • Stamps British • Stamps foreign • Waste paper

COLLECTION SERVICE No

■ RSPCA

ADDRESS Clough Road, Hull, E Yorks HU6 7PE

TELEPHONE 01482 631648

CATEGORY Aluminium *tinfoil, not cans* • Arts & crafts equipment • Baby equipment • Bed linen and mattresses *linen only* • Books hardback • Books paperback • Bric-a-brac • Clocks *in full working order* • Clothing adults' • Clothing children's • Household items *ironing boards etc small items preferred* • Jewellery • Knitting wool • Milk bottle tops • Other metals *tin foil* • Petrol vouchers • Pets equipment • Records & tapes • Silver paper & aluminium foil • Stamps British • Stamps foreign • Toiletries • Toys & games • Watches *if in full working order*

COLLECTION SERVICE Yes

■ RSPCA

ADDRESS 137 Radford Road, Carlton, Nottingham, Notts NG7 5DU

TELEPHONE 0115-978 4965

FAX 0115-978 3909

CATEGORY Air miles ● Antique post cards ● Arts & crafts equipment ● Baby equipment ● Bed linen and mattresses ● Bicycles ● Books paperback ● Bric-a-brac ● Clocks ● Clothing adults' ● Clothing children's ● Diy equipment ● Furniture *small items* ● Gardening equipment ● Household items *ironing boards etc* ● Jewellery ● Knitting wool ● Medals ● Money-off coupons ● Musical instruments ● Non perishable foods ● Office equipment and stationery ● Petrol vouchers ● Pets equipment ● Photographic equipment ● Records & tapes ● Sports equipment ● Toiletries ● Toys & games ● Trading stamps ● Watches

COLLECTION SERVICE No

■ RSPCA (Birmingham & District Branch)

ADDRESS Barnes Hill, Weoley Castle, Birmingham, W Midlands B29 5UP

TELEPHONE 0121-427 6111

FAX 0121-421 2599

CATEGORY Bicycles ● Bric-a-brac ● Gardening equipment ● Jewellery ● Records & tapes ● Sports equipment *not large items* ● Stamps British ● Stamps foreign

COLLECTION SERVICE No

■ RSPCA (Bradford & District Branch)

ADDRESS Mount Street, Bradford, W Yorks BD3 9SW

TELEPHONE 01274 723063

CATEGORY Aluminium ● Antique post cards ● Baby equipment ● Books hardback ● Books paperback ● Bric-a-brac ● Clocks ● Clothing adults' ● Clothing children's ● Coins foreign ● Coins old ● Diy equipment ● Fabric remnants ● Furniture ● Household items *ironing boards etc* ● Jewellery ● Knitting, crochet and sewing equipment ● Knitting wool ● Magazines & comics ● Medals ● Musical instruments ● Non perishable foods ● Pets equipment ● Records & tapes ● Spectacles ● Telephone cards ● Toiletries ● Toys & games ● Video/computer games ● Watches

COLLECTION SERVICE Yes

■ RSPCA (Burton-on-Trent & District Branch)

ADDRESS RSPCA Animal Home, Hillfield Lane, Stretton, Burton-on-Trent, Staffs DE13 0BN

TELEPHONE 01283 569165

CATEGORY Aluminium ● Books hardback ● Books paperback ● Bric-a-brac ● Clothing adults' ● Clothing children's ● Jewellery ● Toiletries *new, unwanted gifts for tombolas*

COLLECTION SERVICE Yes

■ RSPCA (Kent Rochester Branch)

ADDRESS 1 Old Cottages, Backfields, Rochester, Kent ME1 1UH

TELEPHONE 01634 842823/845435

CATEGORY Antique post cards ● Arts & crafts equipment ● Books hardback ● Books paperback ● Bric-a-brac ● Clocks ● Clothing adults' ● Clothing children's ● Jewellery ● Musical instruments ● Photographic equipment ● Records & tapes ● Toiletries ● Toys & games ● Watches

COLLECTION SERVICE No

■ RSPCA (Leicestershire Branch)

ADDRESS 190 Scudmore Road, Leicester, Leics LE3 1QU

TELEPHONE 0116-233 6677

FAX 0116-233 0953

CATEGORY Air miles ● Aluminium ● Antique post cards ● Bicycles ● Books hardback ● Books paperback ● Bric-a-brac ● Clocks ● Clothing adults' ● Clothing children's ● Coins foreign ● Coins old ● Computer hardware and software ● Jewellery ● Knitting, crochet and sewing equipment ● Knitting wool ● Magazines & comics ● Medals ● Milk bottle tops ● Money-off coupons ● Office equipment and stationery ● Petrol vouchers ● Pets equipment *includig tinned animal foods* ● Records & tapes ● Silver paper & aluminium foil ● Stamps British ● Stamps foreign ● Telephone cards ● Toiletries ● Toys & games ● Trading stamps ● Used toner cartridges ● Video/computer games ● Watches

COLLECTION SERVICE Yes

■ RSPCA (Marlborough with Andover Branch)

ADDRESS 18 Ham Close, Aughton, Collingbourne, Kingston, Nr Marlborough, Wilts SN8 3SB

TELEPHONE 01264 850500/01264 401500 (shop)

FAX 01264 402500 (shop)

CATEGORY Antique post cards ● Arts & crafts equipment ● Baby equipment ● Bed linen and mattresses ● Bicycles ● Books hardback ● Books paperback ● Bric-a-brac ● Clocks ● Clothing adults' ● Clothing children's ● Coins foreign ● Coins old ● Computer hardware and software ● Diy equipment ● Fabric remnants ● Furniture ● Gardening equipment ● Household items *ironing boards etc* ● Jewellery ● Knitting, crochet and sewing equipment ● Knitting wool ● Magazines & comics ● Medals ● Musical instruments ● Non perishable foods ● Office equipment and stationery ● Pets equipment ● Photographic equipment ● Records & tapes ● Sports equipment ● Stamps British ● Stamps foreign ● Toiletries ● Toys & games ● Video/computer games ● Watches

COLLECTION SERVICE Yes

■ RSPCA (Mayhew Animal Home)

ADDRESS Trenmar Gardens, London NW10 6BJ

TELEPHONE 0181-964 2790

FAX 0181-964 3221

E-MAIL rspca@cix.co.uk

CATEGORY Air miles ● Coins foreign ● Coins old
● Money-off coupons ● Petrol vouchers ● Pets
equipment ● Stamps British ● Stamps foreign
● Trading stamps

COLLECTION SERVICE No

■ RSPCA (Meirionnydd Branch)

ADDRESS Ty Goleu, Llwyngwril, Gwynedd LL37 2UZ

TELEPHONE 01341 250368

CATEGORY Antique post cards ● Arts & crafts
equipment ● Baby equipment ● Bed linen and
mattresses *bed linen only* ● Books hardback
● Books paperback ● Bric-a-brac ● Christmas cards
● Clocks ● Clothing adults' ● Clothing children's
● Coins foreign ● Coins old ● Diy equipment
● Fabric remnants ● Gardening equipment
● Household items *ironing boards etc* ● Jewellery
● Knitting, crochet and sewing equipment
● Knitting wool ● Non perishable foods ● Office
equipment and stationery ● Pets equipment
● Postcards used ● Records & tapes ● Sports
equipment ● Stamps British ● Stamps foreign
● Toiletries ● Toys & games

COLLECTION SERVICE No

■ RSPCA (North Staffs Branch)

ADDRESS Unit G, Burslem Enterprise Centre,
Moorland Road, Burslem, Stoke-on-Trent, Staffs
ST6 1JQ

TELEPHONE 01782 834713

CATEGORY Baby equipment ● Bicycles ● Books
hardback ● Books paperback ● Bric-a-brac ● Clocks
● Computer hardware and software ● Diy
equipment ● Fabric remnants ● Furniture
● Gardening equipment ● Household items
ironing boards etc ● Jewellery ● Knitting, crochet
and sewing equipment ● Knitting wool
● Magazines & comics ● Musical instruments
● Non perishable foods ● Office equipment and
stationery ● Pets equipment ● Photographic
equipment ● Records & tapes ● Sports equipment
● Toiletries ● Toys & games ● Video/computer
games

COLLECTION SERVICE Yes

■ RSPCA (Richmond, Twickenham & Barnes Branch)

ADDRESS 111 Elm Grove Road, Barnes, London
SW13 0BX

TELEPHONE 0181-876 5990

CATEGORY Antique post cards ● Bric-a-brac ● Coins
foreign ● Coins old ● Jewellery ● Knitting wool
● Stamps foreign ● Toiletries

COLLECTION SERVICE No

■ RSPCA (Swindon Branch)

ADDRESS PO Box 478, Swindon, Wilts SN2 1YD

TELEPHONE 01793 528457

CATEGORY Aluminium *drink cans only* ● Bric-a-brac
● Office equipment and stationery *not too large*
● Petrol vouchers ● Pets equipment ● Toiletries
● Toys & games

COLLECTION SERVICE No

■ RSPCA (SYAC)

ADDRESS Blackfirs Farm, Great North Road, Bawtry,
Doncaster, S Yorks DN10 6DE

TELEPHONE 01302 710271

FAX 01302 710958

CATEGORY Air miles ● Aluminium ● Bed linen and
mattresses ● Bicycles ● Books hardback ● Books
paperback ● Bric-a-brac ● Clocks ● Clothing adults'
● Clothing children's ● Computer hardware and
software ● Diy equipment ● Furniture
● Gardening equipment ● Household items
ironing boards etc ● Jewellery ● Knitting, crochet
and sewing equipment ● Knitting wool ● Non
perishable foods ● Office equipment and
stationery ● Petrol vouchers ● Pets equipment
● Rags ● Records & tapes ● Sports equipment
● Stamps British ● Toiletries ● Toys & games
● Trading stamps ● Video/computer games
● Waste paper ● Watches

COLLECTION SERVICE No

■ RSPCA (West Gwynedd Branch)

ADDRESS 'Eiddior', 6 Tan Y Buarth, Bethel,
Caernarfon, Gwynedd LL55 7UP

TELEPHONE 01248 671304

FAX 01248 671304

E-MAIL 101352.3075@compuserve.com

CATEGORY Aluminium ● Arts & crafts equipment
● Books hardback ● Books paperback ● Bric-a-brac
● Diy equipment *non-electrical* ● Gardening
equipment *non-electrical* ● Household items
ironing boards etc small, non-electrical
● Jewellery *costume jewellery or any sort*
● Knitting, crochet and sewing equipment
● Knitting wool ● Musical instruments ● Pets
equipment ● Photographic equipment ● Records
& tapes ● Sports equipment ● Toiletries ● Toys &
games ● Watches *in working order only*

COLLECTION SERVICE Yes

■ RSPCA (Wiltshire North & Chippenham Branch)

ADDRESS 15 Matsfield Road, Chippenham, Wilts
SN15 1JX

TELEPHONE 01249 653478

CATEGORY Antique post cards ● Books hardback
● Bric-a-brac ● Clocks ● Clothing adults' *good
quality only* ● Clothing children's *good quality only*
● Fabric remnants ● Household items *ironing
boards etc* ● Jewellery ● Knitting, crochet and
sewing equipment ● Knitting wool ● Medals ●

Petrol vouchers • Pets equipment • Photographic equipment • Records & tapes • Stamps British • Stamps foreign • Toiletries • Toys & games • Trading stamps

COLLECTION SERVICE No

■ RSPCA (Wimbledon & District)

ADDRESS Unit 111, Armdale Centre, Wandsworth, London SW18

TELEPHONE 0181-542 5619

CATEGORY Bed linen and mattresses *no mattresses* • Books hardback • Books paperback • Bric-a-brac • Clothing adults' • Clothing children's • Jewellery • Knitting wool • Magazines & comics • Records & tapes • Toiletries • Toys & games

COLLECTION SERVICE No

■ The Russell Street Project Limited

ADDRESS 22 Russell Street, Keighley, W Yorks BD21 2JP

CATEGORY Arts & crafts equipment • Baby equipment • Clothing adults' • Clothing children's • Computer hardware and software • Diy equipment • Fabric remnants • Furniture • Gardening equipment • Household items *ironing boards etc* • Knitting, crochet and sewing equipment • Knitting wool • Musical instruments • Non perishable foods • Office equipment and stationery • Photographic equipment • Sports equipment • Toiletries • Video/computer games • Wedding clothes for hire

COLLECTION SERVICE No

■ St Barnabas Hospice Shops

ADDRESS 2 Dean Road, Lincoln, Lincs LN2 4DR

TELEPHONE 01522 560517

CATEGORY Antique post cards • Bed linen and mattresses *mattress to comply with safety standards* • Books hardback • Books paperback • Clothing adults' • Clothing children's • Fabric remnants • Furniture • Gardening equipment • Household items *ironing boards etc* • Jewellery • Knitting, crochet and sewing equipment • Knitting wool • Magazines & comics • Photographic equipment • Rags • Records & tapes • Spectacles • Toys & games • Waste paper • Watches • Wedding clothes for hire

COLLECTION SERVICE Yes

■ St Bridget's Cheshire Home

ADDRESS Ilex Close, Rustington, W Sussex BN16 4DW

TELEPHONE 01903 787610

FAX 01903 859235

CATEGORY Antique post cards • Bric-a-brac • Clocks • Clothing adults' *new or nearly new* • Clothing children's *new or nearly new* • Coins foreign • Coins old • Jewellery • Petrol vouchers •

Stamps foreign • Toys & games • Trading stamps • Watches

COLLECTION SERVICE No

■ St Cecilia's Cheshire Home

ADDRESS 32 Sundridge Avenue, Bromley, Kent BR1 2PZ

TELEPHONE 0181-460 8377

FAX 0181-466 8292

CATEGORY Antique post cards • Bed linen and mattresses *no mattresses* • Books hardback • Books paperback • Bric-a-brac • Clocks • Clothing adults' • Clothing children's • Coins foreign • Coins old • Fabric remnants • Household items *ironing boards etc small only* • Jewellery • Knitting, crochet and sewing equipment • Knitting wool • Magazines & comics • Medals • Musical instruments • Office equipment and stationery • Petrol vouchers • Photographic equipment • Postcards used • Records & tapes • Spectacles • Sports equipment • Stamps British • Stamps foreign • Telephone cards • Toiletries • Toys & games • Trading stamps • Watches

COLLECTION SERVICE No

■ St Christopher's Hospice

ADDRESS 51–59 Lawrie Park Road, Sydenham, London SE26 6DZ

TELEPHONE 0181-778 9252

FAX 0181-658 8680

CATEGORY Air miles • Antique post cards • Books hardback • Books paperback • Bric-a-brac • Clocks • Clothing adults' • Clothing children's • Coins foreign • Coins old • Diy equipment • Fabric remnants • Household items *ironing boards etc* • Jewellery • Knitting, crochet and sewing equipment • Knitting wool • Medals • Money-off coupons • Musical instruments • Petrol vouchers • Records & tapes • Spectacles • Sports equipment • Stamps British • Stamps foreign • Toys & games • Trading stamps • Watches

COLLECTION SERVICE Yes

■ St George's Community Children's Project Limited

ADDRESS 7 Chilston Road, Tunbridge Wells, Kent TN4 9LP

TELEPHONE 01892 543982/539848

CATEGORY Arts & crafts equipment • Bicycles *only tricycles, or very first bicycle* • Books paperback • Bric-a-brac • Fabric remnants • Knitting wool • Musical instruments • Office equipment and stationery • Sports equipment • Toys & games • Video/computer games • Waste paper *only newspapers or magazines for recycling*

COLLECTION SERVICE No

■ St George's Crypt

ADDRESS Great George Street, Leeds, W Yorks
LS1 3BR

TELEPHONE 0113-245 9061

FAX 0113-244 3646

CATEGORY Baby equipment ● Bed linen and
mattresses *only linen* ● Clothing adults' ● Clothing
children's ● Non perishable foods ● Rags *clean*
● Toys & games

COLLECTION SERVICE No

■ St Helena Hospice

ADDRESS 5 St Botolph's Street, Colchester, Essex
CO2 7DU

TELEPHONE 01206 574995

FAX 01206 561284

CATEGORY Air miles ● Antique post cards ● Arts &
crafts equipment ● Baby equipment ● Bed linen
and mattresses *no mattresses* ● Bicycles ● Books
hardback ● Books paperback ● Bric-a-brac ● Clocks
● Clothing adults' ● Clothing children's ● Coins
foreign ● Coins old ● Diy equipment ● Fabric
remnants ● Furniture ● Gardening equipment
● Household items *ironing boards etc* ● Jewellery
● Knitting, crochet and sewing equipment
● Knitting wool ● Magazines & comics ● Medals
● Musical instruments ● Office equipment and
stationery ● Petrol vouchers ● Pets equipment
● Photographic equipment ● Records & tapes
● Spectacles ● Sports equipment ● Stamps British
● Stamps foreign ● Toiletries ● Toys & games
● Trading stamps ● Video/computer games
● Watches ● Wedding clothes for hire *for sale, not
hire*

COLLECTION SERVICE Yes

■ St Helen's Opportunity for Play

ADDRESS Unit 10, Moorfoot Road, Parr, St Helen's,
Merseyside WA9 2DY

TELEPHONE 01744 22193

CATEGORY Childrens play/craft scrap *non-toxic*
● Fabric remnants

COLLECTION SERVICE Yes

■ St Leonard's Hospice

ADDRESS 185 Tadcaster Road, York, N Yorks
YO2 2QL

TELEPHONE 01904 708553

FAX 01904 704337

CATEGORY Air miles ● Antique post cards ● Arts &
crafts equipment ● Bicycles ● Books hardback
● Books paperback ● Bric-a-brac ● Clocks
● Clothing adults' ● Clothing children's ● Coins
foreign ● Coins old ● Diy equipment ● Fabric
remnants ● Household items *ironing boards etc*
● Jewellery ● Knitting, crochet and sewing
equipment ● Knitting wool ● Medals ● Money-
off coupons ● Musical instruments ● Petrol
vouchers ● Photographic equipment ● Records &
tapes ● Sports equipment ● Stamps British ●

Stamps foreign ● Toiletries ● Toys & games
● Trading stamps ● Watches

COLLECTION SERVICE Yes

■ St Louis Family Service

ADDRESS The Gatehouse, 33 St Andrew's Street
South, Bury St Edmunds, Suffolk IP33 2SB

TELEPHONE 01284 754967

FAX 01284 765083

CATEGORY Baby equipment ● Bed linen and
mattresses ● Bicycles ● Books hardback ● Books
paperback ● Bric-a-brac ● Clocks ● Clothing adults'
● Clothing children's ● Fabric remnants ● Fur coats
● Furniture ● Gardening equipment ● Household
items *ironing boards etc* ● Jewellery ● Knitting,
crochet and sewing equipment ● Knitting wool
● Non perishable foods ● Rags ● Records & tapes
● Spectacles ● Sports equipment ● Toiletries
● Toys & games ● Video/computer games
● Watches

COLLECTION SERVICE Yes

■ St Luke's Hospice

ADDRESS Fobbing Farm, Nethermayne, Basildon,
Essex SS16 5NJ

TELEPHONE 01268 524973

FAX 01268 282483

CATEGORY Air miles ● Antique post cards ● Arts &
crafts equipment ● Baby equipment ● Bed linen
and mattresses ● Bicycles ● Books hardback
● Books paperback ● Bric-a-brac ● Clocks
● Clothing adults' ● Clothing children's ● Coins
foreign ● Coins old ● Computer hardware and
software ● Diy equipment ● Fabric remnants
● Furniture ● Gardening equipment ● Household
items *ironing boards etc* ● Jewellery ● Knitting,
crochet and sewing equipment ● Knitting wool
● Magazines & comics ● Medals ● Money-off
coupons ● Musical instruments ● Office
equipment and stationery ● Petrol vouchers
● Pets equipment ● Photographic equipment
● Records & tapes ● Sports equipment ● Stamps
British ● Stamps foreign ● Toiletries ● Toys &
games ● Trading stamps ● Used toner cartridges
● Video/computer games ● Watches

COLLECTION SERVICE Yes

■ St Margaret's Somerset Hospice

ADDRESS Heron Drive, Taunton, Somerset TA1 5HA

TELEPHONE 01823 259394

FAX 01823 345900

CATEGORY Air miles ● Antique post cards ● Arts &
crafts equipment ● Baby equipment ● Bed linen
and mattresses ● Bicycles ● Books hardback
● Books paperback ● Bric-a-brac ● Clocks
● Clothing adults' ● Clothing children's ● Coins
foreign ● Coins old ● Computer hardware and
software ● Diy equipment ● Fabric remnants
● Furniture ● Gardening equipment ● Household
items *ironing boards etc* ● Jewellery ● Knitting,
crochet and sewing equipment ● Knitting wool
● Magazines & comics ● Medals ● Money-off
coupons ● Musical instruments ● Office

equipment and stationery • Petrol vouchers • Photographic equipment • Rags • Records & tapes • Sports equipment • Stamps British • Stamps foreign • Toys & games • Trading stamps • Video/computer games • Watches • Wedding clothes for hire

COLLECTION SERVICE Yes

■ St Martin's Emmaus

ADDRESS Archcliffe Fort, Archcliffe Road, Dover, Kent CT17 9EL

TELEPHONE 01304 204550

CATEGORY Aluminium • Antique post cards • Arts & crafts equipment • Baby equipment • Bed linen and mattresses • Bicycles • Books hardback • Books paperback • Bric-a-brac • Christmas cards • Clocks • Clothing adults' • Clothing children's • Coins foreign • Coins old • Computer hardware and software • Diy equipment • Fabric remnants • Furniture • Gardening equipment • Household items *ironing boards etc* • Jewellery • Knitting, crochet and sewing equipment • Knitting wool • Magazines & comics • Medals • Motorbike engines, car engines, spare parts • Musical instruments • Non perishable foods • Office equipment and stationery • Other metals • Photographic equipment • Postcards used • Rags • Records & tapes • Sports equipment • Toiletries • Toys & games • Trading stamps • Waste paper • Watches

COLLECTION SERVICE Yes

■ St Oswald's Hospice

ADDRESS Regent Avenue, Gosforth, Newcastle upon Tyne, Tyne & Wear NE3 1EE

TELEPHONE 0191-285 0063

CATEGORY Arts & crafts equipment • Baby equipment • Bed linen and mattresses *not mattresses* • Bicycles • Books paperback • Bric-a-brac • Clocks • Clothing adults' • Clothing children's • Diy equipment • Fabric remnants • Furniture • Gardening equipment • Household items *ironing boards etc* • Jewellery • Knitting, crochet and sewing equipment • Knitting wool • Petrol vouchers • Records & tapes • Toiletries • Toys & games • Trading stamps

COLLECTION SERVICE No

■ St Raphael's Hospice

ADDRESS Tobit Appeal Office, London Road, North Cheam, Sutton, Surrey SM3 9DX

TELEPHONE 0181-337 4156

FAX 0181-335 3089

CATEGORY Air miles • Antique post cards • Arts & crafts equipment • Baby equipment • Bed linen and mattresses *not mattresses* • Bicycles • Books hardback • Books paperback • Bric-a-brac • Clocks • Clothing adults' • Clothing children's • Coins foreign • Coins old • Computer hardware and software • Diy equipment • Fabric remnants • Fur coats • Furniture *small items only* • Gardening equipment • Household items *ironing boards etc* • Jewellery • Knitting, crochet and sewing equipment • Knitting wool •

Magazines & comics • Medals • Money-off coupons • Musical instruments • Office equipment and stationery • Petrol vouchers • Photographic equipment • Records & tapes • Sports equipment • Stamps British • Stamps foreign • Toiletries • Toys & games • Trading stamps • Used toner cartridges • Video/computer games • Watches

COLLECTION SERVICE No

■ St Theresa's House

ADDRESS 13–15 Manor House Street, Peterborough, Cambs PE1 2TL

TELEPHONE 01733 894989

FAX 01733 352506

CATEGORY Baby equipment • Bed linen and mattresses • Bric-a-brac • Clothing adults' • Clothing children's • Money-off coupons • Toiletries • Toys & games • Trading stamps

COLLECTION SERVICE No

■ Saint Vincent De Paul Furniture Store

ADDRESS St Wilfred's Centre, 524 Queen's Road, Sheffield, S Yorks S2 4DT

TELEPHONE 0114-250 0707

CATEGORY Bed linen and mattresses • Furniture *no foam filled items* • Household items *ironing boards etc*

COLLECTION SERVICE Yes

■ Salcare

ADDRESS 2 Fletcher Street, Heanor, Derbys DE75 7PE

TELEPHONE 01773 764562

FAX 01773 710750

CATEGORY Antique post cards • Arts & crafts equipment • Baby equipment • Bed linen and mattresses *must conform to fire standards* • Bicycles • Books hardback • Books paperback • Bric-a-brac • Clocks • Clothing adults' • Clothing children's • Coins foreign • Coins old • Computer hardware and software • Diy equipment • Fabric remnants • Fur coats • Furniture *must conform to fire standards* • Gardening equipment • Household items *ironing boards etc* • Jewellery • Knitting, crochet and sewing equipment • Knitting wool • Magazines & comics • Medals • Musical instruments • Non perishable foods • Office equipment and stationery • Photographic equipment • Postcards used • Records & tapes • Spectacles • Sports equipment • Stamps British • Stamps foreign • Toiletries • Toys & games • Video/computer games • Watches • Wedding clothes for hire

COLLECTION SERVICE Yes

■ The Salvation Army

ADDRESS 55 Northall Street, Kettering, Northants
NN16 8DT

TELEPHONE 01536 415655

FAX 01536 525538

E-MAIL garthw@sarec.teine.com

CATEGORY Bed linen and mattresses *bed linen only*
● Books hardback ● Books paperback ● Bric-a-brac
● Clothing adults' ● Clothing children's ● Fabric
remnants *not selvedges* ● Knitting wool ● Rags

COLLECTION SERVICE Yes

■ The Salvation Army

ADDRESS 4 Auchencrow Street, Easterhouse,
Glasgow, Strathclyde G34 0AL

TELEPHONE 0141-771 4343

CATEGORY Baby equipment ● Bed linen and
mattresses ● Bicycles ● Books paperback ● Bric-a-
brac ● Clocks ● Clothing adults' ● Clothing
children's ● Furniture ● Household items *ironing
boards etc* ● Jewellery ● Musical instruments
● Rags ● Toiletries ● Toys & games

COLLECTION SERVICE Yes

■ The Salvation Army

ADDRESS Gillygate, York, N Yorks YO3 7EA

TELEPHONE 01904 630470

CATEGORY Baby equipment ● Bed linen and
mattresses ● Bicycles ● Books hardback ● Books
paperback ● Bric-a-brac ● Clocks ● Clothing adults'
● Clothing children's ● Diy equipment ● Fabric
remnants ● Household items *ironing boards etc*
● Jewellery ● Knitting, crochet and sewing
equipment ● Knitting wool ● Magazines & comics
● Musical instruments ● Records & tapes
● Spectacles ● Sports equipment ● Toiletries
● Toys & games ● Video/computer games
● Watches

COLLECTION SERVICE No

■ The Salvation Army

ADDRESS 27 Oldfield Road, Salford, Gtr Manchester
M5 4NE

TELEPHONE 0161-833 2400

CATEGORY Antique post cards ● Arts & crafts
equipment ● Baby equipment ● Bed linen and
mattresses *compliance with fire regulations*
● Bicycles ● Books hardback ● Books paperback
● Bric-a-brac ● Clocks ● Clothing adults'
● Clothing children's ● Coins foreign ● Coins old
● Computer hardware and software ● Diy
equipment ● Fabric remnants ● Fur coats
● Furniture *compliance with fire regulations*
● Gardening equipment ● Hearing aids
● Household items *ironing boards etc* ● Jewellery
● Knitting, crochet and sewing equipment
● Knitting wool ● Medals ● Musical instruments
● Non perishable foods ● Office equipment and
stationery ● Photographic equipment ● Records &
tapes ● Spectacles ● Sports equipment ● Stamps

British ● Stamps foreign ● Toiletries ● Toys &
games ● Video/computer games ● Watches

COLLECTION SERVICE Yes

■ The Salvation Army

ADDRESS Providence House, 2 High Street, Rochdale,
Lancs OL12 0NT

TELEPHONE 01706 45151

FAX 01706 759466

CATEGORY Air miles ● Antique post cards ● Arts &
crafts equipment ● Books hardback ● Books
paperback ● Bric-a-brac ● Clothing adults'
● Clothing children's ● Household items *ironing
boards etc* ● Jewellery ● Medals ● Musical
instruments ● Sports equipment ● Toys & games

COLLECTION SERVICE No

■ The Salvation Army

ADDRESS 4 Saxon's Close, Leighton Buzzard, Beds
LU7 8LT

TELEPHONE 01525 373780

CATEGORY Bric-a-brac ● Coins foreign ● Coins old
● Jewellery ● Medals ● Musical instruments
● Stamps British ● Stamps foreign

COLLECTION SERVICE No

■ Salvation Army (Care & Share Shop)

ADDRESS Duke Street, Sheffield, S Yorks S2 5QP

TELEPHONE 0114-273 1778

CATEGORY Arts & crafts equipment ● Baby
equipment ● Bed linen and mattresses ● Bicycles
● Books hardback ● Books paperback ● Bric-a-brac
● Clocks ● Clothing adults' ● Clothing children's
● Computer hardware and software ● Diy
equipment ● Furniture ● Gardening equipment
● Household items *ironing boards etc* ● Jewellery
● Knitting, crochet and sewing equipment
● Knitting wool ● Musical instruments ● Non
perishable foods ● Office equipment and
stationery ● Photographic equipment ● Rags
● Records & tapes ● Sports equipment ● Toiletries
● Toys & games ● Video/computer games
● Watches

COLLECTION SERVICE Yes

■ The Salvation Army Charity Shop

ADDRESS 13–15 Bridge Street, Lisburn, Antrim,
N Ireland BT28 1XZ

TELEPHONE 01846 662622

CATEGORY Antique post cards ● Arts & crafts
equipment ● Baby equipment *must meet latest BS
standards* ● Bed linen and mattresses *bed linen
only* ● Bicycles ● Books hardback ● Books
paperback ● Bric-a-brac ● Clocks ● Clothing adults'
● Clothing children's ● Coins foreign ● Coins old
● Diy equipment *no power tools at present*
● Fabric remnants ● Furniture ● Gardening
equipment ● Household items *ironing boards etc
no electrical items at present* ● Jewellery
● Knitting, crochet and sewing equipment ●

Knitting wool • Magazines & comics • Medals • Musical instruments • Pets equipment *good order* • Photographic equipment • Postcards used • Rags *if for rags, must be marked so* • Records & tapes • Sports equipment • Stamps British • Stamps foreign • Telephone cards • Toys & games • Watches • Wedding clothes for hire *mainly for resale, but hire will be possible if we have a reasonable supply*

COLLECTION SERVICE Yes

■ Sandy Neighbourhood Centre (part of Christian Family Care)

ADDRESS Manor Farm, 76 London Road, Sandy, Beds SG19 1DZ

TELEPHONE 01767 683015

FAX 01767 683015

CATEGORY Arts & crafts equipment • Furniture *storage restricted* • Gardening equipment • Non perishable foods • Toys & games *in good working order and condition* • Waste paper *white paper and newspapers only*

COLLECTION SERVICE No

■ Save the Children

ADDRESS 3 Annandale Gardens, Up-Holland, Lancs WN8 0BA

TELEPHONE 01695 632710

FAX 01695 632710

CATEGORY Air miles • Antique post cards • Arts & crafts equipment • Clocks • Clothing adults' • Clothing children's • Coins foreign • Coins old • Computer hardware and software • Diy equipment • Fabric remnants • Jewellery • Knitting, crochet and sewing equipment • Knitting wool • Medals • Money-off coupons • Musical instruments • Non perishable foods • Office equipment and stationery • Petrol vouchers • Photographic equipment • Records & tapes • Sports equipment • Stamps British • Stamps foreign • Telephone cards • Toiletries • Toys & games • Trading stamps • Video/ computer games • Watches

COLLECTION SERVICE No

■ Scoliosis Association (UK)

ADDRESS 2 Ivebury Court, 323–327 Latimer Road, London W10 6RA

TELEPHONE 0181-964 5343

FAX 0181-964 5343

CATEGORY Bric-a-brac • Clocks • Coins foreign • Coins old • Jewellery • Records & tapes • Stamps foreign • Watches

COLLECTION SERVICE No

■ Scope

ADDRESS 4 Harefield Road, Nuneaton, Warks CV11 4HD

TELEPHONE 01203 348558

CATEGORY Antique post cards • Arts & crafts equipment • Bed linen and mattresses *linen only, no mattresses* • Books hardback • Books paperback • Bric-a-brac • Clocks • Clothing adults' *including footwear and hats* • Clothing children's *includig footwear and hats* • Coins foreign • Coins old • Computer hardware and software *if electrical, we sell only to a dealer due to health and safety regulations* • Fabric remnants • Household items *ironing boards etc* • Jewellery • Knitting, crochet and sewing equipment • Knitting wool • Musical instruments • Office equipment and stationery • Photographic equipment • Records & tapes • Spectacles *donate to opticians for thirld world* • Sports equipment • Toiletries • Toys & games *British Standard* • Video/computer games *sell to dealer* • Watches • Wedding clothes for hire *for sale*

COLLECTION SERVICE Yes

■ Scope in Colchester (Castlegate Centre)

ADDRESS George Street, Colchester, Essex CO1 1TS

TELEPHONE 01206 764633

FAX 01206 764633

CATEGORY Antique post cards • Arts & crafts equipment • Books paperback • Bric-a-brac • Childrens play/craft scrap *paper and board offcuts only* • Christmas cards • Clothing adults' • Clothing children's • Coins foreign • Coins old • Fabric remnants • Household items *ironing boards etc* • Jewellery • Knitting, crochet and sewing equipment • Knitting wool • Medals • Musical instruments • Photographic equipment • Records & tapes • Sports equipment • Stamps British • Stamps foreign • Telephone cards • Toiletries • Toys & games

COLLECTION SERVICE No

■ Scout Holiday Homes Trust

ADDRESS Baden-Powell House, Queen's Gate, London SW7 5JS

TELEPHONE 0171-584 7030

FAX 0171-590 5103

CATEGORY Antique post cards • Coins foreign • Coins old • Medals • Money-off coupons • Petrol vouchers • Stamps British • Stamps foreign • Telephone cards • Trading stamps

COLLECTION SERVICE No

■ Seaford Volunteers

ADDRESS The Old Workhouse, Blatchington Road, Seaford, E Sussex BN25 1A

TELEPHONE 01323 492800

CATEGORY Antique post cards • Arts & crafts equipment • Bric-a-brac • Clocks • Clothing adults' • Coins foreign • Coins old • Diy equipment

• Furniture • Gardening equipment • Jewellery • Medals • Musical instruments • Non perishable foods • Pets equipment • Photographic equipment • Postcards used • Stamps British • Stamps foreign • Toys & games • Watches

COLLECTION SERVICE Yes

■ Seaton & District Hospital League of Friends

ADDRESS S & D Community Hospital, Valley View, Seaton, Devon EX12 2UU

TELEPHONE 01297 20143

FAX 01297 24590

CATEGORY Antique post cards • Arts & crafts equipment • Baby equipment • Bed linen and mattresses *no mattresses* • Books hardback • Books paperback • Bric-a-brac • Clothing adults' • Clothing children's • Diy equipment *not electrical* • Fabric remnants • Furniture *small* • Gardening equipment *not electrical* • Household items *ironing boards etc* • Jewellery • Knitting, crochet and sewing equipment • Knitting wool • Magazines & comics • Musical instruments *not electrical* • Records & tapes • Sports equipment • Toiletries • Toys & games

COLLECTION SERVICE No

■ Selby District AVS Charity Shop

ADDRESS Finkle Court, Finkle Hill, Sherburn-in-Elmet, N Yorks LS25 6EB

TELEPHONE 01757 291111

FAX 01757 290311

CATEGORY Arts & crafts equipment • Baby equipment • Bed linen and mattresses *not mattresses* • Bicycles • Books hardback • Books paperback • Bric-a-brac • Clocks • Clothing adults' • Clothing children's • Diy equipment • Fabric remnants • Fur coats • Furniture *no soft furnishings* • Gardening equipment • Household items *ironing boards etc* • Jewellery • Knitting, crochet and sewing equipment • Knitting wool • Musical instruments • Non perishable foods • Office equipment and stationery • Pets equipment • Photographic equipment • Records & tapes • Sports equipment • Toiletries • Toys & games • Video/computer games • Watches

COLLECTION SERVICE No

■ Service 9 – Bristol's Volunteer Bureau

ADDRESS 66 Gloucester Road, Bishopston, Bristol, Avon BS7 8BH

TELEPHONE 0117-924 7929

CATEGORY Antique post cards • Arts & crafts equipment • Bed linen and mattresses *bed linen only* • Books hardback • Books paperback • Bric-a-brac • Clothing adults' • Clothing children's • Fabric remnants • Household items *ironing boards etc* • Jewellery • Knitting, crochet and sewing equipment • Knitting wool • Magazines & comics • Office equipment and stationery •

Records & tapes • Toiletries • Toys & games • Video/computer games • Watches

COLLECTION SERVICE No

■ Seven Springs Boutique

ADDRESS c/o West Kent CVS, 19 Monson Road, Tunbridge Wells, Kent TN1 1LS

TELEPHONE 01892 522002/530330

CATEGORY Clothing adults' *only ladies' clothing* • Fur coats • Jewellery

COLLECTION SERVICE No

■ Seven Springs Cheshire Home

ADDRESS Pembury Road, Tunbridge Wells, Kent TN2 4ND

TELEPHONE 01892 531138

FAX 01892 511292

CATEGORY Air miles • Antique post cards • Arts & crafts equipment • Bed linen and mattresses • Books hardback • Books paperback • Bric-a-brac • Clocks • Clothing adults' • Clothing children's • Coins foreign • Coins old • Computer hardware and software • Diy equipment • Fabric remnants • Fur coats • Furniture • Gardening equipment • Household items *ironing boards etc* • Jewellery • Knitting, crochet and sewing equipment • Knitting wool • Magazines & comics • Medals • Money-off coupons • Musical instruments • Office equipment and stationery • Petrol vouchers • Photographic equipment • Postcards used • Records & tapes • Spectacles • Sports equipment • Stamps British • Stamps foreign • Toiletries • Toys & games • Trading stamps • Video/computer games • Waste paper • Watches

COLLECTION SERVICE Yes

■ Shaftesbury Resources Centre

ADDRESS 93 Camberwell Station Road, Camberwell, London SE5 9JJ

TELEPHONE 0171-737 7475

FAX 0171-737 7475

CATEGORY Air miles • Antique post cards • Baby equipment • Bed linen and mattresses *no stained mattresses* • Bicycles • Bric-a-brac • Clocks • Clothing children's • Coins foreign • Coins old • Diy equipment • Furniture • Gardening equipment • Household items *ironing boards etc* • Medals • Money-off coupons • Musical instruments • Non perishable foods • Petrol vouchers • Sports equipment • Stamps British • Stamps foreign • Toys & games • Trading stamps • Watches

COLLECTION SERVICE Yes

■ SHCVS

ADDRESS Resource Centre, Rossmore House, 26–42 Park Street, Camberley, Surrey GU15 3PL

TELEPHONE 01276 684979

FAX 01276 684979

E-MAIL shcvs@ukonline.co.uk

CATEGORY Air miles ● Coins foreign ● Computer hardware and software ● Knitting wool ● Money-off coupons ● Non perishable foods ● Office equipment and stationery ● Petrol vouchers ● Spectacles ● Stamps British ● Toiletries ● Toys & games ● Trading stamps

COLLECTION SERVICE Yes

■ Sheffield Family Services Unit

ADDRESS 88 Upper Hanover Street, Sheffield, S Yorks S3 7RQ

TELEPHONE 0114-275 0981

CATEGORY Baby equipment ● Bed linen and mattresses ● Bicycles ● Books hardback ● Bric-a-brac ● Clocks ● Clothing adults' ● Clothing children's ● Computer hardware and software ● Diy equipment *smaller items, ie fridges, but not three piece suites* ● Furniture ● Gardening equipment ● Household items *ironing boards etc* ● Jewellery ● Knitting wool ● Non perishable foods ● Office equipment and stationery ● Records & tapes ● Sports equipment ● Toiletries ● Toys & games ● Watches

COLLECTION SERVICE No

■ Shelter, the National Campaign for Homeless People

ADDRESS 88 Old Street, London EC1V 9HU

TELEPHONE 0171-505 2000

FAX 0171-505 2169

CATEGORY Antique post cards ● Arts & crafts equipment ● Baby equipment ● Bed linen and mattresses *no mattresses* ● Bicycles ● Books hardback ● Books paperback ● Bric-a-brac ● Clocks ● Clothing adults' ● Clothing children's ● Coins foreign ● Coins old ● Computer hardware and software ● Diy equipment ● Fabric remnants ● Gardening equipment ● Household items *ironing boards etc* ● Jewellery ● Knitting, crochet and sewing equipment ● Knitting wool ● Magazines & comics ● Medals ● Musical instruments ● Photographic equipment ● Records & tapes ● Spectacles *only sunglasses and empty frames* ● Sports equipment ● Stamps British ● Stamps foreign ● Toys & games ● Video/computer games ● Watches

COLLECTION SERVICE No

■ Sheltered Work Opportunities Project

ADDRESS Cherry Tree Nursery, Off New Road Roundabout, Northbourne, Bournemouth, Dorset BH10 7DA

TELEPHONE 01202 593537

FAX 01202 590626

CATEGORY Bed linen and mattresses ● Books hardback ● Books paperback ● Clothing adults' ● Computer hardware and software ● Diy equipment ● Furniture ● Gardening equipment ● Jewellery ● Money-off coupons ● Non perishable foods ● Office equipment and stationery ● Petrol vouchers ● Records & tapes ● Toiletries

COLLECTION SERVICE No

■ Shropshire & Mid Wales Hospice

ADDRESS Bicton Heath, Shrewsbury, Shropshire SY3 8HS

TELEPHONE 01743 354450

FAX 01743 233263

CATEGORY Air miles ● Aluminium ● Arts & crafts equipment ● Bicycles ● Books hardback ● Books paperback ● Bric-a-brac ● Clocks ● Clothing adults' ● Clothing children's ● Diy equipment ● Fabric remnants ● Household items *ironing boards etc* ● Jewellery ● Knitting, crochet and sewing equipment ● Knitting wool ● Magazines & comics ● Musical instruments ● Office equipment and stationery ● Petrol vouchers ● Photographic equipment ● Rags ● Records & tapes ● Silver paper & aluminium foil ● Sports equipment ● Toiletries ● Toys & games ● Used toner cartridges ● Waste paper ● Watches ● Wedding clothes for hire

COLLECTION SERVICE Yes

■ Shropshire Children's Scrap Store

ADDRESS Scraddies, Lutwyche Road, Church Stretton, Shropshire SY6 6AT

TELEPHONE 01694 722511

CATEGORY Aluminium ● Arts & crafts equipment ● Bric-a-brac ● Christmas cards ● Clothing adults' ● Clothing children's ● Diy equipment ● Fabric remnants ● Jewellery ● Knitting, crochet and sewing equipment ● Knitting wool ● Money-off coupons ● Office equipment and stationery ● Plastics ● Rags ● Silver paper & aluminium foil ● Sports equipment ● Stamps British ● Stamps foreign ● Toiletries ● Used toner cartridges ● Waste paper

COLLECTION SERVICE Yes

■ Shropshire Children's Scrap Store

ADDRESS Castle House, Clun, Shropshire SY7 8JU

TELEPHONE 01588 640374

CATEGORY Aluminium ● Arts & crafts equipment ● Bric-a-brac ● Christmas cards ● Clothing adults' ● Clothing children's ● Diy equipment ● Fabric remnants ● Jewellery ● Knitting, crochet and sewing equipment • Knitting wool • Money-off coupons • Office equipment and stationery • Plastics • Rags • Silver paper & aluminium foil • Sports equipment • Stamps British • Stamps foreign • Toiletries • Used toner cartridges • Waste paper

COLLECTION SERVICE Yes

■ Sidcup Torch Fellowship for the Blind

ADDRESS Bethany, 6 Hanmer Way, Staplehurst, Kent TN12 0PA

TELEPHONE 01580 891096

CATEGORY Stamps British *if on paper, please leave ¼" margin all round* • Stamps foreign *for paper, please leave ¼" margin all round*

COLLECTION SERVICE Yes

■ SIM International (UK)

ADDRESS Ullswater Crescent, Coulsdon, Surrey CR5 2HR

TELEPHONE 0181-660 7778

FAX 0181-763 1175

CATEGORY Air miles • Stamps foreign

COLLECTION SERVICE No

■ Simon Community

ADDRESS 129 Malden Road, PO Box 1187, London NW5 4HW

TELEPHONE 0171-267 1547

CATEGORY Bed linen and mattresses *including blankets and sleeping bags* • Bicycles • Clothing adults' *men's only, including underwear and shoes* • Computer hardware and software • Diy equipment • Gardening equipment • Household items *ironing boards etc* • Office equipment and stationery

COLLECTION SERVICE Yes

■ Sleaford & District Furniture Recycling Project

ADDRESS c/o Sleaford Training Limited, 49a Southgate, Sleaford, Lincs NG34 7SY

TELEPHONE 01529 307060

FAX 01529 307060

CATEGORY Baby equipment *baby furniture only* • Bed linen and mattresses *clean mattresses only* • Furniture • Household items *ironing boards etc*

COLLECTION SERVICE Yes

■ Slough Furniture Project

ADDRESS Unit A, Wentworth Industrial Court, Goodwin Road, Slough, Bucks SL2 5RE

TELEPHONE 01753 692535

CATEGORY Baby equipment • Bed linen and mattresses • Bric-a-brac *only household, eg*

mirrors, ornaments • Diy equipment • Furniture • Household items *ironing boards etc*

COLLECTION SERVICE Yes

■ SOFA (Peterborough) Limited

ADDRESS 19 Shakespeare Avenue, Peterborough, Cambs PE1 3JT

TELEPHONE 01733 62984

CATEGORY Aluminium • Antique post cards • Arts & crafts equipment • Baby equipment • Bed linen and mattresses • Bicycles • Books hardback • Books paperback • Bric-a-brac • Childrens play/craft scrap • Christmas cards • Clocks • Clothing adults' • Clothing children's • Diy equipment • Fabric remnants • Furniture • Gardening equipment • Household items *ironing boards etc* • Jewellery • Milk bottle tops • Musical instruments • Other metals • Photographic equipment • Plastics • Rags • Records & tapes • Silver paper & aluminium foil • Sports equipment • Toys & games • Waste paper

COLLECTION SERVICE Yes

■ The SOFA Project

ADDRESS 48–54 West Street, St Philip's, Bristol, Avon BS2 0BL

TELEPHONE 0117-941 3322

FAX 0117-941 2567

CATEGORY Bed linen and mattresses • Bicycles • Books hardback • Books paperback • Bric-a-brac • Clocks • Furniture *immediately reusable* • Household items *ironing boards etc*

COLLECTION SERVICE Yes

■ SOS Children's Villages UK

ADDRESS 32a Bridge Street, Cambridge, Cambs CB2 1UJ

TELEPHONE 01223 365589

FAX 01223 322613

CATEGORY Books hardback *only children's books* • Books paperback *only children's books*

COLLECTION SERVICE No

■ South Devon Play and Resource Centre Scrapstore (SPARC)

ADDRESS Frontiers, Woodlands Road, Huxham's Cross, Dartington, Totnes, Devon TQ9 6NS

TELEPHONE 01803 868036

CATEGORY Childrens play/craft scrap • Fabric remnants • Knitting wool • Plastics • Waste paper

COLLECTION SERVICE Yes

■ **South Essex Community Furniture Service**

ADDRESS 212–216 Westborough Road, Westcliff-on-Sea, Essex SS0 9PR

TELEPHONE 01702 430058

FAX 01702 392788

CATEGORY Baby equipment *must meet health & safety regulations* ● Bed linen and mattresses *must meet health & safety regulations* ● Bric-a-brac ● Clocks ● Diy equipment ● Furniture *upholstered items must meet fire safety regulations* ● Gardening equipment ● Household items *ironing boards etc*

COLLECTION SERVICE Yes

■ **South Norwood Animal Rescue**

ADDRESS 7 Farnley Road, South Norwood, London SE25 6PA

TELEPHONE 0181-653 7628

CATEGORY Aluminium ● Antique post cards ● Books paperback ● Bric-a-brac ● Clothing adults' ● Jewellery ● Knitting wool ● Money-off coupons ● Petrol vouchers ● Pets equipment ● Postcards used ● Records & tapes ● Stamps British ● Stamps foreign ● Telephone cards ● Toiletries ● Trading stamps ● Watches

COLLECTION SERVICE No

■ **South Sefton Helping Hand Service**

ADDRESS Waterloo Town Hall, Gt George's Road, Waterloo, Merseyside L22 1RB

TELEPHONE 0151-934 3050

CATEGORY Bric-a-brac ● Furniture

COLLECTION SERVICE Yes

■ **South Shields Ladies Lifeboat Comm**

ADDRESS 54 Lawe Road, South Shields, Tyne & Wear NE33 2AL

TELEPHONE 0191-456 2214

CATEGORY Books hardback ● Books paperback ● Bric-a-brac ● Christmas cards ● Clothing adults' ● Clothing children's ● Glass ● Jewellery ● Knitting, crochet and sewing equipment ● Knitting wool ● Musical instruments ● Non perishable foods ● Toiletries ● Toys & games ● Video/computer games ● Watches

COLLECTION SERVICE No

■ **Southampton Scrap Store**

ADDRESS c/o Eastpoint Centre, Burgoyne Road, Southampton, Hants SO19 6PB

TELEPHONE 01703 402812

FAX 01703 402308

CATEGORY Fabric remnants *large pieces – ends of rolls, etc* ● Knitting wool ● Plastics *contact store*

to check first ● Silver paper & aluminium foil *contact store first* ● Waste paper *unprinted paper*

COLLECTION SERVICE Yes

■ **Southport & District Cerebral Palsy Association**

ADDRESS 38 Westcliffe Road, Southport, Merseyside PR8 2BT

TELEPHONE 01704 568545

CATEGORY Antique post cards ● Arts & crafts equipment ● Baby equipment ● Bed linen and mattresses *not mattresses* ● Bicycles ● Books hardback ● Books paperback ● Bric-a-brac ● Clocks ● Clothing adults' ● Clothing children's ● Diy equipment ● Fabric remnants ● Fur coats ● Gardening equipment ● Household items *ironing boards etc* ● Jewellery ● Knitting, crochet and sewing equipment ● Knitting wool ● Musical instruments ● Non perishable foods ● Office equipment and stationery ● Photographic equipment ● Records & tapes ● Sports equipment ● Toiletries ● Toys & games ● Video/computer games ● Watches

COLLECTION SERVICE No

■ **Spaywatch**

ADDRESS Northey Lodge, North Bank, Newark Common, Peterborough, Cambs PE6 7YZ

TELEPHONE 01733 223185

CATEGORY Antique post cards ● Arts & crafts equipment ● Books hardback ● Books paperback ● Bric-a-brac ● Coins foreign ● Coins old ● Diy equipment ● Fabric remnants ● Gardening equipment ● Jewellery ● Knitting, crochet and sewing equipment ● Knitting wool ● Medals ● Musical instruments ● Non perishable foods ● Office equipment and stationery ● Stamps foreign

COLLECTION SERVICE No

■ **Stafford Furniture Exchange**

ADDRESS Stafford District Voluntary Service, c/o Unit 4, Kenworthy Road, Astonfields Industrial Estate, Stafford, Staffs ST16 3DY

TELEPHONE 01785 220484

FAX 01785 220484

CATEGORY Baby equipment ● Bed linen and mattresses ● Bric-a-brac ● Computer hardware and software ● Furniture *furniture made with pre-1988 foam* ● Household items *ironing boards etc* ● Office equipment and stationery

COLLECTION SERVICE Yes

■ Staffordshire Wildlife Trust

ADDRESS Coutts House, Sandon, Staffs ST18 0DN

TELEPHONE 01889 508534

FAX 01889 508422

E-MAIL staffswt@cix.compulink.co.uk

CATEGORY Aluminium *cans* ● Books hardback *nature conservation related* ● Books paperback *nature conservation related* ● Computer hardware and software ● Diy equipment ● Gardening equipment ● Office equipment and stationery ● Petrol vouchers ● Photographic equipment ● Stamps British ● Stamps foreign

COLLECTION SERVICE Yes

■ Stevenage Furniture Scheme

ADDRESS Roundmead Hall, The Poplars, Stevenage, Herts SG2 9PQ

TELEPHONE 01438 362900

CATEGORY Baby equipment *no upholstered items unless fire resistant* ● Bed linen and mattresses *mattresses must have safety labels* ● Furniture *no upholstered items unless fire resistant* ● Household items *ironing boards etc*

COLLECTION SERVICE Yes

■ Stevenage Haven

ADDRESS Frobisher Drive, Stevenage, Herts SG2 0HH

TELEPHONE 01438 354884

CATEGORY Diy equipment ● Gardening equipment ● Household items *ironing boards etc ironing boards, washing baskets, clothes airers* ● Non perishable foods ● Office equipment and stationery ● Toiletries

COLLECTION SERVICE No

■ The Stort Trust

ADDRESS 45–47 South Street, Bishops Stortford, Herts CM23 3AG

TELEPHONE 01279 465075

FAX 01279 758143

CATEGORY Air miles ● Antique post cards ● Arts & crafts equipment ● Bed linen and mattresses *not mattresses* ● Bicycles ● Books hardback ● Books paperback ● Bric-a-brac ● Clocks ● Clothing adults' ● Clothing children's ● Coins foreign ● Coins old ● Computer hardware and software ● Diy equipment *small tools, not powered* ● Gardening equipment ● Household items *ironing boards etc* ● Jewellery ● Knitting, crochet and sewing equipment ● Knitting wool ● Magazines & comics ● Medals ● Money-off coupons ● Musical instruments ● Office equipment and stationery ● Petrol vouchers ● Photographic equipment ● Postcards used ● Records & tapes ● Spectacles ● Sports equipment ● Stamps British ● Stamps foreign ● Telephone cards ● Toiletries ● Toys & games ● Trading stamps ● Video/computer games ● Watches

COLLECTION SERVICE No

■ Stour Valley Cat Rescue

ADDRESS 44 Sheraton Grange, Norton, Stourbridge, W Midlands DY8 2BE

TELEPHONE 01384 375832/872326

CATEGORY Air miles ● Antique post cards ● Arts & crafts equipment ● Books hardback ● Books paperback ● Bric-a-brac ● Clocks ● Clothing adults' ● Clothing children's ● Diy equipment ● Fabric remnants ● Furniture *small pieces* ● Household items *ironing boards etc* ● Jewellery ● Knitting, crochet and sewing equipment ● Knitting wool ● Magazines & comics ● Medals ● Money-off coupons ● Musical instruments ● Petrol vouchers ● Pets equipment ● Photographic equipment ● Postcards used ● Records & tapes ● Stamps British ● Stamps foreign ● Toiletries ● Toys & games ● Trading stamps ● Watches

COLLECTION SERVICE Yes

■ Strut Limited

ADDRESS Strut Charity Shops, 35 St Catherine's, Lincoln, Lincs LN5 8LW

TELEPHONE 01522 534994

CATEGORY Baby equipment ● Bed linen and mattresses *not mattresses* ● Bicycles ● Books hardback ● Books paperback ● Bric-a-brac ● Christmas cards ● Clocks ● Clothing adults' ● Clothing children's ● Diy equipment ● Fabric remnants ● Furniture *not upholstered goods* ● Gardening equipment ● Household items *ironing boards etc* ● Jewellery ● Knitting, crochet and sewing equipment ● Knitting wool ● Magazines & comics ● Money-off coupons ● Musical instruments ● Petrol vouchers ● Photographic equipment ● Rags ● Records & tapes ● Sports equipment ● Toiletries ● Toys & games ● Trading stamps ● Video/computer games

COLLECTION SERVICE Yes

■ Sudan Church Association

ADDRESS 16 Marks Close, Ingatestone, Essex CM4 9AR

TELEPHONE 01277 352464

CATEGORY Antique post cards ● Postcards used ● Telephone cards

COLLECTION SERVICE Yes

■ Sue Ryder Foundation

ADDRESS Unit 2, Victoria Square, Widnes, Cheshire WA8 2UT

TELEPHONE 0151-495 2280

CATEGORY Antique post cards ● Baby equipment ● Bicycles ● Books hardback ● Books paperback ● Bric-a-brac ● Clocks ● Clothing adults' ● Clothing children's ● Coins foreign ● Coins old ● Computer hardware and software ● Diy equipment ● Fabric remnants ● Furniture ● Gardening equipment ● Household items *ironing boards etc* ● Jewellery ● Knitting, crochet and sewing equipment ● Knitting wool ● Magazines & comics ● Medals ● Musical instruments ● Office equipment and stationery ●

Photographic equipment • Records & tapes
• Spectacles • Sports equipment • Stamps British
• Stamps foreign • Toiletries • Toys & games
• Trading stamps • Wedding clothes for hire

COLLECTION SERVICE Yes

■ **Sue Ryder Foundation**

ADDRESS Unit 23, Thistle Business Park, Broxburn, Lothian EH52 5AS

TELEPHONE 01506 852183

FAX 01506 852183

CATEGORY Air miles • Antique post cards • Arts & crafts equipment • Baby equipment • Bed linen and mattresses • Bicycles • Books hardback • Books paperback • Bric-a-brac • Clocks • Clothing adults' • Clothing children's • Coins foreign • Coins old • Computer hardware and software • Diy equipment • Fabric remnants • Fur coats • Furniture • Gardening equipment • Household items *ironing boards etc* • Jewellery • Knitting, crochet and sewing equipment • Knitting wool • Magazines & comics • Medals • Milk bottle tops • Money-off coupons • Musical instruments • Office equipment and stationery • Other metals • Petrol vouchers • Pets equipment • Photographic equipment • Rags • Records & tapes • Spectacles • Sports equipment • Stamps British • Stamps foreign • Toiletries • Toys & games • Trading stamps • Used toner cartridges • Video/computer games • Watches • Wedding clothes for hire

COLLECTION SERVICE Yes

■ **Surrey Community Recycling and Play Project**

ADDRESS Scrapp Centre, William Road, Guildford, Surrey GU1 4QZ

TELEPHONE 01483 453143

FAX 01483 453143

CATEGORY Aluminium • Arts & crafts equipment • Baby equipment • Bed linen and mattresses • Bicycles • Bric-a-brac • Childrens play/craft scrap • Clocks • Clothing adults' • Clothing children's • Computer hardware and software • Diy equipment • Fabric remnants • Fur coats • Furniture • Household items *ironing boards etc* • Jewellery • Knitting, crochet and sewing equipment • Knitting wool • Magazines & comics • Milk bottle tops • Office equipment and stationery • Rags • Records & tapes • Silver paper & aluminium foil • Spectacles • Sports equipment • Toys & games • Video/computer games • Waste paper • Watches

COLLECTION SERVICE Yes

■ **Sussex Emmaus**

ADDRESS Manor Road, Portslade, E Sussex BN41 2GA

TELEPHONE 01273 410146

CATEGORY Air Miles • Aluminium • Antique postcards • Arts and crafts equipment • Baby equipment • Bed linen and mattresses • Bicycles • Books hardback • Books paperback • Bric-a-brac • Children's play/craft scrap • Clocks • Clothing

adults' • Clothing children's • Coins forein • Coins old • Computer harware and software • DIY equipment • Fabric remnants • Fur coats • Furniture • Gardening equipment • Glass • Hearing aids • Household items *ironing boards, etc* • Jewellery • Knitting, crochet, sewing equipment • Knitting wool • Magazines and comics • Medals • Milk bottle tops • Money-off-coupons • Motorbike engines, car engines, spare parts • Musical instruments • Non-perishable foods • Office equipment and stationery • Other metals • Petrol vouchers • Pets' equipment • Photographic equipment • Plastics • Rags • Records and tapes • Silver paper and aluminium foil • Spectacles • Sports equipment • Stamps British • Stamps foreign • Telephone cards • Toiletries • Toys and games • Trading stamps • Used toner cartridges • Video/computer games • Waste cards • Watches

COLLECTION SERVICE No

■ **Swindon Children's Scrapstore**

ADDRESS Oakfield School, Marlowe Avenue, Walcot, Swindon, Wilts SN3 3HW

TELEPHONE 01793 513982

CATEGORY Arts & crafts equipment • Childrens play/craft scrap • Christmas cards • Fabric remnants • Knitting, crochet and sewing equipment • Knitting wool • Office equipment and stationery *stationery only* • Postcards used • Silver paper & aluminium foil • Toys & games

COLLECTION SERVICE No

■ **Swindon Gingerbread**

ADDRESS Acorn Building, Marlowe Avenue, Swindon, Wilts SN5 9UD

TELEPHONE 01793 513662

CATEGORY Furniture *we cannot strore items, so we have them as needed* • Gardening equipment • Household items *ironing boards etc* • Money-off coupons • Non perishable foods • Petrol vouchers

COLLECTION SERVICE Yes

■ **Tayside Furniture Project**

ADDRESS 4a Ainslie Street, Broughty Ferry, Dundee, Tayside DD5 3RR

TELEPHONE 01382 775629

FAX 01382 779315

CATEGORY Baby equipment • Bed linen and mattresses • Bicycles *only children's* • Bric-a-brac • Clocks • Clothing adults' • Clothing children's • Computer hardware and software • Fabric remnants • Furniture *all kinds of household articles, but DTI approved soft furniture for recycling* • Household items *ironing boards etc* • Office equipment and stationery *not paper* • Toys & games • Video/computer games

COLLECTION SERVICE Yes

■ Teg Down Residents' Association

ADDRESS 11 Goringfield, Teg Down, Winchester, Hants SO22 5NH

TELEPHONE 01962 853336

CATEGORY Antique post cards • Medals • Milk bottle tops • Postcards used • Silver paper & aluminium foil • Stamps British • Stamps foreign

COLLECTION SERVICE No

■ Tendring Furniture Scheme

ADDRESS 92 Pier Avenue, Clacton-on-Sea, Essex CO15 1NJ

TELEPHONE 01255 476068

FAX 01255 830219

CATEGORY Furniture

COLLECTION SERVICE Yes

■ Thames Valley Hospice

ADDRESS Pine Lodge, Hatch Lane, Windsor, Berks SL4 3RW

TELEPHONE 01753 842121

FAX 01753 832886

CATEGORY Air miles • Antique post cards • Arts & crafts equipment • Baby equipment • Bicycles • Books hardback • Books paperback • Bric-a-brac • Clocks • Clothing adults' *clean and wearable, not torn* • Clothing children's *clean and wearable, not torn* • Coins foreign • Coins old • Diy equipment • Fabric remnants • Fur coats • Furniture • Gardening equipment • Household items *ironing boards etc* • Jewellery • Knitting, crochet and sewing equipment • Knitting wool • Medals • Money-off coupons • Musical instruments • Petrol vouchers • Pets equipment • Photographic equipment • Records & tapes • Spectacles • Sports equipment • Stamps British • Stamps foreign • Toiletries • Toys & games • Video/computer games • Watches

COLLECTION SERVICE Yes

■ Thanet Mind (Mental Health Day Centre)

ADDRESS Ramsgate Community Centre, Royal Road, Ramsgate, Kent CT11 9LF

TELEPHONE 01843 586875

CATEGORY Arts & crafts equipment • Books hardback • Books paperback • Christmas cards • Fabric remnants • Gardening equipment • Jewellery • Knitting, crochet and sewing equipment • Knitting wool • Magazines & comics *no children's comics* • Musical instruments • Photographic equipment • Postcards used • Records & tapes • Sports equipment

COLLECTION SERVICE No

■ Thanet Phobic Group

ADDRESS 47 Orchard Road, Westbrook, Margate, Kent CT9 5JS

TELEPHONE 01843 833720

CATEGORY Anitique postcards • Office equipment and stationery *suitable for group use* • Stamps British *commemorative & Scots, Welsh & Irish* • Stamps foreign • Telephone cards

COLLECTION SERVICE No

■ Tools For Self Reliance

ADDRESS 35 The Esplanade, Seaford, E Sussex BN25 1JJ

TELEPHONE 01323 492014

CATEGORY Clothing adults' *safety workwear only* • DIY equipment *including woodwork tools* • Gardening equipmet • Books hardback *DIY books only* • Books paperback *DIY books only*

COLLECTION SERVICE Yes

■ Tools Mission Workshop

ADDRESS Friendship House, 484 Southchurch Road, Southend-on-Sea, Essex SS1 2QA

TELEPHONE 01702 601147

FAX 01702 601147

CATEGORY DIY equipment *not decorating* • Fabric remnants *only if suitable for making clothes* • Knitting, crochet, sewig equipmet *sewing machines – all types needed* • Knitting wool

COLLECTION SERVICE Yes

■ Tools with a Mission

ADDRESS Unit 3, Perry Barn, Burstall Lane, Sproughton, Ipswich, Suffolk IP8 3DJ

TELEPHONE 01473 652029

FAX 01473 652029

CATEGORY DIY equipment *not decorating* • Fabric remnants *only if suitable for making clothes* • Knitting, crochet, sewig equipmet *sewing machines – all types needed* • Knitting wool

COLLECTION SERVICE Yes

■ Totton & Eling Community Association

ADDRESS Civic Centre Building, Library Road, Totton, Southampton, Hants SO40 3AP

TELEPHONE 01703 863769

CATEGORY Antique post cards • Arts & crafts equipment • Knitting, crochet and sewing equipment • Knitting wool • Petrol vouchers • Stamps British • Stamps foreign • Trading stamps

COLLECTION SERVICE No

■ Toynbee Hall

ADDRESS 28 Commercial Street, London E1 6LS

TELEPHONE 0171-247 6943

FAX 0171-247 8748

CATEGORY Baby equipment ● Bed linen and mattresses ● Bicycles ● Books hardback ● Books paperback ● Bric-a-brac ● Clocks ● Clothing adults' ● Clothing children's ● Computer hardware and software ● Diy equipment ● Fabric remnants ● Furniture ● Gardening equipment ● Household items *ironing boards etc* ● Jewellery ● Knitting, crochet and sewing equipment ● Knitting wool ● Musical instruments ● Non perishable foods ● Office equipment and stationery ● Photographic equipment ● Records & tapes ● Sports equipment ● Toys & games ● Video/computer games ● Watches

COLLECTION SERVICE Yes

■ Track 2000

ADDRESS 1 Hope Terrace, Splott, Cardiff, S Glamorgan CF2 2AU

TELEPHONE 01222 489441/486600

FAX 01222 495190

CATEGORY Air miles ● Antique post cards ● Arts & crafts equipment ● Baby equipment ● Bed linen and mattresses ● Bicycles ● Books hardback ● Books paperback ● Bric-a-brac ● Clocks ● Clothing adults' ● Clothing children's ● Coins foreign ● Coins old ● Computer hardware and software ● Diy equipment ● Fabric remnants ● Fur coats ● Furniture ● Gardening equipment ● Household items *ironing boards etc* ● Jewellery ● Knitting, crochet and sewing equipment ● Knitting wool ● Medals ● Money-off coupons ● Motorbike engines, car engines, spare parts ● Musical instruments ● Office equipment and stationery ● Petrol vouchers ● Photographic equipment ● Rags ● Records & tapes ● Spectacles ● Sports equipment ● Stamps British ● Stamps foreign ● Toys & games ● Trading stamps ● Video/computer games ● Watches ● Wedding clothes for hire

COLLECTION SERVICE Yes

■ Treetops Hospice

ADDRESS Derby Road, Risley, Derbys DE72 3SS

TELEPHONE 0115-949 1264

FAX 0115-939 5901

CATEGORY Air miles ● Antique post cards ● Arts & crafts equipment ● Baby equipment *no prams or cots* ● Bed linen and mattresses *no mattresses* ● Books hardback ● Books paperback ● Bric-a-brac ● Clocks ● Clothing adults' ● Clothing children's ● Coins foreign ● Coins old ● Diy equipment ● Fabric remnants ● Furniture *small items only* ● Gardening equipment ● Household items *ironing boards etc* ● Jewellery ● Knitting, crochet and sewing equipment ● Knitting wool ● Magazines & comics ● Medals ● Musical instruments ● Petrol vouchers ● Photographic

equipment ● Rags ● Records & tapes ● Sports equipment ● Stamps British ● Stamps foreign ● Telephone cards ● Toys & games ● Watches

COLLECTION SERVICE No

■ Trinity Hospice

ADDRESS 30 Clapham Common, North Side, London SW4 0RN

TELEPHONE 0171-787 1000

FAX 0171-720 3878

CATEGORY Antique post cards ● Baby equipment ● Bicycles ● Books hardback ● Books paperback ● Bric-a-brac ● Clocks ● Clothing adults' ● Clothing children's ● Coins foreign ● Coins old ● Computer hardware and software ● Diy equipment ● Fabric remnants ● Fur coats ● Furniture *small items only, no soft furnishings* ● Gardening equipment ● Household items *ironing boards etc* ● Jewellery ● Knitting, crochet and sewing equipment ● Knitting wool ● Medals ● Musical instruments ● Photographic equipment ● Records & tapes ● Spectacles ● Sports equipment ● Stamps foreign ● Video/computer games ● Watches

COLLECTION SERVICE Yes

■ Turntable Furniture Project

ADDRESS The Old Pumping Station, Exeter City Council Recycling Park, Exton Road, Exeter, Devon EX2 8LX

TELEPHONE 01392 499477

CATEGORY Baby equipment ● Bed linen and mattresses ● Diy equipment ● Furniture ● Gardening equipment ● Household items *ironing boards etc* ● Office equipment and stationery

COLLECTION SERVICE Yes

■ Uttlesford Council for Voluntary Service

ADDRESS c/o Saffron Walden Community Hospital, Radwinter Road, Essex

TELEPHONE 01799 513626

CATEGORY Milk bottle tops ● Silver paper & aluminium foil ● Waste paper

COLLECTION SERVICE No

■ Vincent Harkins Day Care Centre

ADDRESS 7 Cardigan Avenue, Birkenhead, Wirral, Merseyside L41 4NH

TELEPHONE 0151-647 2120

CATEGORY Books hardback ● Books paperback ● Bric-a-brac ● Clocks ● Clothing adults' ● Knitting wool ● Magazines & comics ● Non perishable foods ● Toiletries ● Toys & games ● Watches

COLLECTION SERVICE No

■ Vision Aid Overseas

ADDRESS 56–66 Highlands Road, Leatherhead, Surrey KT22 8NR

TELEPHONE 01372 360822

FAX 01372 360823

CATEGORY Spectacles

COLLECTION SERVICE No

■ Voluntary Action (Haringey)

ADDRESS Selby Centre, Selby Road, London N17 8ND

TELEPHONE 0181-365 1873

FAX 0181-801 8957

CATEGORY Computer hardware and software ● Office equipment and stationery

COLLECTION SERVICE No

■ Voluntary Service (Aberdeen)

ADDRESS 38 Castle Street, Aberdeen, Grampian AB1 1AB

TELEPHONE 01224 586395

FAX 01224 580722

CATEGORY Antique post cards ● Arts & crafts equipment ● Baby equipment ● Bed linen and mattresses ● Bicycles ● Books hardback ● Books paperback ● Bric-a-brac ● Clocks ● Clothing adults' ● Clothing children's ● Coins foreign ● Coins old ● Computer hardware and software ● Diy equipment ● Fabric remnants ● Fur coats ● Furniture ● Gardening equipment ● Household items *ironing boards etc* ● Jewellery ● Knitting, crochet and sewing equipment ● Knitting wool ● Magazines & comics ● Medals ● Musical instruments ● Office equipment and stationery ● Photographic equipment ● Rags ● Records & tapes ● Sports equipment ● Stamps British ● Stamps foreign ● Toiletries ● Toys & games ● Video/computer games ● Watches

COLLECTION SERVICE Yes

■ Voluntary Service (Belfast)

ADDRESS 70–72 Lisburn Road, Belfast, Antrim, N Ireland BT9 6AF

TELEPHONE 01232 329499

FAX 01232 321797

CATEGORY Arts & crafts equipment ● Baby equipment ● Bed linen and mattresses ● Books hardback ● Books paperback ● Bric-a-brac ● Clocks ● Clothing adults' ● Clothing children's ● Diy equipment ● Fabric remnants ● Fur coats ● Furniture ● Gardening equipment ● Household items *ironing boards etc* ● Jewellery ● Knitting, crochet and sewing equipment ● Knitting wool ● Magazines & comics ● Musical instruments ● Non perishable foods ● Pets equipment ● Photographic equipment ● Records & tapes ● Sports equipment ● Toiletries ● Toys & games ● Watches

COLLECTION SERVICE Yes

■ Wallis Centre

ADDRESS De La Warr Road, East Grinstead, W Sussex RH19 3BS

TELEPHONE 01342 321585

CATEGORY Arts & crafts equipment ● Fabric remnants ● Musical instruments ● Petrol vouchers ● Records & tapes ● Sports equipment ● Toys & games ● Video/computer games

COLLECTION SERVICE No

■ Walsall Gingerbread Advice Centre

ADDRESS 93–95 Caldmore Road, Walsall, W Midlands WS1 3NR

TELEPHONE 01922 641588

FAX 01922 641588

CATEGORY Air miles ● Antique post cards ● Arts & crafts equipment ● Baby equipment ● Bed linen and mattresses ● Bicycles ● Books hardback ● Books paperback ● Bric-a-brac ● Childrens play/craft scrap ● Christmas cards ● Clocks ● Clothing adults' ● Clothing children's ● Coins foreign ● Coins old ● Computer hardware and software ● Diy equipment ● Fabric remnants ● Furniture ● Gardening equipment ● Household items *ironing boards etc* ● Jewellery ● Knitting, crochet and sewing equipment ● Knitting wool ● Magazines & comics ● Money-off coupons ● Musical instruments ● Non perishable foods ● Office equipment and stationery ● Petrol vouchers ● Pets equipment ● Rags ● Records & tapes ● Sports equipment ● Stamps British ● Stamps foreign ● Telephone cards ● Toiletries ● Toys & games ● Trading stamps ● Video/computer games ● Watches

COLLECTION SERVICE Yes

■ Walthamstow After School Club

ADDRESS 98 Edinburgh Road, Walthamstow, London E17 7QB

TELEPHONE 0181-521 6293

CATEGORY Air miles ● Aluminium ● Arts & crafts equipment ● Bicycles ● Books hardback ● Books paperback ● Bric-a-brac ● Childrens play/craft scrap ● Clocks ● Computer hardware and software ● Diy equipment ● Fabric remnants ● Gardening equipment ● Jewellery ● Knitting, crochet and sewing equipment ● Knitting wool ● Musical instruments ● Non perishable foods ● Office equipment and stationery ● Petrol vouchers ● Silver paper & aluminium foil ● Sports equipment ● Toiletries ● Toys & games ● Video/computer games ● Watches

COLLECTION SERVICE Yes

■ Wandsworth Housing Support Project

ADDRESS 307 Battersea Park Road, London SW11 4LU

TELEPHONE 0171-498 1208

FAX 0171-498 7026

CATEGORY Baby equipment ● Bed linen and mattresses ● Bicycles ● Books hardback ● Books paperback ● Bric-a-brac ● Clothing adults' ● Clothing children's ● Computer hardware and software ● Diy equipment ● Furniture ● Household items *ironing boards etc* ● Jewellery ● Knitting wool ● Musical instruments ● Office equipment and stationery ● Records & tapes ● Spectacles ● Sports equipment ● Toys & games ● Video/computer games ● Watches

COLLECTION SERVICE Yes

■ War on Want (NI)

ADDRESS 1 Rugby Avenue, Belfast, Co Antrim, N Ireland BT7 1RD

TELEPHONE 01232 232064

FAX 01232 328019

CATEGORY Air miles ● Bed linen and mattresses ● Books hardback ● Books paperback ● Bric-a-brac ● Clocks ● Clothing adults' ● Clothing children's ● Fabric remnants ● Furniture ● Gardening equipment ● Household items *ironing boards etc* ● Jewellery ● Knitting wool ● Magazines & comics ● Musical instruments ● Petrol vouchers ● Postcards used ● Records & tapes ● Spectacles ● Sports equipment ● Toiletries ● Toys & games ● Video/computer games ● Waste paper ● Watches

COLLECTION SERVICE Yes

■ Waste Not Recycling

ADDRESS 24 Rossendale Street, Hackney, London E5 8TA

TELEPHONE 0181-880 0325

FAX 0181-880 0282

CATEGORY Aluminium *drinks cans only* ● Bed linen and mattresses *not mattresses* ● Clothing adults' ● Clothing children's ● Fabric remnants *must be larger than 12" x 12"* ● Fur coats

COLLECTION SERVICE Yes

■ Wastesavers Recycling Association

ADDRESS Unit 11, Crawford Street, Newport, Gwent NP9 7AY

TELEPHONE 01633 216855/216856

FAX 01633 216856

CATEGORY Aluminium *cans only* ● Clothing adults' ● Clothing children's ● Fabric remnants ● Magazines & comics ● Other metals ● Rags ● Used toner cartridges ● Waste paper *office and household*

COLLECTION SERVICE Yes

■ Wearside Women in Need

ADDRESS The Elms, Front Street, Concord, Washington, Tyne & Wear NE37 2BA

TELEPHONE 0191-416 3550

CATEGORY Aluminium ● Baby equipment ● Bed linen and mattresses ● Bric-a-brac ● Clothing adults' *women's clothing* ● Clothing children's ● Furniture ● Non perishable foods ● Office equipment and stationery ● Toys & games

COLLECTION SERVICE Yes

■ Wellington Basins Project

ADDRESS Rose Cottage, Tracebridge, Wellington, Somerset TA21 0HG

TELEPHONE 01823 672135

CATEGORY Arts & crafts equipment ● Books hardback ● Gardening equipment ● Photographic equipment ● Postcards used ● Stamps British ● Stamps foreign

COLLECTION SERVICE Yes

■ Welwyn Hatfield CVS

ADDRESS The Bill Salmon Centre, 88 Town Centre, Hatfield, Herts AL10 0JW

TELEPHONE 01707 274861

FAX 01707 258845

CATEGORY Baby equipment ● Bed linen and mattresses *must meet fire and safety regulations* ● Furniture ● Gardening equipment ● Household items *ironing boards etc*

COLLECTION SERVICE Yes

■ Wesley Community Project

ADDRESS Royce Road, Hulme, Gtr Manchester M16 5BP

TELEPHONE 0161-226 9051

FAX 0161-226 9604

E-MAIL wes@wes.nwnet.co.uk

CATEGORY Aluminium ● Arts & crafts equipment ● Baby equipment ● Bed linen and mattresses ● Bicycles ● Books hardback ● Books paperback ● Bric-a-brac ● Clocks ● Clothing adults' ● Clothing children's ● Computer hardware and software ● Diy equipment ● Fur coats ● Furniture ● Gardening equipment ● Hearing aids ● Household items *ironing boards etc* ● Jewellery ● Knitting, crochet and sewing equipment ● Knitting wool ● Magazines & comics ● Musical instruments ● Non perishable foods ● Office equipment and stationery ● Photographic equipment ● Records & tapes ● Spectacles ● Sports equipment ● Toys & games ● Used toner cartridges ● Video/computer games ● Watches

COLLECTION SERVICE Yes

■ Wessex Cancer Trust

ADDRESS Bellis House, 11 Westwood Road, Southampton, Hants SO17 1DL

TELEPHONE 01703 672200

FAX 01703 672266

CATEGORY Air miles • Arts & crafts equipment • Books hardback • Books paperback • Bric-a-brac • Clothing adults' • Clothing children's • Diy equipment • Fabric remnants • Furniture • Gardening equipment • Household items *ironing boards etc* • Jewellery • Petrol vouchers • Sports equipment • Toiletries • Toys & games • Used toner cartridges

COLLECTION SERVICE Yes

■ West Somerset Council for Voluntary Service

ADDRESS The Old Post Office, Parkhouse Road, Minehead, Somerset TA24 5AA

TELEPHONE 01643 707484

CATEGORY Books hardback • Books paperback • Bric-a-brac • Furniture • Jewellery • Magazines & comics • Money-off coupons • Petrol vouchers • Postcards used • Records & tapes • Stamps British • Stamps foreign • Toys & games • Trading stamps

COLLECTION SERVICE Yes

■ West Sussex Dyslexia Association

ADDRESS c/o John Clark, 47 Cranleigh Road, W Sussex BN14 7QN

TELEPHONE 01903 212058

CATEGORY Computer hardware and software

COLLECTION SERVICE No

■ West Wiltshire Council for Voluntary Service

ADDRESS Bridge House, Stallard Street, Trowbridge, Wilts SN13 9XW

TELEPHONE 01225 767993

FAX 01225 776313

CATEGORY Diy equipment • Gardening equipment

COLLECTION SERVICE Yes

■ Windhill Community Furniture Store

ADDRESS Church Street, Windhill, Shipley, W Yorks BD18 2NR

TELEPHONE 01274 588831

CATEGORY Baby equipment • Bed linen and mattresses • Bric-a-brac • Furniture *not fridges* • Household items *ironing boards etc*

COLLECTION SERVICE Yes

■ Wirral Rehab T/AS Speaks Volumes

ADDRESS 48–50 Grange Road West, Birkenhead, Wirral, Merseyside L41 4DA

TELEPHONE 0151-647 6076

FAX 0151-647 3532

CATEGORY Antique post cards • Books hardback *our main emphasis is on sale of secondhand books, but we will also collect other items* • Books paperback • Magazines & comics • Postcards used • Records & tapes

COLLECTION SERVICE Yes

■ Women's Aid to Former Yugoslavia

ADDRESS 20 Tennyson Road, Portswood, Southampton, Hants SO17 2GW

TELEPHONE 01703 551094

FAX 01703 554434

E-MAIL waty@gn.apc.org

CATEGORY Clothing adults' *new, especially underwear* • Clothing children's *new* • Computer hardware and software • Fabric remnants *useable pieces 1metre minimum* • Knitting, crochet and sewing equipment • Knitting wool *complete balls only* • Non perishable foods *in date only* • Office equipment and stationery • Toiletries *unused*

COLLECTION SERVICE No

■ Women's Royal Voluntary Service

ADDRESS 1 Collingdon Street, Luton, Beds LU1 1RT

TELEPHONE 01582 24696

CATEGORY Baby equipment • Bed linen and mattresses *linen only* • Bric-a-brac • Clothing adults' • Clothing children's • Knitting wool • Magazines & comics • Silver paper & aluminium foil • Spectacles • Toys & games

COLLECTION SERVICE No

■ Women's Royal Voluntary Service

ADDRESS Taunton Deane District Office, 27 Canon Street, Taunton, Somerset TA1 1SW

TELEPHONE 01823 275626

CATEGORY Bed linen and mattresses *not mattresses* • Clothing adults' • Clothing children's • Knitting wool

COLLECTION SERVICE No

■ Worcestershire Association for the Blind

ADDRESS 13 Wylds Lane, Worcester, Hereford & Worcs WR5 1DA

TELEPHONE 01905 351311

FAX 01905 764442

CATEGORY Stamps British • Stamps foreign

COLLECTION SERVICE No

■ **Work-Link Project**

ADDRESS Units 1 & 3, Mansfield House, Upper Bond Street, Hinckley, Leics LE10 1RJ

TELEPHONE 01455 636506

CATEGORY Arts & crafts equipment ● Baby equipment *must comply with latest regulations* ● Bed linen and mattresses *must comply with latest regulations* ● Bicycles ● Books hardback ● Books paperback ● Bric-a-brac ● Diy equipment *non-electrical only* ● Fabric remnants ● Furniture *foam-filled must comply with latest regulations* ● Gardening equipment *non-electrical only* ● Household items *ironing boards etc* ● Knitting, crochet and sewing equipment ● Knitting wool ● Musical instruments ● Office equipment and stationery ● Records & tapes ● Toiletries ● Toys & games *must comply with latest regulations*

COLLECTION SERVICE Yes

■ **The Worldwide Fund for Nature (WWF)**

ADDRESS Banbury Supporters Group, 1 Old Bridge Road, Bloxham, Oxon OX15 4LY

TELEPHONE 01295 721630

FAX 01295 721060

CATEGORY Air miles ● Clocks ● Coins foreign ● Coins old ● Jewellery ● Medals ● Money-off coupons ● Musical instruments ● Petrol vouchers ● Stamps British ● Stamps foreign ● Trading stamps ● Watches

COLLECTION SERVICE Yes

■ **WWF UK North London Office**

ADDRESS 13 Redston Road, London N8 7HL

TELEPHONE 0181-347 8171

FAX 0181-347 8171

E-MAIL 100661.2757@compuserve.com

CATEGORY Air miles ● Stamps British ● Stamps foreign

COLLECTION SERVICE No

■ **YMCA Day Camps**

ADDRESS Warlies Park House, Horseshoe Hill, Upshire, Waltham Abbey, Essex EN9 3SL

TELEPHONE 01992 652272

FAX 01992 652273

CATEGORY Arts & crafts equipment ● Childrens play/craft scrap ● Computer hardware and software ● Diy equipment *paint, wood & tools only* ● Office equipment and stationery ● Sports equipment

COLLECTION SERVICE No

■ **Zaire Evangelistic Mission**

ADDRESS 355 Blackpool Road, Preston, Lancs PR2 3AB

TELEPHONE 01772 717830

FAX 01772 719322

E-MAIL zem@compuserve.com

CATEGORY Air miles ● Antique post cards ● Petrol vouchers ● Postcards used ● Stamps British ● Stamps foreign ● Trading stamps

COLLECTION SERVICE No

Useful addresses

Electronic equipment

■ Industry Council for Electronic Equipment Recycling (ICER)

ADDRESS 6 Bath Place, Rivington Street, London EC2A 3JE

TELEPHONE 0171-729 4766

Further information on recycling of electronic equipment

General

■ Community Recycling Network

ADDRESS 10-12 Picton Street, Montpelier, Bristol, Avon BS6 5QA

TELEPHONE 01179 420142

Promotes community recycling and highlights best practice

■ Department of the Environment Waste Policy Division

ADDRESS Room A222, Romney House, 43 Marsham Street, London SW1P 3PY

TELEPHONE 0171-276 8473

For general recycling enquiries

■ Department of the Environment – Environment, Business and Management Division

ADDRESS Room C9/02, 2 Marsham Street, London SW1P 3EB

TELEPHONE 0171-276 6307

Information on Government policy on recycling

■ Department of Trade and Industry Environment Directorate

ADDRESS 4.104 (Red Zone), 151 Buckingham Palace Road, London SW1W 9SS

TELEPHONE 0171-215 1036

Recycling advice for industry

■ Institute of Wastes Management

ADDRESS 9 Saxon Court, St Peter's Gardens, Northampton, Northamptonshire NN1 1SX

TELEPHONE 01604 20426

Promotes scientific, technical and practical aspects of wastes management, including refuse collection, waste disposal, street cleansing and recycling

■ Local Authority Recycling Advisory Council (LARAC)

ADDRESS London Waste Regulation Authority, Hampton House, 20 Albert Embankment, London SE1 7TJ

TELEPHONE 0171-587 3000

■ National Recycling Forum

ADDRESS 74 Kirkgate, Leeds, West Yorkshire LS2 7DJ

TELEPHONE 0113-243 1562

Information on issues concerning recycling, also Save Waste and Prospect (SWAP) Ltd on 0113-243 8777

■ Shell Better Britain Campaign

ADDRESS Victoria Works, 21a Graham Street, Hockley, Birmingham, West Midlands B1 3JR

TELEPHONE 0121-212 9221

Produces Interactive Annual Magazine and A-Z Guide to contacts and publications.

■ Tidy Britain Group

ADDRESS The Pier, Wigan, Lancashire WN3 4EX

TELEPHONE 01942 824620

Runs campaigns, education programmes and award schemes

■ Warmer Bulletin

ADDRESS World Resource, Foundation Bridge House, High Street, Tonbridge, Kent TN9 1DP

TELEPHONE 01732 368333

Produced six times a year and distributed in over 140 countries. Information on waste management and recycling

■ Waste Management Information Bureau

ADDRESS AEA Technology, F6, Culham, Abingdon, Oxon OX14 3DB

TELEPHONE 01235 463162

National centre for information and advice on waste management, including reclamation and recycling

■ Waste Watch

ADDRESS Gresham House, 24 Holborn Viaduct, London EC1A 2BN

TELEPHONE 0171-248 1818

Produces National Recycling Directory containing information for local authorities and community groups. Lists recycling facilities and has networking section

Glass

■ British Glass Recycling Co Ltd

ADDRESS Northumberland Road, Sheffield, South Yorkshire S10 2AU

TELEPHONE 0114-268 4067

Trying to encourage charities to collect glass for recycling

Metals

■ Alcan Aluminium Can Recycling

ADDRESS 3rd Floor, Eldon House, Regent Centre, Gosforth, Newcastle upon Tyne, Tyne & Wear NE3 3PW

Freephone information line: 0800 262465 Information on aluminium can recycling and group collecting

■ Aluminium Can Recycling Association

ADDRESS 5 Gatsby Court, 176 Holliday Street, Birmingham, West Midlands B1 1TJ

TELEPHONE 0121-633 4656

Promotion of aluminium drinks cans recycling by the public. Has a directory of recycling centres listed by county

■ Aluminium Foil Recycling Campaign

ADDRESS Bridge House, 53 High Street, Bidford on Avon, Warwickshire B50 4BG

TELEPHONE 01789 490609

Offers general information to encourage recycling

■ British Aerosol Manufacturers Association

ADDRESS Kings Building, Smith Square, London SW1P 3JJ

TELEPHONE 0171-828 5111

The Trade Association for the aerosol industry offering expert advice on aerosol recycling

■ British Secondary Metals Association (Non-Ferrous)

ADDRESS Park House, 25 Park Road, Runcorn, Cheshire WA7 4AA

TELEPHONE 01928 572400

Disposal of brass, copper, zinc, lead, aluminium, etc

■ British Scrap Federation (Ferrous)

ADDRESS 16 High Street, Brampton, Huntingdon, Cambridgeshire PE18 8TU

TELEPHONE 01480 455249

Information on the disposal of iron and steel

■ Steel Can Recycling Information Bureau

ADDRESS 69 Monmouth Street, London WC2H 9DG

TELEPHONE 0171-379 1306

Leading authority on steel can recycling, offering information, promotional and educational material

Packaging

■ British Fibreboard Packaging Association/REPAK

ADDRESS 2 Saxon Court, Freeschool Street, Northampton, Northamptonshire NN1 1ST

TELEPHONE 01604 21002

Information on environmental issues and recycling

■ Industry Council for Packaging and the Environment

ADDRESS Tenterden House, 3 Tenterden Street, London W1R 9AH

TELEPHONE 0171-409 0949

A source of information on the use of packaging materials, and recycling

■ Institute of Packaging

ADDRESS Sysonby Lodge, Nottingham Road, Melton Mowbray, Leicestershire LE14 0NU

TELEPHONE 01664 500055

Information on packaging and the environment and further information on recycling

■ Timber Packaging and Pallet Confederation

ADDRESS 42 Heath Street, Tamworth, Staffordshire B79 7JH

TELEPHONE 01827 52337

Concerned with environmental and industrial relations matters in the industry and a source of information on recycling

Paper and Board

■ Autobar Environmental Group

ADDRESS Autobar House, 41-42 Kew Bridge Road, Brentford, Middlesex TW8 0DY

TELEPHONE 0181-560 7485

Information on Save-a-Cup scheme

■ Aylesford Newsprint Limited

ADDRESS Recycling Development, Newsprint House, Bellingham Way, Aylesford, Kent ME20 7BR

TELEPHONE 01622 796194

Information on setting up recycling initiatives

■ British Paper & Board Industry Federation

ADDRESS Papermakers House, Riverhall Road, Westlea, Swindon, Wiltshire SN5 7BE

TELEPHONE 01793 866086

01793 879229 (PAPER BACK Helpline: Waste paper and board recycling) Information on waste-based paper/board products. Can supply lists of local waste paper merchants if they have a postcode

■ British Waste Paper Association

ADDRESS Alexander House, Station Road, Aldershot, Hampshire GU11 1BQ

TELEPHONE 01252 344454

Information service on the collection of waste paper

■ Community Recycling Scheme

ADDRESS Richardsons Farm, Crowhurst Lane, West Kingsdown, Kent TN15 6JE

TELEPHONE 01474 854532

Collects old papers and magazines and provides paperbanks for use with the scheme

■ Davidsons Waste Paper

ADDRESS Folds Road, Bolton, Greater Manchester GL1 2SW

TELEPHONE 01204 372717

There are eight branches in the UK and a telephone call will put you in touch with the nearest

■ Independent Waste Paper Processors Association

ADDRESS 25 High Street, Daventry, Northamptonshire NN11 4BG

TELEPHONE 01327 703223

Association with a wide membership across the UK. Local contact details can be supplied

■ Kayjon International

ADDRESS Kayjon House, Upper Tooting Road, London SW17 7PG

TELEPHONE 0181-767 2207

Purchases paper in bulk to send to African countries

■ Liquid Food Carton Manufacturers Association

ADDRESS St Mary's Centre, Oystershell Lane, Newcastle upon Tyne, Tyne & Wear NE4 5QS

TELEPHONE 0191-232 1985

Represents manufacturers of cartons and addresses environmental issues of recovery and recycling

Plastics

■ British Plastics Federation

ADDRESS 6 Bath Place, Rivington Street, London EC2A 3JE

TELEPHONE 0171-457 5000

A Trade Association and Information Service promoting the benefits, use and recycling of plastics. Produces a directory costing £15

■ RECOUP - Recycling of used plastic containers

ADDRESS 9 Metro Centre, Welbeck Way, Woodston, Peterborough, Cambridgeshire PE2 7WH

TELEPHONE 01733 390021

Information on recycling of plastic containers

Textiles

■ British Textile Fibres Association

ADDRESS Thorncliffe, 115 Windsor Road, Oldham, Lancashire OL8 1RQ

TELEPHONE 0161-624 3611

Processes waste fibres

■ The Reclamation Association

ADDRESS 16 High Street, Brampton, Huntingdon, Cambridgeshire PE18 8TU

TELEPHONE 01480 455249

UK Trade Association. Represents mainly textile reclaimers, recyclers, processors and wiping cloth manufacturers.

■ Oxfam Wastesaver

ADDRESS Unit 4-6, Ringway Industrial Estate, Beck Road, Huddersfield, West Yorkshire HD1 5DG

TELEPHONE 01484 542021

Will pay money for all kinds of clothes

■ Textile Recycling Association

ADDRESS PO Box 124, Huntingdon, Cambridgeshire PE18 7DP

TELEPHONE 01480 386398

Helpline for disposing of textiles

Stamps

■ Firm Jurgen Wolff

ADDRESS Sammeln und Service GmbH, Steinweg, 23 D-51107 Koln, Germany

■ W H Hirst

ADDRESS 49 Priory Road, West Bridgford, Nottingham, Nottinghamshire NG2 5HX

TELEPHONE 0115-981 3828

Purchases only foreign and commonwealth stamps in quantity

Toner Cartridges etc

■ ACA Ltd

ADDRESS Unit 35, Lords Wood Industrial Estate, Gleaming Wood Drive, Walderslade, Chatham, Kent ME5 8HY

TELEPHONE 01634 868824

Will purchase ink jet cartridges and toner cartridges to recycle

■ Ecotone Ltd

ADDRESS Supply Partners (UK) Ltd, 16a Crawley Mill, Witney, Oxon OX8 5TJ

TELEPHONE 01993 709007

Purchases used laser printer cartridges for recycling

■ Logical Computer Supplies Ltd

ADDRESS Kerry House, Kerry Street, Horsforth, Leeds, West Yorkshire LS18 4AW

TELEPHONE 01132 580808

Will purchase used inkjet or laser toner cartridges for recycling

■ United Kingdom Cartridge Recyclers Association

ADDRESS PO Box 41, Eccles, Greater Manchester M30 0RT

TELEPHONE 0161-487 4288

To promote recycling especially of computer printer consumables, toner and ink cartridges, ribbons etc.